Deep-Sky Observing
With Small Telescopes
A Guide and Reference

David J. Eicher

and the Editors of *Deep Sky*

ENSLOW PUBLISHERS, INC.

Bloy St. & Ramsey Ave.   P.O. Box 38
Box 777   Aldershot
Hillside, N.J. 07205   Hants GU12 6BP
U.S.A.   U.K.

To Dr. John H. Eicher, chemist and father *par excellence*, and to the memory of Susan Ann Arne Eicher, dear departed mother

Library of Congress Cataloging-in-Publication Data

Deep-sky observing with small telescopes : a guide and reference /
    David J. Eicher and the editors of Deep sky magazine.
        p. cm.
    Bibliography: p.
    "The Messier catalog": p.
    Includes index.
    ISBN 0-89490-075-7
    1. Astronomy—Amateurs' manuals. 2. Astronomy—Observers'
manuals. I. Eicher, David J., 1961-   . II. Deep sky.
QB63.D45 1989
522'.2—dc20   89-7653
CIP

Printed in the United States of America

10 9 8 7 6 5 4 3 2 1

ILLUSTRATION CREDITS:
Jon Almada, fig. 5-19; American Association of Variable Star Observers, figs. 3-2, 3-3, 3-4, 3-5, 3-6; Jay Anderson, figs. 4-27, 6-29; Robert Brooks, fig. 7-27; K. Alexander Brownlee, figs. 8-8, 8-11; Norman Butler, figs. 4-17, 5-27, 5-28, 6-24, 6-33; Celestron International, figs. 1-2, 1-6, 1-10, 1-12; Glenn F. Chaple, Jr., figs. 2-3, 2-4, 2-5, 4-15, 4-19, 6-22; Lee C. Coombs, figs. 4-2, 4-11, 4-12, 4-28, 5-6, 5-9, 6-37, 7-9, 8-15; Jeffrey Corder, figs. 5-18, 5-26, 7-26, 8-18; Clarence P. Custer, fig. 6-25; Ulf Danielsson, figs., 4-16, 4-20, 4-23; Thomas L. Dessert, figs., 4-7, 4-13; Tom Eby, figs. 7-3, 7-12, 8-4; Edmund Scientific Co., fig. 1-4; David J. Eicher, figs. 4-14, 4-22, 5-15, 5-21, 6-23, 6-32, 7-15, 7-21, 7-22, 7-25; John H. Eicher, fig. 1-11; Al Ernst, fig. 5-23; Rex M. Evans, figs. 4-21, 7-14, 8-19; James Garasich, figs. 4-18, 8-28; Martin C. Germano, figs. 4-10, 5-3, 5-4, 5-5, 5-7, 5-11, 5-12, 5-13, 5-22, 6-3, 6-4, 6-6, 6-7, 6-8, 6-9, 6-10, 6-15, 6-16, 6-17, 6-18, 6-19, 6-26, 6-27, 6-28, 6-30, 7-1, 7-4, 7-7, 7-13, 8-2, 8-3, 8-6, 8-9, 8-10, 8-12, 8-13, 8-29, 8-30, 8-31; Alan Goldstein, figs. 5-20, 8-20, 8-21; Walter E. Hamler, fig. 4-6; David Healy, foreword, figs. 4-1, 4-5, 6-1, 7-18, 8-1, 8-16, appendix 3; Thomas L. Hunt, appendix 4; Rick Hunter, figs. 8-23, 8-24; Preston Justis, figs. 4-9, 4-26, 7-10; John A. Leoder, fig. 5-10; David H. Levy, fig. 1-8; Alfred Lilge, preface, figs. 5-1, 5-2, 5-8, 6-2, 7-5; Randy Lutz, figs. 5-16, 5-25, 6-14, 6-31; Eric Maddox, fig. 8-22; Jack B. Marling, figs. 6-5, 7-19, 8-5, 8-7, 8-14; Meade Instruments Corp., figs. 1-7, 1-9; Jack Newton, figs. 4-3, 5-24, 6-20; Daniel C. Oakes, fig. 4-24; John W. Parker, appendix 2; Matt Penn, figs. 5-14, 8-27; Ron Potter, figs., 6-35, 7-6, 7-8, 7-11, 7-20, appendix 1; Kevin Ritschel, fig. 1-5; Paul Roques, figs. 1-1, 7-2; Chesley Runyon, Jr., figs. 4-25, 5-17, 6-11, 8-26; John Sanford, figs. 2-1, 3-1; Brian Skiff, figs. 4-4, 4-8; Mike Walters, fig. 6-34; Richard P. Wilds, figs. 7-16, 7-17, 7-23, 7-24, 7-28, 8-17, 8-25; Debra J. Williams: fig. 2-2; F. Michael Witkoski, figs. 6-12, 6-13, 6-21; Howard F. Zeh, 1-3, 6-36.

Contents

The Andromeda Galaxy

Foreword

Walter Scott Houston

Americans, with much justification, have often been accused of having a cult of bigness. Professional astronomers have always rated their jobs with the size of the telescopes they use. Amateur astronomers who started with homemade 6-inch telescopes in 1928 were already boasting 12-inch instruments by 1930. Only the lack of availability of larger pieces of glass saved them from making even bigger telescopes.

Yet there is much to be said for the small telescope. It has advantages in portability and economy. It can be truly handy. Such an instrument will show more than 10,000 worthy objects in the sky and it will take years before the owner can justly contend that he has exhausted the capabilities of this piece of equipment. The small telescope, in the opinions of many eminent amateur astronomers such as the great observer Leslie Peltier (1900-1980), is the finest training ground for serious observers of the sky. The person who starts with a 16-inch scope somehow never really seems to learn astronomy and build an understanding of the universe quite as solidly.

Amateur astronomers were confined to instruments of under 3 inches in aperture for a couple of centuries following the invention of the telescope in 1610. Yet the record of performance of those early observers still carries luster. All of the Messier objects can be seen in just a 1-inch telescope if it has a magnifying power of 40x. Countless double stars just outside the artificial limits of the catalogues await recording. A 2-inch telescope is perfectly sensible as an instrument for the discovery of supernovae in spiral galaxies.

So this observing manual for small telescope owners comes as a most timely contribution. Deep Sky magazine and its host of cooperative observers has produced a much needed book. The next Leslie Peltier will undoubtedly come from this volume's readership.

Walter Scott Houston

East Haddam, Connecticut

The Great Nebula in Orion

Preface

David J. Eicher

The world of astronomy was very different six score years ago. Professional observatories housed magnificently crafted refracting telescopes, and their research interests were centered on double star astronomy, spectroscopy, and the burgeoning process of astronomical photography. The nature of galaxies and nebulae was almost a complete mystery. Very few hobbyists had telescopes they could use to see the wonders of the universe beyond the solar system. Even more so than today, we were a civilization curious about the stars but unable to decipher a good deal about them.

Just before the Civil War, the English observer Rev. Thomas W. Webb, Vicar of Hardwicke in Herefordshire, authored a book called Celestial Objects for Common Telescopes that would become a classic for casual star gazers in the late 19th-century. In fact, it is still available in a two-volume paperback reprint edition.

When I picked up a copy of this book in 1976, I was astounded at its content. Mind you, it is of great historical interest, but the coverage of objects reflects those thought to be important or interesting in 1859 and the information provided is, of course, badly outdated. Since the publication of this book, astronomers have discovered the fundamental nature of the Milky Way, the nature of external galaxies, and the nature of star clusters and nebulae. Such gigantic leaps in understanding objects in the sky radically improved information about deep-sky objects, as clusters, nebulae, and galaxies came to be known, and consequently I thought that a similar sort of observing guide needed to appear for late 20th-century observers. Thus the idea for Deep Sky Observing with Small Telescopes was born.

The idea for this book grew along with Deep Sky Monthly (DSM), a magazine for deep-sky observers I started in 1977. Several writers for DSM became interested in contributing to the book and the project became a collaboration, work beginning in earnest in 1980. This book went through an extraordinarily problematic development since I had to redo it on three non-compatible computer systems, one as a student in Ohio, and two after starting my job in Wisconsin as editor of Deep Sky, a quarterly reincarnation of DSM, and assistant editor of ASTRONOMY. But I finally finished the project, and you hold in your hands the result.

Many people deserve thanks for support, encouragement, and practical advice on seeing this project through. First and foremost are my parents, Prof. John Harold Eicher and my late mother Susan Ann Arne Eicher, without whom none of my astronomical interests or projects, this book included, would have flourished. My sister Nancy deserves credit for giving me a nudge to keep moving ahead at critical times.

Many other friends helped out. David H. Levy of the University of Arizona and Brian Skiff of Lowell Observatory have provided an enormous amount of support and encouragement. The contributing authors, Levy, Kevin Ritschel, Glenn F. Chaple, Jr., Mike Witkoski, and Alan Goldstein, supplied me not only with manuscripts but with helpful suggestions. Walter Scott Houston, the greatest popularizer of deep-sky objects in this century, has graciously contributed a foreword. Many amateur astronomers contributed photographers and sketches of deep-sky objects. My colleagues at Astronomy magazine, most notably Richard Berry, have helped greatly with informative suggestions. Lynda Goodnetter has always been around to keep me going when things looked bleak.

Finally, I must thank Ridley M. Enslow, Christopher Carr, and Pat Culleton of Enslow Publishers for their patience and understanding. Their talents and unique abilities were invaluable during the production of this work.

I hope that <u>Deep Sky Observing with Small Telescopes</u> provides you with enjoyable reading and browsing, and that it ultimately becomes an indispensible reference book on your astronomy bookshelf, and a fun companion in your adventure of backyard astronomy.

David John Eicher
Brookfield, Wisconsin

23 September 1988

Fig. 1-1. **The Pleiades**

1

An Introduction to Deep-Sky Observing

Kevin Ritschel

When you looked at the cover of this book, you probably thought, "What is deep-sky observing?" It is the backyard activity of visually inspecting and studying celestial objects that inhabit the universe beyond our local solar system. Deep-sky objects comprise the vast majority of the objects you can see with your telescope. They include: double stars--two stars that appear close together either because they are physically linked or merely optically aligned; variable stars--stars that vary in brightness; open star clusters--congregations of newly formed stars in our Milky Way galaxy; globular star clusters--enormous balls of old stars orbiting in our galactic halo; planetary nebulae--shells of hot hydrogen gas thrown out from dying stars; bright and dark nebulae--emission, reflection, and dark gas and dust clouds in our galaxy's spiral arms; and galaxies--huge stellar systems composed of billions of stars. Recognizing that our sun is one star out of billions in the Milky Way galaxy--which in turn is one of billions of galaxies in the observable universe--makes for an awesome awakening to the immensity of the cosmos, an awakening you can fully experience with your telescope on any clear dark night.

Kevin Ritschel
Irvine, California

About the Author: Kevin Ritschel is an accomplished amateur astronomer, author, lecturer, and photographer. An astronomy graduate of the University of California at Irvine, he is a member of the American Astronomical Society, the Astronomical Society of the Pacific, and the American Association for the Advancement of Science. Responsible for much of the success of the California astronomy groups' Western Observatorium and the Rio Hondo College Astrophysical Observatory, he has published work in such magazines as Astronomy, Deep Sky, and Telescope Making.

Fig. 1-2. **A typical backyard Schmidt-Cassegrain telescope**

Fig. 1-3. **A Typical Backyard Observatory**

AN ADVENTURE IN ASTRONOMY

Today, astronomy is a popular science. Thanks to the space program, we have stepped on the surface of the moon, examined the satellites of Jupiter, and studied the myriad rings of Saturn. New technology makes the beauty and excitement of the universe around us more and more accessible, boldly projecting it into living rooms around the world. People are becoming familiar with the cosmos, and they want to know more. It is only human nature to seek knowledge about the vast spaces around us.

Even with the modest optical aid of a pair of binoculars, the cosmos becomes less mysterious than it used to be. It transforms into familiar place, not a freightening void. With a telescope you can indeed study the solar system quite well; changes are visible over relatively short periods of time. But the solar system, earth's "backyard," offers only eight other planets, their moons, our moon, a number of asteroids, and an occasional comet. Deep-sky observing, on the other hand, offers almost endless variety--even with a small 3-inch refractor, you'll never run out of things to look at. In this chapter we will discuss how the telescope, the primary instrument for observation, can be used for an adventure in backyard astronomy that could change your entire perspective on the world around you.

Modern astronomy has revealed many new and almost unbelievable objects throughout the universe. Most of the stranger phenomena are out of the reach of backyard telescopes, but you can routinely observe examples of seven broad classes of deep-sky objects.

1. Double and Multiple Stars. Astronomers have discovered that more than half of all stars are not single stars, as they appear to the naked eye, but rather systems of two (double) or more (multiple) stars. Indeed it is a pleasant pasttime to spend observing time "splitting" these multiple stars into their components. You can use any type of telescope for this, although refractors offer some advantages over reflectors for this work. Larger telescopes will, of course, permit higher resolution, letting you separate progressively closer pairs.

2. Variable Stars. Most stars appear as a point of constant brightness. This isn't the case with all stars, however, for there are literally tens of thousands of stars that vary their light output. By carefully comparing the variables to steady stars, you can monitor the fluctuating lives of these exotic stars. This is one area in which backyard observers can make very useful contributions to science--because of the sheer number of stars to watch, professional astronomers don't have time to keep an eye on all the variables in the sky.

3. Open Star Clusters. If you scan the Milky Way with binoculars you'll see that stars often lump together in clusters of a few dozen to many thousands--in fact, stars are born in groups like these. Since many of them are bright and easily observable, these are some of the most rewarding targets for small telescopes.

4. Globular Star Clusters. These objects are concentrated toward the direction of the constellation Sagittarius; you can find them throughout the sky. Globular star clusters are huge balls of 50,000 to half a million stars, all united by the bond of their mutual gravity.

The stars are packed so densely that no space between the stars near the cluster's centers is visible from our vantage point on earth. They are located in a huge sphere called the galactic halo which surrounds the nucleus of our Milky Way galaxy. Small telescopes show about 100 globulars orbiting in our galaxy. Some are visible in other galaxies as well, but they are very faint and nearly impossible to observe with small telescopes.

5. Planetary Nebulae. Like people, stars are born, live out a finite lifetime, and die. When their nuclear fuel is spent, some stars puff their outer atmospheres and form a shell of gas around the the dying sun. This gives rise to the class of objects known as planetary nebulae, named such for their resemblance to the planets in small telescopes. They are beautiful objects, and fine details of their internal structure vary from example to example.

6. Bright and Dark Nebulae. All other nebulae--clouds of gas and dust--in our galaxy get lumped into four subclasses: emission nebulae, hot clouds of bright gas; reflection nebulae, clouds of interstellar dust that become visible by reflecting starlight; supernovae remnants, glowing last traces of exploded stars; and dark nebulae, cold black clouds of dust visible only when they block brighter objects. The latter type is among the most difficult of sky objects to observe, but many can be seen with small telescopes.

7. Galaxies. The objects discussed above are relatively nearby; they are all part of the Milky Way galaxy, as is our own sun. There are billions of other galaxies--whole island stellar systems--in the universe, and you can observe several thousand of them with your small telescope. Most are so far away that they appear as a mere faint blur, but many yield fine details to backyard telescopes. No two galaxies are alike, but there are several subclasses: spirals, those with pinwheel-shaped structure (the Milky Way is a spiral); ellipticals, more or less spherical galaxies with little or no gas and dust and composed of old stars; lenticular galaxies, lens-shaped systems that represent a cross between spirals and ellipticals; and irregular and peculiar galaxies, those that show little or no organized form and lots of gas and dust.

Once you spend several nights under the stars looking at various faint fuzzy patches, you'll begin to gain an appreciation of the different types of deep-sky objects and what their light represents. It will take time for your eye to become used to seeing subtle details, but such a variety awaits you that learning the sky will be a pleasure, not an undertaking.

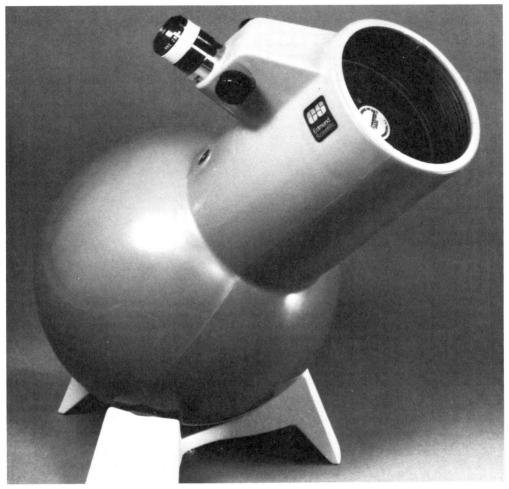

Fig. 1-4. **A portable 4¼-inch wide-field Newtonian**

Fig. 1-5. **A California amateur's refractor**

Fig. 1-6. **11x80 binoculars for deep-sky observing**

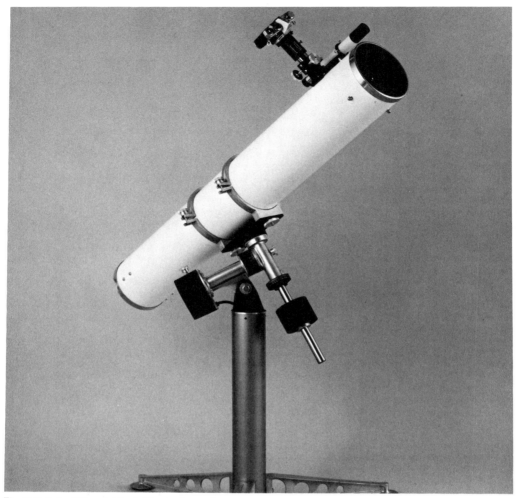

Fig. 1-7. **A traditional 6-inch Newtonian reflector**

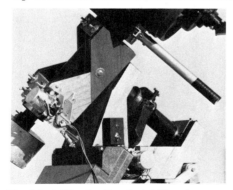

Fig. 1-8. **A Wooden Equatorial Mount**

Fig. 1-9. A 4-inch Schmidt-Cassegrain

TOOLS OF THE TRADE

A telescope is a tool--it allows you to see much more than you could with your eyes alone. But what exactly does it do? Many people answer that a telescope makes things bigger. It does that, but its primary and most important job is to collect light.

Think of light as information. Light from the Moon, a planet, or a distant galaxy is the only source of energy that our senses pick up. Luckily, nature codes an incredible amount of information about the physical nature of a radiant or reflecting object in its light. By simply analyzing the light coming from a star, astronomers can assess the star's chemical composition, the relative abundances of its elements, temperatures, the presence of magnetic fields, and much more. As with any type of communication, the more information that's available, the more you can learn. The reason for using telescopes is that gather lots of information in the form of light in a short time. Thus the larger the telescope, the more information you can gather.

You don't have to be a professional astronomer to enjoy studying the sky. A telescope can be your transportation to stellar vistas, where beautiful objects await you. And you don't have to own a large telescope--even a small one will show you hundreds of times more light than your eye does. Telescopes show you sights that the greatest minds of past centuries could only dream about. All you have to do is look.

Telescopes are simple to operate. Once you've mastered a few basic rules of thumb, using your telescope will become as routine as riding a bicycle. You just point and look. The secret is knowing where to look. You simply can't point a telescope anywhere in the sky and see exploding galaxies. There is a lot of space out there--vast distances and huge voids--so you must seek out distant deep-sky targets carefully.

Telescopes come in many different sizes, shapes, optical configurations, and today, even various colors. There are mass-produced ready-to-use telescopes, parts for assembling your own instrument, and raw glass from which to grind mirrors from scratch. All scopes are composed of two basic parts: a mounting that allows you to point it anywhere, and a tube assembly, consisting of the light-gathering optics and an eyepiece used for focusing the image.

There are two basic types of telescope mountings, from which other variations have been produced. The simplest is the altazimuth mounting, which allows you to move the telescope in two axes--up and down, left and right. This is the type of mounting found on the simplest "toy" telescopes. Recently amateur astronomers have produced Dobsonian mountings--so named for San Francisco telescope builder John Dobson--much like the altazimuth, which permit large telescopes to be mounted inexpensively. Huge professional telescopes now use altazimuth mounts coupled to computer-controlled guidance systems that follow the stars. Yes, follow the stars. Objects in the sky "move," not because of their own motion, but because the earth rotates. They are themselves rapidly moving, but are so far away that we see them as stationary objects. The earth's rotation causes stars to rise in the east and set in the west--which allows designing a tracking system that moves a telescope on one axis so that a single motion keeps an object conveniently centered in the eyepiece.

Such a mounting is called an equatorial; it, too, has two basic motions, right and left, and up and down, but the right/left axis on an equatorial mount can be tilted parallel to the earth's axis, so that a simple single motion can track any object in the sky. The left/right axis on an equatorial is called the polar axis or the Right Ascension axis. If you place a small motor on this axis and track it at the same rate of the earth's rotation (but in an opposite direction), the telescope automatically follows objects, providing it is aligned. Most commercial telescopes arrive on an equatorial mount supplied with a clock drive, and this is a very handy accessory.

Now that you're familiar with various types of telescope mountings, let's look at the optical tube assemblies that lie on top. There are three major types of telescopes commonly available in small apertures: refractors, reflectors, and catadioptrics (the latter including Schmidt-Cassegrain and Maksutov designs).

Refractors use only lenses to collect light and form an image. This type was the original telescope, used by Galileo in 1609 to show the world that Jupiter had satellites and that the Milky Way was made up of millions of stars. It is also the classic picture that comes to mind when a layman thinks of a telescope: a long, skinny, brass tube with a lens at one end and an astronomer peering into the other.

Reflectors are the traditional telescopes and use mirrors to collect light and form an image. The simplest and most common type is a Newtonian reflector that uses a single large mirror and a small diagonal mirror. This type of instrument is inexpensive to build and rewards its owners with excellent image quality. You could spend a few hundred dollars on a commercial, ready to use Newtonian and come away with a 6-inch telescope capable of showing you thousands of interesting objects. These telescopes are free of color aberration, a fault of refractors. Their disadvantages include bulkiness and weight: a 6-inch Newtonian is around 4 to 5 feet long and tips the scales at 50 pounds or more.

The catadioptric designs, of which the Schmidt-Cassegrain and Maksutov-Cassegrain are the commonest types, use both mirrors and lenses to form images. They bounce incoming light between two mirrors to yield a very powerful, long focal length telescope in a short, light tube. They are very portable, and for that reason are the most common large telescopes today.

The larger diameter the telescope's mirror or lens, the more light you can collect and, generally, the more detail you'll be able to see due to high resolution. Twenty years ago nobody mass-produced telescopes, and those that were commercially available were very expensive. So small telescopes were very common. Today's technology has made 4-inch and 6-inch telescopes affordable, but if you want to save money you can buy the parts and build one yourself.

You can easily go overboard with telescope: a 12-inch Newtonian shows many more objects than a 6-inch Newtonian, but the 12-incher is so big that you'll need a station wagon or truck to haul it to dark sky sites. It is indeed sad to see someone sink a thousand dollars into a large telescope only to   store it away in the garage because "it's "too darn heavy to put in the car." You'll do well to get a small telescope first, see if you enjoy becoming a backyard sky gazer, then perhaps move up to a costlier instrument.

Approach the purchase of a telescope carefully. Consult telescope dealers, astronomy instructors, planetarium people, telescope owners, and astronomy club members. Take the advice of people who own and know telescopes. And remember that in the telescope business you usually get what you pay for. If you live near a college or in a city, there may well be an astronomy club in your town. Clubs hold "star parties" where you may take a look through telescopes before deciding what you want. If you don't know where to look for a club, contact one of the following: the

Astronomical League, Science Services Building, Washington, DC 20036; the Western Amateur Astronomers, 2215 Martha Avenue, Orange, Cal. 92267; or the Astronomical Society of the Pacific, 1290 24th Avenue, San Francisco, Cal 94122. These groups are composed of networks of astronomy clubs and will be happy to assist you in finding information. If you purchase a telescope, you can also contact the manufacturer for information, instruction manuals, help from their dealers, or lists of reference books, atlases, and magazines that will help you enjoy the heavens.

Before you use a telescope, you should be familiar with the constellations and know how to use a star chart to find objects in the sky. Such charts appear in many books and are printed monthly in Astronomy and Sky and Telescope magazines, the two most influential U.S. astronomy publications. A pair of 7 x 35 or 7 x 50 binoculars can be a great aid in locating objects and familiarizing yourself with the heavens. And when you do start looking around in the sky with your telescope, try to observe a few times with an experienced skywatcher--that will get you off to a good start in your cosmic adventure.

As you get used to your telescope, you'll become quite agile with it. You'll see which eyepieces work best for which objects you like to observe. After you find an object, don't take just a casual glance--take some time to look carefully--since then you'll see details that "show themselves" after a bit of looking. Seeing conditions--the atmosphere's steadiness--will sometimes play tricks on you: as you watch, there will be periods of good seeing when the image will look as crisp as a painting, and occasional turbulence that will soften the image. As you gain experience your eyes will become "educated" and you'll see more than you did when you first started. Repeating observations also helps you to see more: the 35th time you look at the Great Nebula in Orion, you'll see it quite differently than you did the 2nd time. If you keep a logbook of your observations, a valuable item in later months and years, you'll be able to monitor the growth of your observing skills.

When a beginner skygazer asks me to recommend a telescope, I take several factors into account. The following types are best for certain kinds of deep-sky observing.

Newtonians and Dobsonians. A 4-inch to 6-inch Newtonian reflector with a focal ratio of f/5 to f/8 is a good all-around observational telescope, and will show many deep-sky objects. This type is the most economical--especially when mounted Dobsonian-style--and is excellent for image brightness, wide field of view, and ease of use.

Schmidt-Cassegrains. If you want maximum portability and good capability for astrophotography, you'll probably want a Schmidt-Cassegrain. Inch for inch, they are more expensive than Newtonians. Because of their long focal ratios (f/10 or greater), they show lots of detail and work well on small deep-sky objects, but their relatively narrow fields of view prohibit observing the largest deep-sky objects. You can avoid this problem by adding a visual compressing lens, which reduces the effective focal ratio to f/5 or so and increases the field of view by 100%.

Richest Field Telescopes. An "RFT," a short focal length Newtonian, makes an excellent low power telescope that gives bright images of large deep-sky objects. It is not a good scope for small objects like galaxies and planetary nebulae, but complements the standard types and thus makes a fine "second telescope." Look for them in focal ratios of f/3.5 to f/5.

Refractors. Although they are expensive and offer only narrow fields of view because of their f/10 to f/15 focal ratios, refractors offer fine resolution for tiny details and are excellent instruments for double stars.

Properly used, even a tiny 2-inch refractor can show you the rings of Saturn or the soft glow of the Andromeda Galaxy. Be patient as a budding stargazer, and realize that the views in telescopes won't equal long-exposure observatory photos of the far-away objects. You'll experience the colored hues of twin-star systems orbiting each other; fuzzy patches of nebulous gas with hot star clusters in their bellies; and wispy distant spiral galaxies, so huge but so silent. You'll be seeing the objects "live," unprocessed by electronics or photography, and you will experience a unique view of a certain object through your telescope. As you gain experience as an observer, you'll gain a realization of exactly how profoundly and startlingly real those faint galaxies are.

Fig. 1-10. **A 3½-inch Maksutov telescope**

Fig. 1-11. **Schmidt-Cassegrain and Friend**

Fig. 1-12. **A 5-inch Schmidt-Cassegrain**

STARTING TO LOOK

When you first get a telescope, look at a few objects on the ground during the daytime. You'll soon learn how to point your telescope and understand how small its field of view is. After you become fairly comfortable using it, try it out on the moon and some of the bright planets. After you have some experience moving it around, switching magnifications, and getting your eye adjusted, you can turn to the great diversity of deep-sky objects. The following is a list of some of the brightest and best objects, suggested for first-time deep-sky observers.

Object	Constellation
M8, the Lagoon Nebula	Sagittarius
M20, the Trifid Nebula	
A pair of emission nebulae, where gas is condensing into newborn stars.	
M13, the Hercules Cluster	Hercules
A huge globular star cluster.	
M27, the Dumbbell Nebula	Vulpecula
A fine bow-tie shaped planetary nebula.	
M31, the Andromeda Galaxy	Andromeda
The closest large spiral galaxy.	
M42, the Orion Nebula	Orion
A bright emission nebula.	
M44, the Beehive Cluster	Cancer
A large open star cluster.	
M45, the Pleiades	Taurus
An open cluster mixed with a faint nebula.	
M51, the Whirlpool Galaxy	Ursa Major
A nice face-on spiral galaxy.	
The Double Cluster	Perseus
Twin bright open star clusters.	
Alcor and Mizar	Ursa Major
A naked-eye double star; Mizar is itself a telescopic double.	

These targets are easy to find and will give you a good start in your effort to observe the universe. They'll also give you an idea of what to expect. Because of the large sizes of most of these objects, binoculars or small RFTs provide excellent views.

Because modern cities are chock-full of lights that pollute the night sky, you should observe as far away from them as possible. Streetlights, cars, houses, businesses, and so on create a huge bowl of light around metropolitan areas. Unfortunately, man's artificial lights reflect off of atmopsheric dust and smog and return to Earth, making the nighttime sky very bright, relatively speaking. This light pollution will drastically affect what you can see through your telescope, and it is as important a consideration as telescope aperture itself. If you get away from city lights--perhaps only 20 or 30 miles out--your telescope will show you many objects that were completly invisible from near the city.

It is also important to "dark-adapt" your eyes: don't set up your telescope, run inside your house to get warm, and run out to observe again. You must stay outside, with no exposure to bright lights, for at least 15 minutes (and probably closer to 40 minutes) to become fully sensitive to faint light. When your eyes are fully dark-adapted, their pupils open up to about 7mm diameter. You will thus see faint objects far better than when you first came outside. Don't use an unfiltered flashlight when you read a star chart: either buy a red-filtered flashlight that is pretty dim, or create one by placing a red filter over a flashlight you already own. Human eyes are far less sensitive to faint red light, and so it will barely affect your dark-adapted eyes.

Atmospheric stability is another important consideration. On unsteady nights, telescopic images of the moon or bright stars seem to "flicker" or "wiggle," as if you were viewing them from the bottom of a swimming pool. This motion is not caused by activity on the Moon or stars, but by turbulence in the earth's atmosphere. Astronomers call the measure of this turbulence "seeing."

If you observe the same object wih the same telescope from the same place on several different nights, you'll notice that the seeing--how well you can see an object--varies a bit from night to night. Sometimes it is very good, sometimes it is bad. You'll see that on nights of bad seeing the images will be so distorted that you'll probably want to only use low powers--which don't accentuate the bad seeing as much as high powers--or not to observe at all.

What can you do about bad seeing conditions? Not much, except wait for another night. Different parts of the country exhibit very different seeing conditions. And local geographical features such as lakes, mountain ranges, or even houses, can also alter the seeing. Never observe looking over a house or other heat-emitting surface, since the turbulent air above it will surely distort the images. On the other hand, lakes seem to steady telescopic images.

The atmosphere does more than distort your views of astronomical objects--it also filters their light, causing them to appear much dimmer than they would, say, from space. The lower parts of earth's atmosphere contain lots of water vapor, dust, and man-made contaminants. All of these particles scatter starlight, substantially reducing the image quality. If you go to a high elevation, you'll be amazed at how dark the sky appears. At high elevations, less light is absorbed and scattered by the atmosphere: about 45% more light gets through at 8,000 feet than at sea level. This is exactly why major observatories like Palomar, Kitt Peak, and McDonald are perched high on mountaintops.

To be a deep-sky observer, you must learn how to successfully avoid the moon. Try observing an object like M42 every night as the moon changes from new (invisible) to its full phase. You'll see that as the Moon approaches full, the sky becomes brighter and more "washed out," making views of deep-sky objects unbearably bad. In a sense the moon acts as a huge streetlamp, reflecting scattered sunlight back onto the "dark" side of the Earth. Scattered moonlight overpowers faint objects, so use nights when the Moon is bright to plan observing sessions, to maintain your equipment, and to dream of the views you'll get when the big satellite once again gets out of the way. You can observe double stars and bright open clusters when the moon is partially lit, but forget observing nebular objects--they'll be completely wiped out.

Your eye is a remarkable instrument. It can discern detail in bright daytime light, and it can perceive the faint, delicate details of a distant galaxy. This property, the ability to see such a huge variety of brightnesses, is called having a large dynamic range. This construction of your eye is such that different parts of it are more sensitive to faint light than others. When you look directly at an object the cornea and lens of your eye form an image on one part of your retina, the structure sensitive to bright light and color. This central area, called the fovea, hosts a high concentration of color receptors called cones, and very few faint light receptors (termed rods). When you look slightly away from an object--with the "side" of your eye--you use many rods, and can therefore see faint details very well. This is using "averted vision," a valuable tool for deep-sky observers. Using this trick will make faint objects pop into view better, and sometimes you'll look at objects that are so faint you'll have to use averted vision to see them at all!

Before you worry too much about how to observe deep-sky objects, you must know how to find them. Finding deep-sky objects is often confusing to beginners, but it isn't too hard to learn after short intervals of practice. It's possible to get a telescope and launch right into observing deep-sky objects, but if you carefully look at a map of the sky beforehand you'll know your way around much better. Familiarize yourself with the constellations and where objects lie in relation to bright stars. Get hold of one of the very simple charts showing the brightest stars (the ones printed in Astronomy or Sky and Telescope, for example) and also one that is more detailed. The following is a list of the most popular star atlases and their relative usefulness to small telescope observers.

British Astronomical Association, B.A.A. Star Charts. Drawn by Wil
     Tirion. Enslow Publishers, Box 777, Hillside, NJ, 1983. An
     inexpensive set of five charts showing all stars down to and
     including magnitude 6.5. Includes many deep-sky objects.
Becvar, Antonin, Skalnate Pleso Atlas of the Heavens. Sky Publishing
     Corp., Cambridge, MA, 1962.
     This is an excellent atlas, and shows many thousands of deep-sky
     objects. However it is now superseded by Tirion's updated version.
Dickinson, Terence, Chaple, Glenn F., and Costanzo, Victor, Mag. 6 Star
     Atlas. Edmund Scientific, Barrington, NJ, 1982.
     A nice atlas showing a moderate number of deep-sky objects.
Howard, Neale E., A Telescope Handbook and Star Atlas. Thomas Y. Crowell
     Publishers, New York, 1975.
     Unfortunately this nice work--which contains an atlas bound into
     sections of text--suffers because its deep-sky object overlays
     don't exactly register with the underlying starfields.
Norton, Arthur P., Norton's Star Atlas and Reference Handbook. Sky
     Publishing Corp., Cambridge, MA, 1973.
     This atlas--a classic for many years--shows a moderate number of
     deep-sky objects, but suffers from cluttered, old-fashioned
     notation.
Scovil, Charles E., AAVSO Star Atlas. Sky Publishing Corp., Cambridge,
     MA, 1982.
     An excellent atlas for variable star observers, it plots deep-sky
     objects but doesn't label them. You can't help but wonder why.
Tirion, Wil, Sky Atlas 2000.0. Cambridge University Press, Cambridge,
     U.K., and Sky Publishing Corp., Cambridge, MA, 1981.
     An updated version of the classic Becvar work, this is absolutely
     the finest and most detailed deep sky atlas, showing thousands of
     objects.
Vehrenberg, Hans, and Blank, Dieter, Handbook of the Constellations. Sky
     Publishing Corp., Cambridge, MA, 1973.
     This is a fine work for deep-sky observers, labeling a moderate
     number of objects and produced in an easy to use style.

To learn the constellations, you must learn how to use a star chart. Star charts are simply maps of the sky and represent stars and deep-sky objects projected onto flat paper. They exhibit the same types of slight distortion as do flat maps of the earth's surface--some more than others--because they project three dimensions onto a two-dimensional sheet of paper.

It isn't difficult to use a star chart to find a deep-sky object.

First find the chart that shows the approximate part of the sky in which
the object lies. Then locate that part of the sky by picking a bright
star nearby and finding it on the chart. Now relocate the object on the
chart and note its position relative to the closest bright star. You can
now approach the job of finding the object in your telescope by one of
two methods--"star-hopping" or using coordinates. Star-hopping is simply
finding the bright locator-star in your finderscope and hopping over to
the object's position by using chains and patterns of stars. Or you can
use the telescope's setting circles and coordinates, a method explained
in detail later.

A good quality 6 x 30 or 8 x 50 (preferably 8 x 50) finderscope
should ride atop your telescope, and you should check its alignment--its
collimation with the main telescope--before each observing session.
Finderscopes are simply small refracting telescopes attached to the side
of the main instrument. They are fitted with a crosshair and adjusting
screws so that you can align the intersection of the crosshairs with the
center of your telescope's field of view. Finders show an inverted image
(unless they are fitted with a right-angle eyepiece, in which case the
image is only backwards) and range in size from approximately 25mm to
80mm aperture and in magnifications from 5x to 11x. The larger your
telescope is, the larger you'll want your finder to be. Large
finderscopes make it easy to pick up faint objects but also
characteristically have smaller fields of view. They are primarily
available as straight-through instruments, but you can add a star
diagonal to allow right-angle viewing.

On most star charts you'll see a grid of lines, much like lines of
latitude and longitude on earth. These grids compose a coordinate system
designed to help astronomers find objects in the sky; you can think of
them as an extension of the earth's latitude and longitude up onto the
celestial sphere.

Projecting the earth's axis of rotation and equator up to where
they intersect the imaginary celestial sphere creates the north and
south celestial poles and the celestial equator. Just where an
astronomical object lies in relation to the celestial poles and
equator--the equivalent of earth's latitude--is the measure of
declination. Position on a sphere, either with regard to the earth or
the sky, is measured in degrees. So where your city has a latitude in
degrees above the earth's equator, a sky object has a declination north
(+) or south (-) of the celestial equator. An object at the celestial
equator has a declination of 0°, while an object at the north celestial
pole--near Polaris, the North Star--has a declination of +90°.

To measure east/west positions, geographers use longitude.
Astronomers decided to measure the celestial sphere in terms of hours,
minutes, and seconds of right ascension because the east/west motion of
the stars was once used to measure time. One complete trip around the
sky in the east/west direction equals 24 hours of right ascension
(R.A.). Since one revolution is also 360°, we see that one hour of R.A.
angle is 15° (360 divided by 24 = 15). In one hour, then, a sky object
travels about 15°, east to west.

In the sky, as on earth, we have arbitrarily decided that the zero
mark in R.A. (and longitude) starts in a certain spot and that R.A.
increases eastwardly until we reach 24 hours, the same spot.

Thus all objects in the sky are assigned a unique position in terms
of right ascension and declination. For example: the Orion Nebula, M42,
has the coordinates 5 hours 33 minutes (R.A.) and -05° 25' (Dec.). This
means that it lies 5 hours 33 minutes (83.25°) east of the Vernal

Equinox--the Sun's position on the first day of spring--and about 5.5° below the celestial equator. No other object has that precise position. The right ascension system was arbitarily selected to start at the Vernal Equinox; there's nothing so special about that spot, just as there's nothing special about Greenwich, England as the earth's "zero point."

You can use right ascension and declination to locate objects providing your telescope is equipped with setting circles, a pair of disks with graduated marks. They are located on each axis of an equatorial telescope, the polar axis (R.A.) and the declination axis. The declination circle reads from +90° (the north celestial pole) to 0° (the celestial equator) to -90° (the south celestial pole). The right ascension axis reads like a clock: its divisions add up to 24 hours.

To use setting circles, you must first polar-align your telescope (see the telescope's instruction manual), a relatively simple job that takes about 10 minutes. If you've accurately polar-aligned the scope, the setting circles will read accurately and the clock drive will track on target. After polar-aligning, point the telescope at a star of known coordinates that lies in the same general area as the objects you want to view and center it in the telescope. Then manually adjust the setting circles to read the coordinates of the star. The setting circles are now calibrated. Now move the telescope's axes--not the setting circles--until the markers show the coordinates of the deep-sky object you're hunting. If you have good polar-alignment and good calibration, the object should be in the telescope's field of view or at least close by. To make this job as easy as possible, always use a low power eyepiece to find objects. After you find that faint galaxy you can switch to a higher powered ocular, but make things easy on yourself. If you know you're in the right area but can't find the object, check the finderscope which may show it.

With most telescopes, setting circles are very accurate over a short slice of sky, say 15° to 25°: but if you calibrate on a star and try to find an object in the opposite part of the sky, you may find that the object is not dead center in the field. With most commercial telescopes, the R.A. circle is driven by a clock motor, so once you've calibrated the circles, they'll remain aligned all night. But it is still a good idea to recalibrate every half hour or so. If your telescope is not motor-driven, you'll have to recalibrate every time you use the circles to move to another object.

A telescope, like a car, has limits to its performance. Perhaps the most misunderstood limitation is magnification. Telescopes do indeed magnify objects, but there is a practical limit. Magnification is the focal length of the telescope divided by the eyepiece's focal length (focal length is the distance from an optical system to the point where it forms an image). Telescope focal lengths are supplied by the manufacturers; eyepiece focal lengths are printed on the eyepieces themselves.

By changing the focal length of the eyepiece in your telescope, you can get nearly any power you want. But as we've said there is a limit: a rule of thumb is that the maximum useable telescopic power is 50 to 60 times the mirror diameter in inches. So if you have a 6-inch f/8 telescope--which has an effective focal length of 48 inches--the most power you can get away with is around 300x. You can certainly put a higher power eyepiece in your telescope, but you'll get a dimmer, more distorted image. But in deep sky observing you generally want to use low power eyepieces anyway, since the objects are fairly large and the wide field of low-power eyepieces gives bright images of faint fuzzy things like galaxies.

A limiting factor in using high magnifications is the steadiness of the atmopshere. On some nights the air is more stable than on others: on these really clear, steady nights, use high powers on close double stars and tiny planetary nebulae; on more average nights, use low powers.

Magnification also affects the brightness of the telescope's image. A telescope's optics compress the incoming light into a focused beam called the "exit pupil." The diameter of this focused beam of light affects how bright the object appears to be. To find the exit pupil of your telescope, divide the diameter of the mirror in millimeters by the telescope's magnification. If your eye is fully dark-adapted, the maximum diameter of your pupil can be as much as 7mm. If you use an eyepiece with so low a magnification that the exit pupil is larger than 7mm, some of the light will never enter your eyes. On the other hand, if you use a high power eyepiece and make the exit pupil smaller than 7mm, the images of faint objects will be relatively dim but may contrast well with the slightly darker sky background. So to get the brightest possible images of deep-sky objects, get a low power eyepiece with a large exit pupil, but not so large that you waste lots of light.

You'll find that some objects need more magnification than others for the best possible view. Objects like the Orion Nebula and the Andromeda Galaxy are best viewed with low power. But you may well give up some of the exit pupil to use slightly higher magnifications on objects like the Hercules Cluster: with a 60mm eyepiece on a 5-inch f/10 scope, it appears very bright, but a 24mm ocular with the same telescope retains a pretty bright image and resolves more of the cluster's stars. The name of the game in using eyepieces is experimentation--see what powers please you the most on different types of objects, and pretty soon you'll know what eyepiece to use when.

Despite most of the wonderful things you can do with your telescope, it is primarily a visual instrument--in other words, you'll use it for just plain old looking rather than photography. You point the scope, pop in an eyepiece, and focus. But what type of eyepiece you use affects the quality of the image you see. The two most important characteristics for eyepieces are focal length and optical design. The smaller the focal length of the eyepiece, the higher the magnification. Large magnifications cause small fields of view and relatively dim images. With a 5-inch f/10 telescope (50 inches or 1270 millimeters focal length) a 32mm focal length eyepiece (resulting in 40x) or a 24mm eyepiece (53x) usually does a nice job of providing a crisp wide field and bright images.

Just as significant to your telescope's performance is the optical design of the eyepieces you use. Four types are currently of particular use to deep-sky observers.

1. Kellner. The Kellner eyepiece and its derivatives are the ones which are supplied as standard equipment with most commercial telescopes. They provide much better image quality than the more primitive Ramsdens and Huygenians--the eyepieces that are supplied with department store telescopes--but they can give ghost reflection images from bright stars. They work well at low powers, and are most useful in focal lengths of 12mm to 30mm. They perform best with telescopes in the f/8 to f/15 range, and show an apparent field of view of about 40°.

2. Orthoscopic. Orthoscopic oculars are constructed of six optical elements and yield superior images to those offered by Kellners. They provide better color correction, contrast, edge sharpness, and show markedly fewer ghost images. They are valuable oculars for double star observing, and for looking at small objects like planetary nebulae and globular clusters. Commercial orthoscopic designs range from 4mm to

40mm in focal length, and they work well with short-focus instruments.

3. Erfle. The Erfle design is one of the most useful for deep-sky observing. It offers huge apparent fields of view, so that you get the effect of looking through a wide angle lens at the sky--and the images are very bright. They are usually available in focal lengths of 15mm to 60mm: try one on the Orion Nebula or the Double Cluster and you'll no doubt be pleased with its performance.

4. Plossl. The Plossl design is certainly one of the best. It contains four elements so that it loses less light than an Orthoscopic or Erfle eyepiece, and many observers claim to see more with Plossls than with Erfles. The Plossls also offer very wide apparent fields (up to 50°) and superior image definition.

You can get eyepieces in many different optical configurations and focal lengths. But you can't buy everything--what should you get? You'll probably receive some oculars, and probably pretty good ones, with your telescope. But they may not be the best types for deep-sky observing, or they may not cover all of your needs. The following is a list of oculars that cover most uses.

1. A low power ocular. You'll certainly need a good low power eyepiece with a focal length designed to give you a large exit pupil (and therefore high image brightness on faint objects). Best buy: a 28mm to 50mm Plossl or Erfle.

2. A medium-power wide angle ocular. You'll want a higher powered version of #1 to see sharp definition in star clusters and nebulae. Best buy: either a 20mm to 25mm Erfle or Plossl, or a 2x Barlow lens--a device used with an eyepiece to increase its power--coupled to eyepiece #1 to double its power.

3. A medium power ocular. You'll want a normal medium power eyepiece for small deep-sky objects. Best buy: a 12mm Orthoscopic or Plossl.

4. A high-power ocular. A good high-power eyepiece is essential for checking the alignment of your telescope, observing planetary nebulae, and splitting close double stars. Best buy: a 6mm to 10mm orthoscopic or Plossl.

You'll have to determine the exact focal lengths in the four catagories to match your particular system and needs. You don't rigidly need four oculars either--you'll like certain types as you use your telescope more, and you may end up satisfied with only two oculars or two oculars and a Barlow lens.

Deep-sky observing strains the eye and mind: in it you try to capture as many precious photons of faint light as possible. The smallest amount of city light can be crucially damaging, so if you must observe near light pollution of some kind you may want to get a polarizing "light pollution filter."

Polarizing filters allow you to reject scattered light and light that is preferentially vibrating in one direction (light acts--at least on occasion--as a wave). To do this the filter's molecular structure is aligned such that it is parallel. Artificial lighting around a city is composed primarily of streetlamps emitting specific colors. And so is a nebula's light: the nebula filter is constructed such that it allows only light of the nebular type to pass though it, thus blocking out the bothersome artificial light. The filters aren't perfect: some light leaks and cities have a few types of light very close to that of nebulae. But city-bound observers will probably find that a nebular filter is a great help for observing certain objects.

A telescope permits you to reach out into the depths of space and explore the universe around you. Whether you gaze from the backyard or travel several hundreds of miles to a remote spot, remember to make yourself comfortable on the long voyage. If you've never taken your telescope to a dark-sky site for a star party, you've got a real treat in store, but if you don't dress right you've got another thing coming. Remember to take your red filtered flashlight, your telescope, your star charts, something warm to drink, and appropriate clothing. After you realize what you'll need on such an expedition, you can prepare for an unabashed star party out in the "wilds." Make a checklist of items to take: it's an unpleasant experience to drag your family out 100 miles and realize you forgot the eyepieces and the star chart!

The most important thing to remember is to dress warmly. Even during the summer--at high elevations--the temperature can drop rapidly after sunset. Always take an extra jacket or sweater--after all, you can remove too much clothing, but you'll have to pack up and leave if you don't have enough. Get a warm sleeping bag or lots of blankets for overnight ventures. Goose down seems to be about the best filler for sleeping bags--why not visit a mountaineering shop to start preparing your cold weather gear?

But don't go overboard at first. Astronomy can be an expensive hobby if you make mistakes. Prepare sensibly: if you're not already a diehard observer, get a basic good quality telescope with one or two eyepieces. Then grow with the interest--you can always get more accessories or a bigger telescope later. You probably have enough warm clothing already, but your first star party or two will tell you whether you need more.

When assembling your cold weather gear, pay careful attention to your hands, feet, and head: get gloves, sturdy shoes (insulated snow boots are great) and a wool cap. Bring some friends and hot drinks along--the company will at least help you ignore the cold!

Fig. 2-1. Alcor and Mizar in the Big Dipper's handle

2 Double Stars

Glenn F. Chaple, Jr.

To the unaided eye, Albireo is an ordinary second magnitude star, found at the base of the Northern Cross. Through the eyepiece of any small telescope, however, an amazing transformation takes place: Albireo becomes __two__ stars! On top of that, the brighter one is rich golden-yellow in color, while its partner is deep blue. The surrounding darkness accents this striking color contrast. One stares in trancelike wonder at this celestial marvel, reluctant to leave the eyepiece.

The beauty of double stars is simple, yet compelling. It manifests itself in exquisitely-hued pairs like Albireo. It is further evident in the bright "twin" systems that glow like a cat's eyes from the inky blackness of space. Even faint double stars have a uniquely delicate beauty that captivates the visual sense.

The heavens abound with double stars suitable for small telescopes. Over a thousand of the more interesting pairs are presented by constellation in the Catalog section of this chapter. Preceding the list is background information on the history of double stars, their physical nature, observing hints, and telescopic sketches. I hope that this double star section will serve as a useful guide to small telescope owners who want to explore the fascinating realm of double stars.

This section is dedicated to the following people, all of whom contributed immensely to the completion of this work: Ray Gerbi, a high school friend who introduced me to amateur astronomy and showed me my first double star; My parents, who encouraged my study of astronomy by purchasing my first telescope; Dave Eicher, whose energy and enthusiasm got this book started; and my wife, Regina, who has patiently endured many hours as an astronomy "widow" while I was outdoors observing double stars or indoors writing about them.

Glenn F. Chaple, Jr.
Townsend, Massachusetts

About the Author: Glenn F. Chaple, Jr. is a high school science teacher whose keen interest in astronomy dates back to 1963. After earning a BS in astronomy from the University of Massachusetts, Mr. Chaple spent two years in the army and then lectured on astronomy at the Alice G. Wallace Planetarium in Fitchburg, Massachusetts. With Terence Dickinson and Victor Costanzo he authored the Edmund Mag. 6 Star Atlas, and has written many articles for astronomical magazines, including Astronomy, Star and Sky, Odyssey, and Deep Sky. He is a contributing editor of Deep Sky magazine and an active member of the American Association of Variable Star Observers, the Amateur Astronomers Association, and the Amateur Telescope Makers of Boston.

HISTORICAL BACKGROUND

The term double star seems to have been coined by the Greek-Egyptian astronomer Claudius Ptolemy (ca. 140 A.D.), who used it to describe the naked-eye pair ν^1, ν^2 Sagittarii. It was not the only such object known. Indeed, the best-known naked-eye double is probably Mizar and Alcor, located at the crook in the handle of the Big Dipper. Because Alcor is five times fainter than its partner and just one-fifth degree from it, an individual's ability to see both stars was considered by the Arabians of medieval times to be a sure sign of keen eyesight.

Several decades after the invention of the telescope, Mizar played an historic role in astronomy as the first double star discovered with this optical tool. We might well imagine the surprise when Jean Baptiste Riccioli, in 1650, looked through his telescope at this bright star and found a diminutive companion shining far closer to it than its traditional neighbor--Alcor. The discovery was purely accidental, as were ensuing finds by 17th-century skywatchers. These discoveries include θ' Orionis (1656), Capricorni and 61 Cygni (1659), γ Arietis (1664), α Crucis (1685), and α Centauri (1689). During the next century, astronomers continued to stumble across double stars while chasing comets or casually scanning the skies.

An era of systematic double star discovery opened in 1781 with the appearance of the first double star catalog. Published by the Jesuit priest Christian Mayer, it listed the 80 pairs that he and his assistant Johann Metzger found with the 8-foot mural quadrant at Mannheim. The following year William Herschel, a musician turned astronomer who immigrated to England from his native Germany, presented to the Royal Society a catalog of 269 double stars. And in 1784 the same indefatigable observer produced a second catalog, this time containing an additional 434 entries.

The importance of Herschel's catalogues goes beyond mere numbers. Both contain reasonably accurate measures of separation and position angle for each double star listed--a result of Herschel's belief that double stars (especially those of unequal brightness) would provide a natural means of determining stellar parallax. "As the earth orbits the sun," he reasoned, "the brighter star--being the nearest--should undergo a cyclic displacement relative to its distant, fixed neighbor."

This assumption that double stars might be chance optical alignments of unrelated stars agreed with the prevalent belief of the times. Arguments by Lambert in 1761 and Mitchell in 1767 stressed the possibility that some stellar pairs might be gravitationally-bound systems, but failed for lack of visual evidence. When Herschel reobserved his double stars at the end of the century, his dream of detecting stellar parallax and the resultant stellar distances all but vanished. (The actual accomplishment required the more accurate instrumentation of F. W. Bessel, some forty years later.) He did, however, find that a few dozen pairs underwent position changes. This could only be explained by orbital motions resulting from gravitational interactions between the component stars. Dubbing them binary stars, he announced their discovery in an extraordinary paper published in 1803. Thus did William Herschel reap triumph out of failure.

A brief lull in double star observations ended in 1816 when John Herschel, later assisted by James South, began reviewing and extending his father's work. In doing so, he discovered position changes in more binary stars. From 1833 to 1838, the younger Herschel surveyed the heavens from an observatory erected at Capetown, South Africa. The relatively uncharted southern skies produced thousands of new pairs.

The next major step in double star astronomy is credited to Wilhelm Struve, whose greatest contributions came while he was director of the Dorpat Observatory in what is now Estonia. Using the observatory's 9.5-inch refractor--then the world's largest--he conducted a search for double stars that lasted from November 1824 to February 1827. He checked all stars brighter than 9th magnitude and north of -15 degrees declination for possible companions. The pace was incredible: in an average hour, 400 stars passed before his eyes. The result of his labor appeared in three monumental volumes--Catalogus Novus described the 3,110 double stars Struve found, Mensurae Micrometricae included measures of these pairs, and Positiones Mediae documented the locations of the Struve doubles. Of the three, the Mensurae Micrometricae is the most noteworthy. Here, for the first time, are measures of separation and position angle that rival modern standards.

Struve's son Otto carried on his double star work. During the last months of 1841 and most of 1842, Otto Struve used Pulkova's 15-inch refractor to resurvey the northern heavens. The 514 new pairs he found, supplemented by 33 later discoveries, formed the Pulkovo Catalogue.

The Struves ended an era of double star discovery that Mayer and the Herschels opened. Double star astronomy in the mid-1800's became the realm of observers who carefully measured known pairs and computed orbits for those showing binary motion. The best known of these double star statisticians was astronomer Baron Ercole Dembowski of Naples who, during the last thirty years of his life, made over 20,000 sets of measures. Dembowski's contemporaries included the Rev. W.R. Dawes, J.H. Madler, Father Angelo Secchi, and F.W. Bessel.

Despite a reduction in new discoveries, the mid-1800's was not a period of stagnation for double star astronomy. In 1840, Bessel cracked the code of stellar distances by determining the parallax of 61 Cygni. Distance determinations of Vega (by Wilhelm Struve) and α Centauri (by Henderson and Maclear) quickly followed. If a star whose distance is known happens to be a visual binary (as are 61 Cygni and α Centauri), it provides a special bonus -- the masses of the component stars can be calculated through a simple application of Kepler's Harmonic Law of Orbits. Even today, the gravitational interaction between members of a binary star system provides the only direct means astronomers have of determining stellar masses. Bessel's penchant for accuracy also led to the discovery, in 1844, of a wavelike pattern in the proper motion of Sirius. This he correctly attributed to the gravitational pull from an invisible companion in orbit around the brilliant star. Bessel discovered the first astrometric binary. A visual sighting of Sirius companion came in 1862. The mid-1800's also saw the arrival of photography in astronomy; G. P. Bond created the first double star photograph by making a plate of Mizar in 1857. In time, photography proved its value to double star specialists, especially where they needed accurate measurements of pairs wider than 2 arcseconds' separation.

Thirty years after the appearance of the Pulkovo Catalogue, a new era of double star discovery began. One might expect the initiator to be a prominent professional astronomer, equipped with a massive refracting telescope, but this was not the case. In 1873, Sherburne Wesley Burnham, an amateur astronomer who served as clerk of the Federal District Court in Chicago, published a list of 81 new pairs found with a 6-inch Alvan Clark refractor mounted in his backyard. Burnham's method of locating new pairs was not as systematic as Struve's. His first discoveries came during a survey of double stars listed in the Rev. T.W. Webb's Celestial Objects for Common Telescopes. After observing each pair, Burnham carefully scanned the immediate area for new pairs whose separation was 10 arcseconds or less.

Burnham's reputation for keen eyesight eventually gained him access to several of America's finest observatories. Yet despite brief stints at Lick and Yerkes, the Vermont-born observer primarily remained an amateur astronomer. In 1906, he published his two-part General Catalog of Double Stars Within 121° of the North Pole. Part I listed 13,665 pairs, while Part 2 provided measures and notes on each. By the time of his death in 1921, S.W. Burnham had discovered about 1300 double stars and made thousands of accurate and valuable measures.

Burnham's lifetime coincided with some dramatic innovations in double star astronomy, including a way to uncover binary pairs too close together to be resolved visually. In 1889, Harvard Professor E.C. Pickering found that the spectrum of Mizar's brighter component appeared double at regular intervals. His correct assumption was that this star is a binary system whose components move swiftly around their center of mass in orbits that are nearly edge-on to our line of sight. The splitting of their composite spectrum was due to a Doppler shift of their individual spectra at the times when their orbital motion is in recession or approach. Mizar, the first double star discovered with the telescope and the first to be photographed, thus became the first spectroscopic binary.

Not long after Pickering's discovery, Professor H.C. Vogel, at Potsdam, announced that the famous variable Beta Persei (Algol) was a spectroscopic binary. Here was final proof for a hypothesis set forth by John Goodricke over a hundred years earlier, that such highly regular variables are binary systems whose edge-on orbits permit the periodic eclipse of a bright component by a faint companion. Objects like these are now known as eclipsing binaries.

Thanks to the efforts of S.W. Burnham, the end of the ninteenth century and first few decades of the twentieth saw a renaissance in double star discoveries. Thousands of new pairs were brought to light by the American astronomers G.W. Hough and T.J.J. See, the English astronomers T.E.H. Espin and W. Milburn, and the French astronomer Robert Jonckheere. The southern skies, which remained unassailed since the days of John Herschel, yielded their bounty to the watchful eyes of R.T.A. Innes, W.H. van den Bos, W.S. Finsen, and R.A. Rossiter.

The premier double star observer of the time undoubtedly was Robert Grant Aitken. A native Californian, he began his double star work at the Lick Observatory in 1895. Four years later, he decided to emulate Struve by examining all stars in the massive catalog, the Bonner Durchmusterung, which were as bright as magnitude 9.0 and north of -22 degrees declination. Assisted during part of the search by Professor W.J. Hussey, Aitken uncovered 4,432 new double stars--most closer than 5 arcseconds in separation. The number found by these two observers might have been greater, had they not forced by harsh winter weather to abandon some areas south of -18 degrees.

In 1932 Aitken published the New General Catalog of Double Stars within 120° of the North Pole, a revision of Burnham's catalog which contained 17,181 entries. Around that time Innes, at the Union Observatory in South Africa, produced a "sister" catalog of southern double stars. Three years after the appearance of his catalog, Aitken published The Binary Stars, still a valuable guide for serious double star observers.

During the latter part of Aitken's life (he died in 1951), double star astronomy had ebbed in popularity. In 1923 Edwin Hubble discovered that the so-called white nebulae are actually galaxies like our own Milky Way. This caused a shift in attention from local objects like double stars. During the next decade, experiments by Karl Jansky led to the discovery of radio energy from space. The ensuing development and refinement of the radio telescope was as important a stage in the history of astronomy as the invention of the telescope over 300 years earlier.

Likewise, amateur astronomers in the 20th century began showing more interest in galaxies, nebulae, and star clusters (the Messier and NGC objects), while turning away from double stars. The change is obvious when one compares observing guides written a century ago with those of today. Early guides like Webb's Celestial Objects for Common Telescopes and Olcott's Field Book of the Skies listed hundreds of double stars while giving scant attention to clusters and nebulae. The 1978 edition of Burnham's Celestial Handbook, on the other hand, balanaces the double stars with extensive lists of galaxies, nebulae, and clusters. It is probably safe to say that today most amateurs observe many more Messier objects than double stars.

Double star astronomy is far from dead, though. X-ray astronomers are busy studying what seem to be binary systems in which blue supergiant stars are orbiting massive--but invisible--companions. There is the exciting possibility that these unseen objects may be black holes--remnants of once-huge stars that burned out and collapsed. So intense is their gravity that even light cannot escape from them, and material from their unfortunate partners is drawn into them. Like the sailor who lets out a final cry before being swallowed up by the whirlpool, so do these gases emit a flourish of X-rays before forever disappearing.

The visual and spectroscopic pairs are still watched and measured by a handful of dedicated observers. In many instances, their equipment is the same as that used by their counterparts of a century ago. A notable exception is the use of interferometry on close, nearly equal pairs. The two-slit interferometer, first used in 1920, shows the duplicity of pairs that are actually too close to be resolved by normal visual means. It does this by producing an interference pattern that reveals the relative magnitudes, separation, and position angle of stars separated by as little as a few hundredths of a second of arc. The recent development of speckle interferometry permits the discovery of even closer pairs. Astronomers photograph a star under high magnification in a narrow band of wavelength. The resultant image shows a speckle pattern, caused by atmospheric turbulence. If the star is double, the speckle pattern will be doubled. With the help of a laser, which illuminates the negative of the speckly pattern, the image is "regrouped" into a fringe pattern that reveals the basic data about the double star.

A chief sourcebook for today's double star observer is the Index Catalogue of Visual Double Stars (IDS), published by Lick Observatory in 1963. Covering the entire sky, it contains data on almost four times the number of pairs encompassed by Aitken's catalogue. The list of visual double stars and pertinent measures is constantly being updated at the world center for double star observations, currently being maintained by Charles Worley at the U.S. Naval Observatory in Washington DC. Data on the 75,000 currently known pairs appear on over 400,000 punch cards.

As the number of known double stars increased, so has the number of binary stars with known orbits. In 1900, astronomers knew about the orbits of 50 such systems: nowadays, the figure exceeds 500. Every year new orbits appear; others are revised and updated, providing us with more knowledge about the stars that populate our Galaxy. Thanks to the efforts of our modern-day caretakers of the double stars, the efforts of the Herschels, the Struves, Burnham, Aitken, and others are not in vain.

THE NATURE OF DOUBLE STARS

The term "double star" describes any two stars that appear together in
the sky, whether they are gravitationally bound or merely optically
aligned. They can be wide enough to be seen as double with the naked
eye, or so close that only the largest telescopes will resolve them.
Even an apparently single star--whose duplicity is revealed only by the
spectroscope or by its periodic wobbling motion--can still be rightly
called a double star. For a more complete understanding of the nature
of double stars, let's review the various kinds.

     If two stars are at great distances from each other, but happen to
lie along the same line of sight from our perspective, they form an
optical double. Such pairs are of little use to astronomers except,
perhaps, for parallax determinations. A fine example of an optical
double is   Herculis.

     Most visual double stars are true physical systems. Their
component stars orbit each other in periods that vary from a few years
to many millions of years. These are the visual binary stars; once the
orbit of such a star is determined, it is possible to calculate the mass
of each of the component stars. In general, the closer together the
stars appear to be, the faster they move in their orbits. Nevertheless,
several years must pass before some of the swifter visual binaries show
any noticeable change. Castor (α Geminorum) is a classic example of a
visual binary whose member stars are widening, while Porrima--the star
γ Virginis--is a binary that is rapidly closing. Most wide binaries
have shown practically no orbital motion since accurate double star
measurements began a century and a half ago. That their components are
physically bound is evident only in the fact that they share a common
proper motion. Observations by many generations of astronomers will be
required before pairs like Mizar (ζ Ursae Majoris) and Polaris--also
known as α Ursae Minoris--join the ranks of the visual binary stars
whose orbits are known.

     Binaries that are too close to be resolved with telescopes move
swiftly enough in their orbits to create a periodic Doppler shift in
their spectra--provided that their orbits are edge-on to our line of
sight. When the component stars of such a system move across our line
of sight, there is no Doppler shift and their spectra are superimposed.
At other times, the rapid motion of one star toward the earth as its
partner recedes produces Doppler shifts in their spectra. (The spectrum
of the approaching star shifts toward the blue, while that of its
receding partner becomes red-shifted). Such pairs are known as
spectroscopic binaries, and about 2000 are known. As with the visual
pairs, it is possible to compute the orbit of a spectroscopic binary
and, therefore, the masses of its component stars. The visual
components of Mizar as well as nearby Alcor are spectroscopic binaries.

     An eclipsing binary is a spectroscopic binary whose orbit is
exactly edge-on to our line of sight. In this case, the two stars
alternately pass in front of one another as they orbit the system's
center of mass. Viewers on earth see this as a periodic dip in the
brightness of what appears to be a single star. The best-known
eclipsing binary is Algol (β Persei).

     In certain instances, spectroscopes can reveal the duplicity of a
close pair whose orbit is not edge-on to us. This occurs with systems
that match stars of drastically different spectral types. The resultant
spectrum, which may contain lines characteristic of hot stars
intermingled with those found only in cool stars, is unlike anything
that could possibly be produced by a single star. The astronomer who
encounters such a phenomenon has found a spectrum binary.

Since both members of a binary star system orbit a point in space that is coincident with their center of mass, we can detect an otherwise invisible companion by its orbital interaction with the primary star. Instead of a straight-line motion across the heavens, the primary star will trace out a wavelike path as it reacts to the gravitational tug of its partner. The first known astrometric binary is Sirius, whose faint companion eluded telescopes from the mid-1840's until 1862.

The first double stars discovered were regarded as celestial curiosities. Three centuries and thousands of new pairs later, we now realize that they form a very substantial part of our galaxy's population. If a census of the nearest stars is any indication, over half of all stars are double or multiple systems. It is odd to think that our sun--a single star--may be the exception, rather than the rule.

When you look up the description of double stars, optical or binary, you'll encounter three important pieces of information: magnitude, angular separation, and position angle. The magnitudes, of course, refer to the brightness of each star. An equally bright pair is much easier to resolve than an unequal pair of similar separation. Bright pairs are much more readily split than their fainter brethren. The angular separation--or distance--is how far apart the two stars appear to be, and is measured in seconds (") of arc. One arcsecond is just 1/3600 degree and is approximately equal to the width of a penny viewed from a distance of 2.5 miles! Under ideal conditions, a good 2-inch telescope splits a bright, equal double star whose components are just 2.3 arcseconds apart. A 3-inch telescope reduces that figure to 1.5 arcseconds. Close doubles are popular with amateur astronomers who like to put their eyesight and the quality of their telescopes to the ultimate test. The position angle, developed a century and a half ago by John Herschel, is the location of the fainter star relative to the brighter one. If the stars are equally bright, the astronomer who first measures them assigns the role of "primary" to one. As Herschel defined it--and as is now standard convention--the position angle (p.a.) is the angle between a line running northward from the primary star and one joining the two stars, measured around to the east. Astronomers use position angle, in combination with angular separation, to make accurate positonal plots that are later used to determine orbits of double stars.

BEGINNING TO OBSERVE

Don't try to observe double stars (or any other kind of deep-sky object) until you are reasonably competent in the use of your telescope, have a basic familiarity with the major stars and constellations, and can use at least a simple star atlas (like Inglis' Popular Star Atlas or the Edmund Mag 6 Star Atlas) to locate sky objects. Proficiency in observing comes only with practice. For a start, try aiming your telescope and focusing your various eyepieces on daylight objects. At night, you can "cut your teeth" on the moon--an ideal target for the novice astronomer. Later on, try for any available planets or bright stars. The latter won't provide much detail--just a pinpoint of light--but they'll offer practice in critical focusing. In a short time, you'll begin to feel comfortable in the use of your telescope--ready to use it to unlock the heavens' secrets.

While getting to know your telescope, you should also be learning what's up in the sky. A few evenings spent outside with a star finder or atlas (or even better, with a friend who knows the constellations and can point them out to you) is a crucial exercise for anyone who wants to avoid becoming hopelessly confused by the myriad nighttime stars. Once you've learned a few basic constellations, you can begin using your star atlas to identify the various naked-eye stars they contain. Use the atlas to find the location of dimmer constellations and the new ones that keep rising in the east as the night progresses.

When you've mastered the basic sky watching skills, you're ready to track down your first double stars. But which ones will you observe? Beginners should start with pairs that are at least 8 to 10 arcseconds apart and whose component stars are brighter than 6th magnitude. Mizar (ζ Ursae Majoris) and Albireo (β Cygni) are popular first doubles for small instruments. Take a look through the Catalog section of this chapter; using it you can prepare a list of doubles to try spotting. Don't go for pairs which will be at low elevations when you are observing.

Your first list, comprised of bright showpiece pairs located in various sectors of the sky, will be but a prelude to later lists you will glean from the catalogue of double stars that follows. Preparing such lists might seem like a tedious task, but each one will organize your observing by eliminating time wasted in haphazard sweeps for sky objects. To this end, you may eventually want to focus your attention on one constellation per night. For the sake of sanity, try to limit yourself to no more than eight to twelve double stars for each hour spent outside.

When setting up your telescope, stick to two basic rules of deep-sky observing. First, select a viewing site with a good horizon in all directions and away from stray light. Next, give your eyes about 20 to 30 minutes to dark-adapt before seriously observing. During this waiting period, you can check the alignment of your finderscope and pinpoint the locations of the doubles you'll be working on. If this isn't enough, relax and watch for meteors, or casually scan starfields with your telescope. Since you'll need a flashlight, be sure to cut down its glare by covering the lens with a sheet or two of red cellophane, held in place with tape or a rubber band.

The best double star in the sky for beginners is Mizar. Not only are its components bright and easily separated, but Mizar is also the easiest of all doubles to find: just set your sights on the middle star in the handle of the Big Dipper. If your eyesight is reasonably good, you won't need optical aid to see tiny Alcor, shining bravely beside its big brother. Binoculars or finderscopes separate Mizar and Alcor even further, but telescopes complete the trick. With an eyepiece that magnifies around 60x--an ideal power for beginners' doubles--you should see Mizar and Alcor at nearly opposite sides of the field. Roughly between them is an 8th magnitude star with the rather unwieldy name, Sidus Ludovicianum. Now look closely at Mizar: Does your telescope reveal Mizar and its companion, shining together like a distant automobile with one weak headlight? If so, congratulations! You've found your first double star.

After you've seen a few double stars, you'll want to document all of your observations. Although not essential, a careful record of your activities with the telescope is a valuable future reference. Try keeping a notebook in which you make a sketch of each double star, supported by descriptive notes. In the back of the notebook, set up a list--perhaps arranged by constellation--of the pairs you see. Or you may prefer to record the sketches and notes on 5"x 8" file cards and arrange them by constellation or by increasing right ascension. If you decide not to keep records of your observations, at least check off each pair you see in the catalog of double stars.

Sooner or later, you'll want to try observing double stars that offer more of a challenge than the wide, bright pairs. If you want to try your luck on pairs whose components lie between 4 and 8 arcseconds apart, be sure to choose a night when the seeing is good. A magnification of 60x or so may do the job, but 100x will do better. Be patient--if you can't split a close pair right away, keep looking for a minute or two. Often the atmosphere settles momentarily.

A different kind of challenge comes from unequal pairs whose faint components play hide and seek behind the glare of their primaries. With a low-power eyepiece, look directly at Polaris (α Ursae Minoris): you'll see a yellowish 2nd magnitude star. Look slightly away, however, and voila, a little 9th magnitude star pops into view. The secret behind this trick lies in the fact that a sideward glance allows the light from faint objects to fall on a more sensitive part of the retina, making them visible.

Averted vision also works on pairs whose member stars are both faint. Here are sky objects whose challenge is leveled at your ability to locate them. To work your way down from 5th and 6th magnitude pairs to 7th or 8th necessitates getting an atlas like the Sky Atlas 2000.0. You can carefully pencil in locations of faint pairs once you know their coordinates. Finding a faint double star in your telescope is a relatively simple matter: first center your finder on a bright nearby star and star-hop, alternating glances between finder and atlas, until the site comes into the finder. This done, a careful sweep with a medium-power eyepiece should bring the faint pair to light. One word of caution: avoid faint double stars that lie near the plane of the Milky Way. Here, amid the tangle of starfields, double stars are scattered everywhere. Finding a particular pair in such surroundings can be a frustrating task for beginners.

How long before you'll become an all-knowing double star expert? Probably never! There is always something new to learn, no matter how long you've been telescopically plying the heavens. You might gauge your progress by asking yourself a few questions: (1) Can I efficiently operate my telescope? (2) Can I use a detailed atlas like Becvar's Atlas of the Heavens or Tirion's Sky Atlas 2000.0 to locate double stars? (3) Can I split bright pairs down to 3 or 4 arcseconds when the seeing is good? (4) On clear nights, can I see the faint companions to bright stars like Polaris? (5) Can I plot faint doubles onto my atlas and easily find them in the sky? If you answer yes to each of these questions, you're ready for the next section.

ADVANCED OBSERVING TECHNIQUES

The methods I outlined for beginners are applicable, with minor refinements, to experienced double star observers. The most challenging pairs can be placed into three distinct groups:

1) <u>Close, bright double stars</u>. Skilled amateur astronomers push their eyesight and the optics of their telescopes to the limit by testing them on extremely close pairs. One way of determining the closest double star a telescope will separate (its resolving power) is by the Dawes Limit, or 4.56" divided by A, where A = telescope aperture in inches. The equation, produced by the Rev. William Rutter Dawes--a noted 19th century amateur astronomer--is reliable for equally bright pairs of about 6th magnitude. As can be seen, the larger the telescope, the greater its resolving power. Still, we needn't sell small telescopes short. Applied to a standard 2.4-inch refractor, the Dawes Limit yields a value of just under 2 arcseconds. A 3-inch telescope does even better, at 1.5 arcseconds, while a 4.25-inch reflecting telescope will just about reach one arcsecond--a mighty angular distance, indeed!

Whether you can reach (or even exceed) the Dawes Limit for your telescope depends on the quality of its optics and the optics of your high-power eyepieces, your visual acuity, and the sky conditions. Nights when star images are crisp and steady are a rarity in most localities. When you encounter such an evening, make the most of it! Magnifications of 40x-50x per inch of telescope aperture are a must for pairs separated by one or two arcseconds. A double star is considered "resolved" when it appears as two distinct points of light. Experienced eyes can often recognize an unresolved pair by its elongated shape.

2) <u>Unequal double stars</u>. For double stars whose individual brightnesses differ by more than a couple of magnitudes, the Dawes Limit does not apply. Studies by T.L. Lewis in 1914 showed that the resolving limit for unequal pairs (mean magnitudes 6.2 and 9.5) is about 16.5 arcseconds/A, while for very unequal pairs (mean magnitudes 4.7 and 10.4) it arises to 36.0 arcseconds/A. Thus, Rigel (β Orionis -- magnitudes 0.1 and 6.7, separation 9.4") is an extremely difficult target for a 3-inch telescope. As mentioned in the beginner's section, averted vision is often the only way you can ferret out a faint star from the glare of a much brighter one. Here, as with the close pairs, high power is often necessary.

If all else fails, try a method I used to view the elusive companion of ϵ Bootis (magnitudes 2.5 and 5.0, separation 2.9"). After repeated failures to split this pair under dark sky conditions, I tried viewing it early in the evening when a touch of remaining twilight still brightened the skies. The light of its primary thus subdued, ϵ Bootis at last revealed its sky partner. Moonlight or very slight haze should also do the trick.

3) <u>Faint double stars</u>. Unless skies are absolutely dark, don't bother with faint doubles. Here again, the standard equation for the Dawes limit doesn't work. While I've split bright pairs down to 1.7" with a 3-inch f/10 reflector, I consider it a triumph when I can separate, with this same instrument, an 8th magnitude pair of just under 5 arcseconds. In the beginner's section, I noted that the biggest challenge from faint pairs comes from locating them with the telescope. We can alleviate the situation by seeking out those that lie in the field of a bright star (like $\Sigma817$, an 8th magnitude pair located a mere 20 arcminutes south of Betelgeuse) or near enough to stars in the finder that we can star hop to them.

But what about faint double stars that are totally isolated from bright guide stars? And, looking at the other extreme, what about those faint pairs that dwell with numerous similar-looking stellar duos in the congested portions of the Milky Way? The solution is obvious: you'll need a detailed star atlas like the Atlas Australis, Atlas Eclipticalis, or Atlas Borealis.

To find a particular faint double, note its position relative to the nearest bright star or group of stars. On a file card, carefully trace the field between this guide star and your quarry. Outside, center your finder on the guide star, then peek into the eyepiece (one of low power--say 30x-50x). After orienting the card to match your eyepiece view, star hop from one field star to the next until you arrive at your double star. Now switch to higher powers for a better view.

To confirm the sighting of any double star that belongs to one of these three groups, it may be necessary to estimate its position angle. From the introductory notes, you may remember that the position angle is the location of the fainter star, relative to the primary, and is defined as the angle between a line running northward from the primary and one that travels from the primary through the companion. Since the position angle is measured from the north around through the east, a star located directly north of the primary has a position angle of 0 degrees, one east of the primary has a p.a. of 90 degrees, southwest 225 degrees, and so on.

Professional astronomers (and a few amateurs) use a filar or bifilar micrometer to obtain precise measures of position angle. You can, however, make an "eyeball" estimate that is accurate to within 10 degrees. To do this, all you have to do is establish the "west" point in the field of the double star. How can this be done? Begin by (A) centering the primary star and (B) letting the pair drift toward the edge of the field. Since stars drift in a westerly direction, the point at which the primary star leaves the field is "west." From this point and traveling clockwise in 90 degree increments, the other cardinal points will be south, east, and north. (The "star diagonals" used for observing by many refractor, Schmidt-Cassegrain, and Maksutov telescope users reverse the field from right to left. Cardinal points clockwise from west will read north, east, and south -- Editor). (C) Now return the double star to the center of the field and estimate the direction of the fainter star from the primary (due east, southwest, one third of the way from west toward north, etc.). Convert this to an angular measure (90°, 225°, 300°, etc.); this is the position angle of the double star. Remember, north = 0 degrees, and the position angle is measured around through the east. If you have trouble visualizing the exact location of west as you peer into the eyepiece, make a sketch of the double star, adding an arrow to show the direction of its drift. The other cardinal points can then be indicated and the position angle determined.

By comparing your position angle estimate with the actual value found in an up-to-date source, you can verify the resolution of a close pair or the sighting of a faint companion star. If your estimate of an equally bright double star is about 180 degrees off, you're still on target. You simply measured the p.a. from the wrong star--an understandable error when it's hard to decide which star is the primary. If you should stumble upon a new and unidentifiable double star, make a rough estimate of its magnitudes, separation, and position angle. If possible, note its location among bright field stars. Indoors, you may be able to use a star atlas to pinpoint the coordinates of your "mystery double."

There is a final, important hint for successful double star observing--have fun! The quiet contemplation of the wonders in the universe is what amateur astronomy is all about.

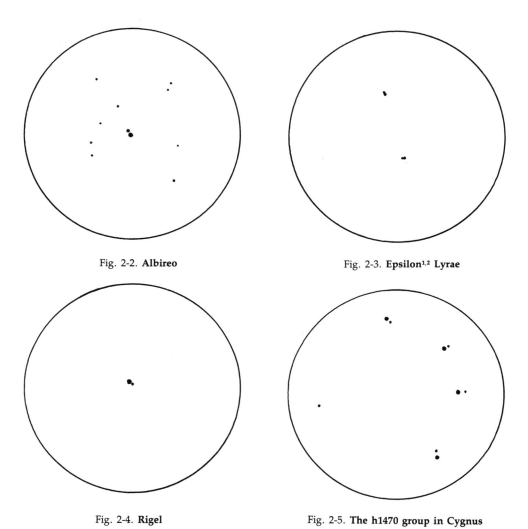

Fig. 2-2. **Albireo**

Fig. 2-3. **Epsilon[1,2] Lyrae**

Fig. 2-4. **Rigel**

Fig. 2-5. **The h1470 group in Cygnus**

Listed on the following pages are 1127 double stars suitable for small telescopes. They have been organized by parent constellation, these being arranged alphabetically. Double stars within each constellation are placed in order of increasing right ascension. Prepared primarily for observers from mid-northern latitudes, this list is as complete as possible down to -20 degrees declination and includes noteworthy pairs between -20 degrees and -40 degrees declination.

I observed over 90 percent of the double stars in this list during an informal ten-year survey, conducted with a 3-inch reflecting telescope. Except for extremely close pairs, which required magnifications of 120x or so, I made all sightings with 60x.

This list is far from complete. Thousands of small telescope doubles are strewn across the heavens. Most, however, are rather faint and require skilled eyes and detailed star atlases. Double stars with primaries fainter than magnitude 9.0 were largely excluded from this list. Anyone interested in tracking down such pairs, should he or she exhaust the offerings in this list, is urged to consult the Lick Observatory's Index Catalogue of Visual Double Stars--1961.0, currently the world's largest double star catalog.

CATALOG NUMBER	R.A. (1950) Dec. h m ° '	Mags.	Sep. "	P.A. °
ANDROMEDA				
OΣΣ2	00 10.8 +26 07	6.9+9.6	17.8	225
Σ17	00 13.9 +29 01	8.0+9.2	26.9	29
	Surrounded by an attractive sprinkling of faint stars.			
Σ24	00 15.9 +25 52	7.2+8.8	5.2	249
Σ40	00 32.5 +36 33	6.8+8.8	11.9	312
	Primary shows a definite ruddy hue.			

CATALOG NUMBER		R.A.(1950)Dec. h m ° '	Mags.	Sep. "	P.A. °
0ΣΣ4	Pi	00 34.2 +33 27	4.1+8.0	36.1	174
Σ47		00 37.7 +23 47	6.7+8.6	16.6	205
ΣI 1		00 43.7 +30 40	7.0+7.3	46.8	50
Σ72		00 51.9 +38 54	8.0+9.0	23.9	178
Σ79		00 57.2 +44 27	6.0+7.0	7.8	193
Σ179		01 50.2 +37 05	6.7+7.7	3.6	160

Requires steady seeing.

(ΣI4)	56	01 53.2 +37 01	5.7+5.8	190.0	300

Optical.   179 lies in same 1/2° field.

Σ205	Gamma	02 00.8 +42 06	3.0+5.0	10.0	63

Almach. One of the finest pairs for small telescopes. Components are golden-yellow and blue. Fainter star is a close binary.

Σ222	59	02 07.8 +38 48	6.7+7.2	16.6	35
Σ245		02 15.5 +40 03	7.0+8.0	11.2	294
Σ2985		23 07.6 +47 41	7.0+8.0	15.3	254
Σ3042		23 49.3 +37 37	7.0+7.0	5.3	88

A beautiful equal pair.   Distance slowly increasing.

_____ANTLIA_____

	Zeta	09 28.6 -31 40	5.9+6.7	8.0	212

Pretty pair, which would be even more attractive were it higher in southern sky. Followed by nice row of stars that includes Zeta².

h4381		10 52.3 -38 29	7.0+8.0	25.8	42

_____AQUARIUS_____

Σ2787		21 19.2 +01 49	7.0+8.3	22.7	20
Σ2809		21 35.0 -00 37	6.0+8.4	31.1	163

1° east and slightly north of Messier 2.

Σ2817		21 39.5 +00 11	8.2+8.5	25.9	156

Nicely wedged between two 7th mag. stars.

Σ2838		21 52.0 -03 33	6.0+8.8	17.6	184
h5524		21 58.8 -15 51	6.0+9.0	103.0	292
Σ2851		21 59.0 -12 14	8.0+8.3	19.1	121
S802	29	21 59.7 -17 13	7.0+7.2	3.9	244

A pretty sight.

Hh753	41	22 11.5 -21 19	6.0+7.6	5.0	114

CATALOG NUMBER		R.A.(1950)Dec. h m ° '		Mags.	Sep. "	P.A. °

AQUARIUS (Continued)

| Hh762 | 53 | 22 23.8 | -17 00 | 6.0+6.5 | 4.0 | 325 |

Distance decreasing.

| Σ2909 | Zeta | 22 26.2 | -00 17 | 4.4+4.6 | 1.8 | 226 |

A fine binary, and a challenge for a 3-inch telescope. Slowing increasing.

| Σ2913 | | 22 27.9 | -08 23 | 7.0-8.0 | 8.2 | 329 |
| Σ2943 | Tau (69) | 22 45.0 | -14 19 | 6.0+9.2 | 25.3 | 119 |

Optical pair; distance slowly decreasing.

| Σ2944 | | 22 45.3 | -04 29 | 7.0+7.5 | 2.5 | 276 |
| | | | | +8.4 | 49.7 | 106 |

Striking triple--all three stars are pretty much in line. 7th magnitude stars are closing.

| Σ2988 | | 23 09.4 | -12 13 | 7.2+7.2 | 3.5 | 101 |

Webb cites a p.a. of 281° (exactly 180° off from Burnham's figure). This is an example of the confusion that can result when the components of a double star are equal in magnitude. A beautiful pair.

| Σ2993 | | 23 11.4 | -09 12 | 7.0+7.8 | 25.5 | 177 |
| ΣII 12 Psi (91) | | 23 13.3 | -09 22 | 4.5+8.5 | 49.6 | 312 |

Mistakenly identified as Psi^2 by Webb. Psi^1, Psi^2, and Psi^3 all form a nice naked-eye group. Σ2993 lies less a degree west of Psi^1.

| Σ2998 | 94 | 23 16.4 | -13 44 | 5.2+7.2 | 13.0 | 350 |
| Σ3008 | | 23 21.2 | -08 44 | 7.0+8.0 | 4.0 | 175 |

Optical pair whose distance is decreasing.

| Hh807 | 107 | 23 43.4m; | -18 57' | 5.3+6.5 | 6.6" | 137 |

Distance slowly increasing.

AQUILA

| Σ2379 | 5 | 18 32.9 | -01 01 | 5.6+7.4 | 13.0 | 121 |

Similar spectra, but difference in brightness causes fainter star to appear bluish in contrast to the white primary.

| Σ2404 | | 18 48.4 | +10 55 | 5.8+7.0 | 3.5 | 183 |
| Σ2424 | 11 | 18 56.8 | +13 33 | 5.7+9.2 | 17.5 | 286 |

CATALOG NUMBER		R.A.(1950)Dec. h m ° '		Mags.	Sep. "	P.A. °
Σ2426		18 57.7	+12 48	6.8+8.2	17.1	259
Σ2425		18 57.8	-08 11	6.9+7.7	31.2	181
Σ2436		18 59.8	+08 41	7.4+8.1	31.9	313
Σ2434		19 00.2	-00 47	7.9+8.4	24.3	106

Optical--fainter star is a close pair.

Hh598	15	19 02.3	-04 06	5.5+7.0	38.4	209

Optical--slowly widening.

Σ2439		19 02.3	-07 13	8.0+9.0	22.0	199
Σ2446		19 03.4	+06 28	6.3+8.3	9.6	153
Σ2447		19 04.0	-01 25	6.7+9.1	13.9	344
Σ2449		19 04.4	+07 05	7.1+7.8	8.0	291
OΣΣ178		19 13.0	+15 00	5.5+7.5	89.7	268

Yellow and blue.

OΣ370		19 14.7	+09 15	7.8+8.2	19.6	15
OΣΣ179	28	19 17.3	+12 17	5.8+8.2	59.3	175
Σ2497		19 17.6	+05 30	6.9+8.0	30.0	357
Σ2498		19 17.7	+03 57	7.2+7.8	12.2	66
Σ2501		19 19.4	-04 51	7.5+9.0	19.8	22
Σ2510		19 20.9	+09 25	8.5+8.5	8.8	181

6th mag. star in field.

Σ2519		19 25.5	-09 38	8.0+8.1	11.4"	124
Σ2533		19 27.5	-00 33	7.2+9.0	22.6	214
Σ2547		19 36.2	-10 27	7.7+9.0	20.8	331

Nice triple attractively arranged in a near-straight row. You might try your luck with 2545 (6+8; 3.7" 324°), located in same field.

Σ2562		19 40.4	+08 16	6.5+8.2	27.1	252

Third star nearby makes this an attractive trio.

Σ2567		19 41.8	+12 15	7.7+9.5	18.4	314
Σ2594		19 51.9	+15 10	5.2+6.2	36.0	170
Hd155		19 55.1	-09 12	7.5+8.5	13.6	119
Σ2613		19 59.0	+10 36	7.0+7.2	4.0	352
Hh671		20 08.7	-00 17	7.0+8.0	55.3	206

Optical. 1° north of θ.

Σ2644		20 10.0	+00 43	7.0+7.5	3.1	206

Fine offering!

OΣΣ202		20 11.7	+06 26	6.9+7.5	43.4	193
Σ2646		20 11.8	-06 12	7.0+8.8	20.0	44

Optical. Distance decreasing.

CATALOG NUMBER		R.A.(1950)Dec. h m ° '	Mags.	Sep. "	P.A. °
Σ2654		20 12.6 -03 40	6.2+7.7	14.2	233
S749		20 24.9 -02 16	6.5+7.0	59.9	189

ARIES

Σ174	1	01 47.4 +22 02	6.2+7.4	2.7	166

This pair requires high power (100-150x) and steady skies.

Σ175		01 48.3 +20 52	8.2+8.5	22.8	355

Optical. Widening.

Σ180	Gamma	01 50.8 +19 03	4.2+4.4	7.8	360

Mesarthim. A "must" object for the small telescope. Both white.

OΣΣ21	Lambda	01 55.1 +23 20	5.0+7.5	37.4	46
Σ196		01 56.8 +20 46	8.5+9.2	30.9	163

1.5° east of β. Closing.

OΣΣ23	14	02 06.5 +25 43	4.9+8.5	93.3	37
			+7.7	105.7	278
Σ224		02 08.2 +13 27	7.5+8.0	6.1	246

Slow distance increase.

Σ1 5	30	02 34.1 +24 26	6.1+7.1	38.6	274
Σ289	33	02 37.8 +26 51	5.8+8.7	28.6	360
Σ291		02 38.3 +18 35	7.4+7.7	3.3	120
			+9.5	65.7	241

Beautiful sight.

Σ338		02 59.1 +10 40	8.2+8.5	19.4	201
Σ376		03 17.5 +19 33	7.9+8.0	7.0	252
Σ394		03 25.0 +20 17	7.0+8.0	6.8	162

AURIGA

Σ603		04 50.4 +49 30	8.0+8.2	8.3	239

Interesting triangle of 7th mag. stars in the field.

Σ613		04 55.2 +44 04	7.7+8.7	14.2	103

Less than 1° northwest of ε

Σ616	Omega	04 55.8 +37 49	5.0+8.0	5.4	359

Difficult object for small telescopes.

9		0502.8 +51 32	5.5+9.5	90.1	61

CATALOG NUMBER		R.A.(1950) Dec. h m ° '		Mags.	Sep. "	P.A. °

AURIGA (Continued)

| Σ648 | | 05 07.8 | +31 59 | 7.4+8.1 | 4.8 | 66 |

A delicate object.

| Σ653 | 14 | 05 12.2 | +32 38 | 5.0+7.2 | 14.6 | 226 |
| Σ669 | | 05 15.3 | +45 231 | 7.8+8.3 | 9.9 | 276 |

Look 1° south of Capella for this charming pair.

	Lambda	05 16.0	+40 10	5.2+8.7	104.0	-
Σ681		05 16.9	+46 65	6.5+8.5	23.2	181
Σ687		05 19.0	+33 45	8.2+9.0	17.3	68
Σ698		05 21.9	+34 49	6.2+7.7	31.2	346
Σ699		05 22.2	+38 00	7.3+8.0	8.8	343
Σ719		05 26.9	+29 31	7.0+9.0	15.0	351

Easily found 1° north of β Tauri.

| Σ718 | | 05 28.5 | +49 21 | 7.2+7.2 | 7.7 | 75 |

Truly lovely pair.

| Σ753 | 26 | 05 35.4 | +30 28 | 5.8+8.0 | 12.4 | 267 |
| Σ764 | | 05 38.2 | +29 28 | 6.3+6.8 | 26.0 | 14 |

Both white. Fine field.

| Hh 209 | | 05 56.7 | +44 35 | 6.5+9.0 | 34.2 | 331 |

0.5° south of π.

OΣ128		06 00.5	+51 35	6.3+8.7	39.0	12
Σ834		06 01.4	+30 14	8.0+8.8	22.9	308
Σ845	41	06 07.8	+48 44	5.2+6.4	7.7	356
Σ872		06 12.3	+36 10	6.0+7.0	11.3	217
	42,43	06 14.3	+46 25	6.0+6.5	450.0	-

Very wide. Data are author's estimates.

Σ884		06 16.8	+47 09	8.5+8.5	9.1	270
Σ896		06 21.9	+51 54	8.3+8.7	18.7	82
Σ918		06 30.0	+52 30	6.7+7.7	4.7	332

Lovely double.

| OΣ147 | | 06 30.9 | +38 07 | 7.0+8.5 | 43.2 | 73 |
| | | | | +9.5 | 46.3 | 117 |

Not bright and flashy, but an interesting triple.

Σ929		06 32.0	+37 46	8.0+8.5	25.6	25
Σ933		06 33.3	+41 11	8.0+8.5	25.6	75
OΣ154		06 40.8	+40 41	6.5+8.5	23.2	103

CATALOG NUMBER		R.A.(1950)Dec. h m ° '	Mags.	Sep. "	P.A. °
0ΣΣ78	Psi^5 56	06 43.1 +43 38	6.0+9.0	36.2	31

Optical. Distance decreasing.

| Σ994 | | 06 56.1   +37 10 | 7.2+7.5 | 26.5 | 56 |

Somewhat faint, but nice.

| Σ1086 | | 07 25.0   +42 51 | 7.5+9.0 | 12.2 | 102 |

_____BOOTES_____

| Σ1785 | | 13 36.8   +27 14 | 7.2+7.5 | 2.8 | 145 |

Binary with a period of 155 years. Distance
was 3.5" in 1830, 1.3" in 1913. A beauty.

0ΣΣ126		13 46.0 +21 31	6.3+6.8	85.9	208
Σ1793		13 56.8 +26 04	7.0+8.0	4.6	242
Σ1821	Kappa	14 11.7 +51 01	5.1+7.2	13.3	236

Companion is a beautiful deep blue. Very
slowly widening. ι in field.

| Σ1829 | | 14 13.6   +50 40 | 7.7+8.2 | 5.4 | 150 |
| ΣI 26 | Iota | 14 14.4   +51 36 | 4.9+7.5 | 38.5 | 33 |

With κ , forms a nice low-power sight.

| Σ1835 | | 14 20.9   +08 40 | 5.5+6.8 | 6.2 | 192 |

Most northerly of an attractive row of 5th
and 6th mag. stars, located in the
extreme southern portion of Bootes.

| Σ1838 | | 14 21.6   +11 28 | 7.2+7.3 | 9.1 | 334 |

A delicately beautiful pair.

Σ1843		14 22.8 +48 03	7.2+8.7	19.9	187
Σ1850		14 26.4 +28 31	6.1+6.7	25.6	262
Σ1864	Pi	14 38.4 +16 38	4.9+6.0	5.6	108
Σ1877	Epsilon	14 42.8 +27 17	2.5+5.0	2.9	338

Izar. Golden-yellow and blue-green.
A popular pair, but difficult for
small Instruments.

| Σ1890 | 39 | 14 48.0   + 48 55 | 5.8+6.5 | 2.9 | 45 |

Nice pair. Easy when skies are steady.

| Σ1888 | Xi | 14 49.1   +19 18 | 4.7+6.6 | 6.9 | 347 |

Binary. Period 150 years. Some observers,
the author included, have noted a pinkish
coloration of the secondary. Primary is
yellow.

| Σ1895 | | 14 55.6   +40 22 | 7.8+8.3 | 12.5 | 43 |

Forms a lovely line with several stars
of similar brightness.

CATALOG NUMBER		R.A.(1950) Dec. h m ° '		Mags.	Sep. "	P.A. °

BOOTES (Continued)

| Sh 191 | | 14 58.1 | +54 04 | 7.0+7.5 | 40.5 | 342 |

Striking, isolated double star.

| OΣ291 | | 14 58.9 | +47 28 | 6.0+8.5 | 35.6 | 29 |
| Σ1909 | 44 | 15 02.2 | +47 51 | 5.2+6.2 | 0.9 | 29 |

Binary with highly eccentric orbit. Currently too close for small telescopes, but will widen to 1.6" by 1990 and 2.2" by 2000.

Σ1910		15 05.2	+09 25	7.0+7.0	4.2	211
Σ1921		15 10.1	+38 51	7.0+7.2	30.4	283
ΣI 27	Delta	15 13.5	+33 30	3.2+7.4	104.0	79
ΣI 28	Mu	15 22.6	+37 33	4.0+6.5	108.0	171

The fainter star is a close binary (6.7+7.3; 2.0").

CAMELOPARDALIS

| Σ362 | | 03 12.3 | +59 51 | 7.7+8.0 | 7.1 | 142 |

Seems to be a part of a little-known open cluster called Stock 23.

| Σ374 | | 03 19.5 | +67 17 | 7.0+8.5 | 10.9 | 295 |

Pretty pair in a nice field.

Σ392		03 26.6	+52 44	7.5+9.5	25.8	347
0 54		03 27.3	+67 25	7.2+8.5	23.6	358
Σ396		03 29.5	+58 36	6.3+8.0	20.4	243
0 36		03 35.5	+63 43	6.3+7.3	46.1	69
97	Pi	03 38.6	+59 49	6.0+8.5	54.8	35
0 39		03 45.3	+56 58	5.9+6.6	58.3	75
455		03 51.9	+69 22	8.2+8.7	11.9	166
485		04 03.4	+62 12	6.1+6.2	18.1	304

Immersed in a sprinkling of 10th and 11th mag. stars that comprise the open cluster NGC 1502. A beautiful sight!

| 474 | | 04 06.0 | +76 06 | 8.5+8.5 | 23.3 | 146 |

Pair in field, just to the east.

| pair | | 04 08.3 | 76 10 | 7.0+8.0 | 45.0 | 200 |

Data are author's estimates.

| 509 | | 04 13.7 | +61 47 | 7.5+8.5 | 38.0 | 248 |

Close to 6th mag. star.

| Kui 16 | | 04 18.7 | +59 30 | 6.0+8.5 | 32.3 | 59 |

CATALOG NUMBER		R.A.(1950)Dec. h m ° '	Mags.	Sep. "	P.A. °

Σ550   1   04 28.1   +53 48   5.1+6.2   10.3   308

Pretty double.   Numerous faint stars in field.

Σ557   04 33.0   +62 53   8.0+8.7   23.4   126

Attractively paired with distant 8th mag. star.

Σ587   04 44.1   +53 02   7.0+8.5   21.0   185
Σ617   04 58.8   +62 56   8.5+8.7   12.6   121

Beautifully paired with 618.

Σ618   04 58.8   +63 00   7.0+7.3   32.6   211
OΣΣ57   Beta   04 59.0   +60 22   5.0+9.0   80.0   208

Primary is yellowish.

ΣI 13   11, 12   05 01.8   +58 54   5.0+6.0   180.0   8
Σ634   05 14.3   +79 12   4.5+7.9   10.4   91

Optical. Distance decreasing.

Σ695   05 33.0   +79 18   8.3+9.0   10.3   157
Σ831   06 05.8   +67 59   8.7+8.7   11.8   76

Difficult for small telescopes because of the faintness of its stars and their relative closeness.

Σ866   06 13.6   +62 13   7.7+8.8   17.8   193
                                              +8.2   78.8   265
Σ973   06 57.5   +75 19   6.6+7.6   12.5   31
Σ1006   07 023   +62 37   7.0+8.0   29.6   73

Has a faint companion (about mag. 9.5) on side of primary opposite 8th mag. partner.

Σ1051   07 20.6   +73 10   6.5+6.7   31.5   82

Beautiful pair.

Σ1122   07 41.2   +65 17   7.1+7.1   15.4   5
Σ1127   07 42.4   +64 11   6.2+8.0   5.3   340
OΣΣ90   07 58.0   +63 14   6.0+6.5   48.6   82
Σ1169   08 08.9   +79 39   7.6+7.9   20.7   15
Σ1539   11 26.9   +81 19   8.0+9.2   19.0   313

Quite close to 6th mag. field star.

OΣΣ117   12 08.8   +81 59   6.0+8.0   66.7   76
Σ1625   12 14.1   +80 25   6.5+7.0   14.4   219
Σ1694   12 48.6   +83 41   4.9+5.4   21.6   326

Fine sight.

CATALOG NUMBER			R.A.(1950) h m	Dec. ° '	Mags.	Sep. "	P.A. °
	CANCER						
Σ1179			08 02.0	+12 13	8.5+8.5	21.4	202

Slowly increasing.

CATALOG NUMBER			R.A. h m	Dec. ° '	Mags.	Sep. "	P.A. °
Σ1177			08 02.6	+27 40	6.5+7.4	3.4	351
Σ1188			08 06.3	+30 30	8.0+8.7	16.1	201
Σ1196	Zeta		08 09.3	+17 48	5.1+6.0	5.8	83

Grand object! Brighter star is a close binary (mags. 5.6+5.9) never wider than 1.2".

Σ1219			08 20.3	+07 48	8.5+8.5	11.6	260
Σ1220			08 22.3	+09 35	8.5+10.0	29.0	214
Σ1224	24		08 23.7	+24 42	6.0+7.1	5.8	47

Mistakenly identified by Webb and Olcott as ^{1}. Pretty pair.

Σ1223	Phi		08 23.8	+27 06	6.3+6.3	5.1	217

Beautiful twin system. Both white.

Σ1227			08 24.5	+23 19	8.0+9.5	24.6	163
Σ1228			08 24.6	+27 44	8.0+8.5	9.0	350
Σ1231			08 26.8	+31 33	8.2+8.7	24.8	211

Σ1236 not far away.

Σ1236			08 28.3	+32 06	8.0+8.5	36.9	113
Σ1245			08 33.2	+06.48	6.0+7.0	10.3	25
Σ584			08 37.1	+19 44	7.0+7.0	45.2	156
					+6.5	92.9	241

Bright triple in the Beehive Cluster (M44).

Σ1254			08 37.5	+19 51	6.5+9.0	20.5	54
					+8.0	63.2	342
					+9.0	82.6	43

Fine group. Also in M44.

Σ1266			08 41.4	+28 38	8.5+9.5	23.4	64
Σ1269	Iota		08 43.7	+28 57	4.4+6.5	30.5	307

Beautiful combination of yellow and blue.

Σ1276			08 44.5	+11 21	7.9+8.1	12.5	354
Σ1283			08 47.2	+15 01	7.0+8.0	16.4	123
	Sigma	(51)	08 49.5	+32 40	6.0+9.5	79.0	23
Σ57			08 51.2	+30 46	6.0+9.0	55.6	199
OΣ195	08		08 51.3	+08 37	7.4+7.9	9.6	139
	Sigma	(64)	08 56.5	+32 37	5.6+8.9	89.6	295
	Sigma	(66)	08 58.3	+32 27	6.1+8.1	4.6	137
Σ1311			09 04.6	+23 11	6.7+7.1	7.5	200

CATALOG NUMBER		R.A.(1950)Dec. h m ° '		Mags.	Sep. "	P.A. °

| Σ1332 | | 09 14.4 | +23 52 | 7.2+7.5 | 5.8 | 26 |

Lovely little double in rather sparse field.

_____CANES VENATICI_____

Σ1607		12 09.0	+36 22	7.8+8.3	27.6	14
Σ1622	2	12 13.6	+40 56	5.7+8.0	11.4	260
Σ1645		12 25.7	+45 04	7.0+7.5	10.2	158
Σ1692	Alpha (12)	12 53.7	+38 35	3.2+5.7	19.6	228

Cor Caroli. Magnificent pair for the small telescope. 1702 in field to east.

| OΣ257 | | 12 54.5 | +45 53 | 7.5+8.2 | 13.0 | 353 |

Preceded by pretty group of 10th mag. stars.

| Σ1702 | | 12 56.2 | +38 33 | 8.0+8.5 | 35.6 | 83 |
| ΣI 24 | 15, 17 | 13 07.4 | +38 48 | 5.5+5.9 | 284.0 | 297 |

Optical pair. Best seen in finder.

| Σ1755 | | 13 30.1 | +37 05 | 7.0+7.9 | 4.1 | 132 |

Faint pair nearby.

Σ1776		13 39.7	+46 28	8.0+8.0	7.4	200
OΣ125		13 44.8	+38 48	5.2+8.2	71.3	238
Σ1789		13 51.8	+33 04	8.0+8.2	6.5	328

Westernmost member of a 1/4° triangle of 8th mag. stars.

_____CANIS MAJOR_____

h3869		06 30.8	-31 59	5.5+7.5	24.9	258
Hh 239	Nu	06 34.2	-18 37	6.0+8.0	17.5	262
S534		06 40.8	-22 24	6.5+8.0	18.2	143

Preceded by an attractive group of stars, mags. 7.5 to 10.

Σ36		06 48.5	-31 39	5.5+7.5	42.9	66
	17	06 52.9	-20 20	6.0+9.0	44.4	147
				+9.0	50.5	184

Another 9th mag. star, about 100" away.

| 145 (h3945) | | 07 14.5 | -23 13 | 5.0+7.0 | 26.6 | 55 |

A sadly underrated pair. · Absolutely beautiful, with stars of gold and blue.

CATALOG NUMBER		R.A.(1950)Dec., h m ° '	Mags.	Sep. "	P.A. °
CANIS MAJOR (Continued)					
Brs 2		07 15.0 -30 48	6.5+8.0	37.9	182
Σ1069		07 15.8 -13 36	8.3+8.3	25.4	193

Webb cites a later p.a. reading of 15°, surely measured from the wrong component.

Σ47		07 22.8 -31 43	5.5+7.5	99.2	342

Yellow and blue.

Σ1097		07 25.5 -11 27	6.5+8.7	20.0	313
CANIS MINOR					
Σ1067		07 16.2 -02 57	7.7+8.7	25.6	266
Σ1082		07 21.0 +10 48	8.0+8.7	19.9	326
Σ1095		07 24.7 +08 51	8.3+8.8	10.1	78
Σ1141		07 44.5 +00 09	8.0+8.7	17.7	9

Two 9.5 mag. comites to sides. Beautiful area. Pair (7.5+9.0;45";360°) 1/2° to north-northeast.

Σ1149		07 46.9 +03 21	7.3+9.0	21.7	41
Hh 284	14	07 55.7 +02 22	6.0+8.0	85.8	75
			+9.0	117.2	151

Main star has yellowish cast. Optical.

Σ1198		08 08.6 +01 25	8.0+8.2	33.0	158
CAPRICORNUS					
	Alpha	20 14.9 -12 40	4.6+9.0	45.4	221
	Alpha	20 15.3 -12 42	3.8+9.5	154.0	140

Gredi. Alpha^1 and Alpha^2 form the naked-eye double I 51 (3.2+4.2; 376"; 291°).

Hh 682	Sigma	20 16.5 -19 17	5.0+8.3	55.9	179
ΣI 52	Beta	20 18.2 -14 56	3.0+6.0	205.0	267
Hh 689	Omicron	20 27.0 -18 45	6.3+6.8	21.9	239
S763		20 45.6 -18 23	6.5+7.0	15.8	294
CASSIOPEIA					
Σ3053		00 00.0 +65 49	6.0+7.3	15.2	70

Gold and blue.

Σ10		00 12.1 +62 34	7.5+8.0	17.6	176
Σ30		00 24.5 +49 42	6.8+8.7	15.3	307
Hh 11	Alpha	00 37.6 +56 16	2.5+9.0	64.4	280

The primary of this optical pair has a distinct yellow color.

CATALOG NUMBER		R.A.(1950) h m	Dec. ° '	Mags.	Sep. "	P.A. °

CASSIOPEIA (Continued)

CATALOG NUMBER		R.A.	Dec.	Mags.	Sep.	P.A.
Σ60	Eta	00 46.1	+57 33	3.4+7.6	12.0	307

Archid. Yellow and reddish. Fine binary, with a period of 480 years. Distance increasing.

OΣ23		01 07.2	+51 29	7.5+8.0	14.6	192
	Phi	01 16.9	+57 58	5.0+7.0	134.0	231

Borders the open cluster NGC 457.

OΣΣ15	35	01 17.6	+64 24	6.5+8.5	53.8	347
Σ117	Psi	01 22.4	+67 52	4.4+8.9	23.2	118
Σ131		01 29.9	+60 26	6.0+9.2	13.8	142

Part of the open cluster M103.

OΣ33		01 34.1	+58 23	7.2+8.3	25.4	76

Faint star about 75" away makes this a triple.

44		01 39.9	+60 18	6.0+10.0	66.0	310

Another 6th mag. star nearby.

Σ163		01 47.6	+64 36	6.2+8.2	34.8	35

Primary sports a striking golden-orange color.

Σ170		01 50.6	+75 59	6.7+7.5	3.3	246

Requires steady skies for clean split.

Σ182		01 52.9	+61 02	7.0+7.0	3.6	123
Σ191		01 58.6	+73 37	6.2+8.5	5.5	195
Σ199		02 01.3	+67 27	8.5+8.5	35.8	21
OΣΣ26		02 16.0	+59 48	6.1+6.6	63.3	200
Σ262	Iota	02 24.9	+67 11	4.2+8.1	7.3	114

A 7.1 mag. star 2.2" from the primary, makes this a fine triple. Unfortunately the third star is beyond the reach of most small telescopes.

Σ312		02 51.0	+72 41	7.0+9.0	42.9	129
Σ329		02 57.2	+58 50	7.5+9.0	16.0	273
Σ335		03 00.4	+63 35	8.0+8.5	24.4	159
Σ349		03 06.6	+63 36	7.4+8.1	6.1	321

Lovely pair. Just east of Σ335.

OΣ485		23 00.6	+54 57	6.0+9.0	20.1	50
				+9.5	56.6	260

CATALOG NUMBER		R.A.(1950) h m	Dec. ° '	Mags.	Sep. "	P.A. °
OΣ496		23 27.7	+58 16	5.4+7.4	75.7	269
				+9.0	43.4	114
				+9.0	67.3	338

Formerly known as 1 Cassiopeiae, a designation that now goes to another star in the constellation.

OΣΣ248		23 43.5	+50 24	7.0+9.0	52.7	140
Σ3037		23 43.6	+60 12	7.0+8.9	29.2	186
OΣ507		23 46.2	+64 36	7.0+8.0	50.4	351
Σ3049	Sigma	23 56.4	+55 29	5.4+7.5	3.0	326

Requires high power and steady seeing.

OΣΣ254		23 58.7	+60 05	var+8.0	58.1	89

Primary is semiregular variable WZ Cas (7.4-10.0; 186 days). Rich field.

CENTAURUS

Σ114		11 37.5	-37 50	6.5+8.0	17.0	95
Σ148	1	13 48.9	-32 45	4.5+5.9	7.9	108
C , C		14 41.5	-35 00	4.0+4.9	-	-

Wide pair, separable by naked eye. Brighter star has ruddy appearance.

CEPHEUS

Σ3052		00 00.4	+71 04	7.2+7.8	33.5	8
OΣΣ1		00 11.5	+75 45	6.4+7.0	76.3	103

Optical.

Σ343		03 18.8	+83 53	8.0+9.0	29.5	325
Σ2675	Kappa	20 10.7	+77 34	4.0+8.0	7.4	122
Σ2796		21 16.8	+78 24	7.3+8.8	25.9	43
Espin 137		21 17.9	+61 39	6.5+9.3	45.5	74

1/2° south of   .

Σ2806	Beta	21 28.0	+70 20	3.5+8.0	13.6	250

Alphirk. Nicely paired with 7th mag. field star.

Σ2810		21 33.1	+58 52	7.5+8.5	17.0	290
Σ2813		21 34.5	+57 15	8.5+9.0	10.2	273

In 1° field with Σ2816 and   Σ2819.

Σ2816		21 37.4	+57 16	6.3+7.9	11.7	121
				+8.0	19.9	339

Beautiful triple.

CATALOG NUMBER		R.A.(1950) Dec. h m ° '		Mags.	Sep. "	P.A. °

| Σ2819 | | 21 38.8 | +57 21 | 7.5+8.5 | 12.4 | 57 |

Combines with neighbor Σ2816 to form a grand small-telescope sight.

| Σ2858 | | 21 39.8 | +86 38 | 8.5+8.7 | 15.0 | 164 |

Nice field.

| OΣ451 | | 21 49.5 | +61 22 | 7.2+8.2 | 4.2 | 221 |

A beauty, when skies are steady.

| Σ2840 | | 21 50.3 | +55 33 | 6.0+7.0 | 18.3 | 196 |

Webb calls this "a splendid pair."

| Σ2873 | | 22 00.4 | +8238 | 6.2+7.0 | 13.7 | 69 |
| Σ2863 | Xi | 22 02.2 | +64 23 | 4.7+6.5 | 7.6 | 278 |

One of the finer pairs in Cepheus.

Σ2872		22 06.9	+59 03	7.2+7.5	21.6	316
Σ2833		22 09.6	+69 53	6.2+8.2	14.7	252
Σ2893		22 12.0	+73 04	5.5+7.6	28.9	348
Σ2896		22 16.8	+62 59	7.5+8.5	21.5	242

Accompanied by a nice group of faint stars.

| Σ2903 | | 22 20.2 | +66 27 | 7.0+8.0 | 4.3 | 96 |
| ΣI 58 | Delta | 22 27.3 | +58 10 | Var+6.3 | 40.7 | 192 |

Primary is the prototype Cepheid variable. Mag. range is 3.6-4.3; period is 5.4 days. Yellow and blue.

Σ1092		22 34.8	+72 37	7.5+8.5	42.2	137
OΣ480		22 44.1	+57 49	7.5+8.2	30.9	117
Σ2947		22 47.3	+68 18	7.2+7.2	4.2	60
OΣ486		23 01.3	+60 10	6.0+8.5	33.9	276

Σ3065		00 05.4	-14 30	8.5+8.5	9.6	108
h1981		00 28.6	-10 22	7.0+8.5	79.2	87
Σ39		00 31.9	-04 49	6.8+8.5	19.7	45
h323		00 38.2	-04 38	6.2+8.7	64.3	289

Optical pair.

Σ80		00 56.8	+00 31	7.0+8.2	25.4	331
Σ84	26	01 01.2	+01 06	6.6+9.0	16.0	253
Σ86		01 02.3	-05 44	8.2+8.7	15.0	145
Σ91		01 04.6	-02 00	6.7+7.5	4.1	317

CATALOG NUMBER		R.A.(1950)Dec. h m ° '		Mags.	Sep. "	P.A. °
I 3	37	01 11.9	-08 12	5.1+7.0	49.7	331
Σ150		01 40.9	-07 20	7.2+7.8	36.2	196
Σ171		01 46.2	-01 40	8.5+8.5	32.5	163
	Chi	01 47.1	-10 56	5.0+7.5	84.0	-
Σ218		02 06.2	-00 40	7.0+8.0	4.9	248
Σ231	66	02 10.2	-02 38	6.0+7.8	16.2	232
Σ265		02 22.0	-01 59	8.2+8.7	12.1	136

Σ266 in the same 1/2° field. Nice sight.

Σ266		02 28.9	+00 52	7.2+7.7	13.5	219
Σ280		02 31.6	-05 51	7.5+7.7	3.6	246

Difficult, unless the seeing is steady.

h3524		02 40.6	-20 30	7.0+7.5	19.4	152
Σ330		02 54.6	-00 47	7.5+9.5	8.8	192

Use averted vision and look for a faint
sparkle of light to the south of the
primary.

Σ332		02 55.3	+00 13	8.5+8.5	12.5	53
ΣI 6		03 05.8	+07 27	7.0+7.0	81.2	163

COMA BERENICES

Σ1596	2	12 01.7	+21 44	6.0+7.5	3.6	237
Σ1615		12 11.6	+33 04	6.0+8.2	26.7	88
Σ1633		12 18.1	+27 20	7.1+7.2	9.0	245

Pretty pair, isolated in its field.

Hh 395	12	12 20.0	+26 07	4.5+8.5	66.1	167
ΣI 21	17	12 26.4	+26 11	4.8+6.0	145.0	251
Σ1657	24	12 32.6	+18 39	4.7+6.2	20.3	271

Yellow and blue. Nice pair.

Σ1678		12 42.9	+14 38	6.3+7.0	34.2	181

Has widened somewhat and may be optical.

Σ1685		12 49.4	+19 27	6.8+7.3	16.0	202
ΣI 23	32, 33	12 49.7	+17 21	6.0+6.5	195.0	49
Σ1687	35	12 50.8	+21 31	5.0+9.0	28.7	126
Σ1756		13 31.0	+23 16	8.5+9.0	14.5	177
Σ1760		13 32.0	+26 32	8.0+8.0	8.6	65

CORONA AUSTRALIS

Σ222	Kappa	18 29.9	-38 46	6.0+6.5	21.4	359

Beautiful "treetop object" for northern
observers.

CATALOG NUMBER		R.A.(1950)Dec. h m ° '	Mags.	Sep. "	P.A. °

_____CORONA AUSTRALIS_(Continued)

| Brs 14 | | 18 57.7   -37 08 | 6.5+7.0 | 12.7 | 281 |

The globular cluster NGC 6723 in
Sagittarius is just 1/2° to the north.

_____CORONA BOREALIS

Σ1935		15 18.2 +30 53	8.5+8.7	8.5	289
Σ1936		15 19.0 +27 13	8.5+9.0	20.3	232
Σ1963		15 35.9 +30 16	7.3+7.7	5.0	296
Σ1964		15 36.3 +36 24	6.8+7.3	15.2	86
Σ1965	Zeta	15 37.5 +36 48	4.2+5.0	6.3	305

Fine pair. Both white.

| Σ1973 | | 15 44.5   +36 36 | 7.3+8.5 | 30.6 | 322 |
| OΣ302 | | 15 53.0   +34 30 | 7.0+9.0 | 28.6 | 52 |

| Σ2032 | Sigma | 16 12.8   +33 59 | 5.7+6.7 | 6.7 | 234 |

Slow-moving binary. Distance increasing.

| ΣI 29 | Nu | 16 20.4   +33 55 | 4.8+5.1 | 371.9 | 166 |

Wide pairs like this are most attractive
when viewed through the finder.

| Hh 511 | | 15 21.0   +32 27 | 6.0+8.5 | 34.7 | 19 |

Located midway between δ and η CrB.

| Σ2044 | | 16 22.4   +37 09 | 7.8+8.0 | 8.5 | 342 |

On the Corona Borealis-Hercules border.

_____CORVUS

| S634 | | 12 07.8   -16 31 | 7.0+8.0 | 5.4 | 291 |

Companion seems to blink out from the side
of the primary.

| | Zeta | 12 17.8   -21 55 | 5.0+6.0 | 400.0 | - |

Wide, but surprisingly attractive.

| Hh 396 | Delta | 12 27.3   -16 14 | 3.0+8.5 | 24.2 | 214 |

Algorab. Requires averted vision and
patience!

| Σ1659 | | 12 33.1   -11 26 | 8.0+8.1 | 27.1 | 352 |

Flanked by two 7th mag. stars.

| Σ1669 | | 12 38.7   -12 44 | 6.5+6.5 | 5.4 | 309 |
| S643 | | 12 51.3   -17 46 | 7.5+9.0 | 23.4 | 294 |

CATALOG NUMBER		R.A.(1950) h m	Dec. ° '	Mags.	Sep. "	P.A. °
CRATER						
Σ1509		11 04.0	-13 09	7.2+9.0	32.9	16
Hh 368		11 14.4	-06 53	7.0+9.0	60.5	97
		Σ1530 less than 1° east.				
Σ1530		11 17.2	-06 37	7.8+8.2	7.7	313
CYGNUS						
ΣΣ2486		19 10.8	+49 45	6.0+6.5	8.2	212
		Pretty pair surrounded by nice field. Slowly decreasing in distance.				
2507		19 18.2	+44 17	8.2+9.3	23.9	137
OΣΣ182		19 25.5	+50 02	6.5+7.5	73.4	300
2534		19 25.9	+36 26	7.8+8.0	7.0	64
		Less than 1/2° northeast of 4 Cyg.				
ΣI 34	Beta	19 28.7	+27 51	3.0+5.3	34.3	54
		Albireo. Considered by many observers to be the finest pair in the northern sky. Stars are golden yellow and blue. A real showpiece.				
Σ2542		19 30.7	+52 53	8.2+8.7	11.3	254
		Nicely complimented by distant 8th mag. star.				
ΣI 46	16	19 40.6	+50 24	5.1+5.3	39.0	134
		Fine sight. Both yellow. The bright planetary NGC 6826 is 1/2° to the east.				
Σ2578		19 43.8	+35 58	6.6+7.4	15.1	125
OΣΣ191		19 44.0	+34 53	6.0+8.0		
		Primary is golden orange.				
Σ1580	Chi (17)	19 44.5	+33 37	5.1+8.1	26.0	70
OΣΣ192		19 44.7	+32 46	6.5+9.0	30.7	197
		Optical. Closing very slowly.				
Σ2588		19 47.4	+44 15	7.0+7.5	9.6	160
h603	19	19 48.8	+38 35	6.0+10.0	54.6	106
OΣ389		19 49.7	+31 01	6.9+8.8	12.5	183
OΣ393		19 56.3	+44 15	7.5+8.4	18.9	228
OΣΣ197	26	20 00.0	+49 58	5.3+8.5	41.7	148

CATALOG NUMBER	R.A.(1950) Dec. h m ° '	Mags.	Sep. "	P.A. °

CYGNUS (Continued)

| pair | 20 01.3 +37 58 | 8.0+9.0 | 43.0 | 30 |

Part of a fascinating semicircle of double stars that includes h1470. Data are author's estimates.

| pair | 20 01.4 +38 07 | 8.0+9.5 | 40.0 | 320 |

Part of h1470 group. Mags. and sep. estimated.

| Σ2624 | 20 01.6 +35 33 | 7.0+9.5 | 42.6 | 328 |

Primary is a very close pair of 7th mag. stars.

| h1470 | 20 01.8 +38 11 | 7.0+9.0 | 28.8 | 337 |

Primary is reddish.

| pair | 20 02.6 +38 13 | 8.5+9.5 | 30.0 | 250 |

Completes h1470 group. Author's estimates.

| Σ440 | 20 04.1 +35 39 | 7.0+8.0 | 36.1 | 28 |

Part of a multiple group that includes several fainter stars.

| Σ2639 | 20 07.0 +35 21 | 7.7+8.7 | 6.2 | 301 |

Faint pair 1/2° east.

| Σ2649 | 20 10.3 +31 56 | 7.7+8.8 | 26.1 | 152 |

Optical. Distance decreasing. Faint pair to northeast.

| Omicron | 20 12.0 +46 35 | 4.0+5.0 | 338.0 | 323 |
| | | +7.0 | 107.0 | 173 |

4th mag. star=31 Cyg; 5th mag. star=30 Cyg. Fine wide triple with very yellow primary and blue attendants.

| Ho. 588 | 20 14.9 +31 21 | 6.5+8.3 | 51.1 | 297 |

Bluish primary. Nice gathering of faint stars nearby.

Σ2667	20 15.9 +45 29	8.2+8.5	8.1	226
Σ2666	20 16.4 +40 35	6.5+8.7	34.2	208
Σ2671	20 17.2 +55 14	6.0+7.4	3.5	338
Espin 800	20 18.6 +51 06	8.5+9.0	28.2	315
		+10.0	40.3	104

CATALOG NUMBER		R.A.(1950) h m	Dec. ° '	Mags.	Sep. "	P.A. °
CYGNUS (Continued)						
0ΣΣ206		20 21.1	+39 03	7.0+8.5	43.0	256

Field 1/2° eastward contains an interesting chain of 8-11 mag. stars.

CATALOG NUMBER		R.A.(1950) h m	Dec. ° '	Mags.	Sep. "	P.A. °
0ΣΣ207		20 12.2	+42 49	7.5+7.7	93.2	63
Σ2681		20 21.5	+53 15	7.5+8.0	39.6	201
Σ2687		20 25.2	+56 28	6.5+8.3	26.6	118
Σ2691		20 27.8	+37 57	8.0+8.2	17.1	33

0.5° southeast of 40 Cyg.

CATALOG NUMBER		R.A.(1950) h m	Dec. ° '	Mags.	Sep. "	P.A. °
Σ2700		20 32.7	+32 20	6.5+8.3	23.7	285
ΣI 53	48	20 35.5	+31 23	6.0+6.1	178.1	175
Σ2707		20 36.2	+47 46	7.1+8.6	22.8	31
				+7.9	55.4	195
Σ2708		20 36.8	+38 28	7.0+8.7	34.2	327

Optical. Distance increasing.

CATALOG NUMBER		R.A.(1950) h m	Dec. ° '	Mags.	Sep. "	P.A. °
0Σ410		20 37.7	+40 24	6.4+7.7	69.1	70
Arg 39		20 40.9	+49 05	8.5+8.5	10.3	157
0Σ414		20 45.5	+42 13	7.2+8.3	10.0	95
	Lambda (54)	20 45.5	+36 18	5.0+9.0	84.6	105
0Σ416		20 50.2	+43 34	7.8+8.1	8.7	124

0.5° southeast of 56 Cyg. Very pretty.

CATALOG NUMBER		R.A.(1950) h m	Dec. ° '	Mags.	Sep. "	P.A. °
Σ2743	59	20 58.1	+47 20	4.7+9.0	20.3	352
Σ2758	61	21 04.4	+38 28	5.3+5.9	28.4	144

Historically important as the first star whose distance was determined. Both golden yellow.

CATALOG NUMBER		R.A.(1950) h m	Dec. ° '	Mags.	Sep. "	P.A. °
Σ2762		21 06.5	+30 00	6.0+9.2	57.8	226

Optical. 8th mag. companion just 3.3" away.

CATALOG NUMBER		R.A.(1950) h m	Dec. ° '	Mags.	Sep. "	P.A. °
Σ159		21 08.7	+47 29	6.0+7.5	135.0	189
Σ2779		21 12.3	+28 52	8.5+8.5	19.2	189
Espin 98		21 17.8	+52 06	6.5+9.0	26.7	311
				+9.0	30.1	87

Nice system. Several doubles in vicinity, including Σ2789.

CATALOG NUMBER		R.A.(1950) h m	Dec. ° '	Mags.	Sep. "	P.A. °
Σ2789		21 18.4	+52 46	7.1+7.1	6.7	115

Part of a neat triangle of stars, the northernmost of which is also double.

CATALOG NUMBER		R.A.(1950) h m	Dec. ° '	Mags.	Sep. "	P.A. °
	69	21 23.7	+36 27	6.0+9.0	54.0	98

CATALOG NUMBER		R.A.(1950)Dec. h m ° '	Mags.	Sep. "	P.A. °

CATALOG NUMBER		R.A.(1950) Dec.	Mags.	Sep.	P.A.

_____CYGNUS (Continued)_____

| Σ2803 | | 21 28.2 +52 42 | 7.4+9.0 | 24.8 | 287 |

Third star (mag. 9) about 70" away. 1/2°
west is a beautiful equilateral triangle
of 7th and 8th mag. stars.

OΣ447		21 37.5 +41 31	7.0+7.9	29.0	45
Espin 825		21 38.1 +48 54	7.5+8.5	55.1	286
75		21 38.2 +43 03	5.2+9.4	57.9	254
79		21 41.3 +38 04	5.5+7.0	151.0	60
	Mu	21 41.9 +28 31	4.7+6.2	200.0	70

Bright component is a close binary.

| Σ2832 | | 21 47.4 +50 16 | 7.8+8.3 | 13.1 | 213 |
| | | | +9.5 | 45.9 | 319 |

_____DELPHINUS_____

Σ2664		20 17.3 +12 51	7.7+8.2	27.7	323
Σ2679		20 22.1 +19 25	7.4+8.7	23.5	78
Σ2680		20 22.5 +14 42	8.3+8.5	16.2	289
Σ987		20 28.0 +19 15	7.0+7.5	106.0	288
Σ2690		20 28.8 +11 05	7.0+7.2	16.7	256
Σ2703		20 34.5 +14 33	7.6+7.6	25.3	290
			+7.6	73.7	235

Nice triple. Easily found between   and
  . Most distant member is optical and is
being left behind.

| | Kappa | 20 36.7 +09 55 | 4.7+9.0 | 214.0 | 101 |

Despite the width of this pair, they seem
to be traveling together through space.

| OΣ409 | | 20 37.8 +03 16 | 7.0+8.0 | 65.3 | 334 |
| Σ2817 | | 20 40.2 +12 33 | 7.4+7.6 | 8.5 | 86 |

Beautiful near-equal pair situated in a
nice field.

| Σ2722 | | 20 41.3 +19 33 | 8.2+8.7 | 7.5 | 307 |
| Σ2725 | | 20 43.9 +15 43 | 7.3+8.0 | 5.7 | 9 |

Incredible sight-delicate as a snowflake.
Found in the same field with the bright
pair γ Del, so there is a nice contrast
between the two.

| Σ2727 | Gamma | 20 44.4 +15 57 | 4.0+5.0 | 10.1 | 268 |

A "must" object for the owner of a small
telescope. Subtle color contrast between
yellowish primary and bluish companion.

CATALOG NUMBER	R.A.(1950)Dec. h m ° '	Mags.	Sep. "	P.A. °

DELPHINUS (Continued)

| Σ2733 | 20 50.4 +07 08 | 8.0+8.3 | 40.2 | 145 |
| Σ2734 | 20 51.7 +12 55 | 8.2+8.7 | 24.8 | 198 |

Gradually closing. Probably optical.

| Σ2735 | 20 53.2 +04 20 | 6.2+7.7 | 1.8 | 285 |

Challenge this one on an evening when skies are especially steady.

| Σ2736 | 20 54.4 +12 48 | 7.5+8.7 | 5.1 | 218 |

Just northeast of 16 Del.

| Σ2738 | 20 56.2 +16 15 | 7.2+8.2 | 14.9 | 254 |

Another pair 1/2° to northeast.

| Σ2750 | 21 02.6 +12 31 | 8.5+9.5 | 16.2 | 280 |

Another faint pair (Σ2754) located 1/2° to northeast.

| Σ2754 | 21 03.9 +12 59 | 8.0+8.7 | 32.7 | - |

Slowly closing. P.a. around 300°.

DRACO

Σ1362	09 33.2 +73 18	7.0+7.0	4.8	129
Σ1437	10 30.2 +74 06	7.0+9.5	23.5	290
Σ1516	11 12.1 +73 45	7.0+7.5	52.0	105

Optical. Separation has increased from 22" in 1905.

| Σ1573 | 11 46.5 +67 36 | 6.6+7.6 | 11.2 | 178 |
| Σ1588 | 11 59.7 +72 38 | 8.5+8.7 | 12.9 | 45 |

Sep. and p.a. have decreased slightly from these 1958 figures. Optical pair.

Σ3123	12 03.5 +68 59	7.0+8.0	26.0	181
Σ1602	12 04.6 +69 21	7.5+9.0	17.1	180
OΣΣ123	13 25.0 +65 00	6.4+6.8	68.9	147
Σ1872	14 39.6 +58 11	7.0+8.0	7.6	47

Beautiful, delicate pair.

| Σ1882 | 14 42.8 +61 19 | 7.2+8.7 | 12.2 | 2 |

Forms a "finder double" with nearby 7th mag. star.

Σ1927	15 10.9 +62 03	7.1+8.0	16.12	354
Σ1948	15 25.3 +55 04	8.0+8.7	12.5	50
Σ1984	15 49.7 +53 03	6.3+8.5	6.5	273

CATALOG NUMBER		R.A.(1950) Dec., h m ° '		Mags.	Sep. "	P.A. °

DRACO (Continued)

Σ2006		15 59.4	+59 04	7.5+8.5	46.2	214

Easily found near θ.

Σ2078	17	16 35.0	+53 02	5.0+6.0	3.2	109

With 5th mag. star 16 Dra. 90" away
forms a grand triple.

Σ2092		16 38.4	+60 48	7.7+8.8	8.2	5
Σ2130	Mu (21)	17 04.3	+54 32	5.8+5.8	1.9	42

Fine challenge. The p.a. of this binary
will decrease to 8° by the end of the
century, with little change in separation.

Σ2138		17 09.1	+54 33	8.0+8.3	22.3	135

Easily found just east of Mu.

Σ2180		17 27.8	+50 55	7.0+7.2	3.2	252

Separable only when skies are steady.

ΣI 35	Nu	17 31.2	+55 13	5.0+5.0	61.9	312

One of the finest wide doubles in the sky.
A striking object, especially when viewed
low power.   Both white.

Σ2241	Psi	17 42.8	+72 11	5.0+6.0	30.3	15
Σ2261		17 57.0	+52 13	7.5+9.5	9.5	262

Through a 3-inch reflector, the companion
is visible at times with averted vision.

Σ2273		17 59.0	+64 09	6.8+7.3	21.1	284
Σ2278		18 02.0	+56 25	6.8+7.3 +7.8	36.9	26

The 7.8 mag. star is 6.1", at p.a. 146°,
from the 7.3 mag. component. A beautiful
triple.

Σ2279		18 03.4	+50 52	8.7+8.8	13.2	181
Σ2308	40, 41	18 03.9	+80 00	5.4+6.1	19.3	232
Σ2302		18 04.7	+75 47	7.0+9.5	23.1	280
Σ2326		18 10.2	+81 28	7.5+8.5	16.4	196
	39	18 23.2	+58 46	4.7+7.1	89.0	21

An 8th mag. star, 3.7" from the primary,
forms the close pair Σ2323.

Σ2348		18 32.8	+52 19	5.9+8.1	25.7	272
Σ2377		18 38.0	+63 29	7.5+9.0	16.5	340

CATALOG NUMBER		R.A.(1950)Dec. h m ° '		Mags.	Sep. "	P.A. °

DRACO (Continued)

Σ2398		18 42.5	+59 30	8.0+8.5	15.3	163

An interesting system, consisting of two red dwarfs. This is one of the nearest pairs to the earth. (11.3 l.y.).

Σ2420	Omicron(47)	18 50.5	+59 20	4.7+7.5	34.2	326

Noted for its orange and blue colors.

Σ2452		18 55.2	+75 43	6.7+7.5	5.7	218
Σ2440		18 56.8	+62 20	6.2+9.0	17.0	123

May require a little patience.

Arg 33		19 02.8	+57 23	var+8.0	10.5	58

Primary is on eclipsing binary - mag 8.0-8.6, period 1.82 days.

Σ2549		19 30.7	+63 12	7.7+8.9	25.8	286
				+7.7	50.7	276

Beautiful triple, arranged in a near-straight line with the faint star in the middle.

Σ2571		19 31.8	+78 09	7.3+8.0	11.3	20
ΣI 44		19 32.4	+60 03	5.2+7.2	76.6	187

Look for Σ2554 in same field.

Σ2554		19 33.4	+60 10	7.9+8.4	18.5	196
Σ2573		19 39.4	+60 23	6.2+8.5	18.2	27
Σ2604		19 52.2	+64 03	6.5+8.7	27.8	184

EQUULEUS

Σ2737	Epsilon(1)	20 56.6	+04 06	5.7+7.1	10.6	70

Primary is a close binary with a period of about a century.

Σ2742	Lambda(2)	20 59.8	+06 59	7.1+7.1	2.8	218

Pretty sight.

5, 6 (ΣI 54)		21 07.9	+09 57	4.2+5.7	352.0	153

Optical. Fine low-power sight.

	Delta	21 12.0	+09 48	5.0+10.0	60.0	-

Optical. Distance increasing. Faint star generally north of primary, which is an extremely close and rapid binary.

Σ2793		21 22.6	+09 10	7.0+8.7	26.6	242

CATALOG NUMBER		R.A.(1950)Dec. h m ° '	Mags.	Sep. "	P.A. °
	ERIDANUS				
	Theta	02 56.4 -40 30	3.4+4.4	8.2	88

Observers in northern states will need an unobstructed southern horizon to catch this beautiful pair.

Σ411		03 29.8 -07 15	7.0+8.0	19.1	88
Σ436		03 38.5 -12 46	7.0+8.2	40.1	236

Optical. Widening.

Δ16	f	03 46.7 -37 46	4.9+5.4	7.9	212
Σ470	32	03 51.8 -03 06	5.0+6.3	6.9	347

Yellow and blue. Pretty sight.

31042		03 56.1 -02 48	7.5+8.5	55.6	93

11th mag. star at p.a. 250°, sep. 39.2".

Σ501		04 06.1 -02 49	8.5+9.5	29.2	296
	Omicron2	04 13.0 -07 44	4.5+9.5	82.8	105

The companion is one of the few white dwarfs visible with small telescopes. It is circled by an 11th mag. red dwarf, 8.5" distant.

h3644		04 19.4 -25 51	7.0+8.5	44.5	41

The brighter star is the close binary β744.

h342		04 20.8 -05 07	8.0+9.0	17.4	235

Forms on attractive row with two 8th mag. stars which precede it.

Σ570		04 32.9 -09 50	7.0+8.0	12.8	259

Pleasant sight.

Σ576		04 35.7 -13 08	6.7+7.2	12.4	172
31236		04 37.5 -21 21	7.5+8/5	40.4	314
Σ590	55	04 41.2 -08 53	7.0+7.0	9.2	317
(Hh 138)	62	04 53.9 -05 15	6.0+8.0	67.3	75

Optical. Slowly separating.

Σ624		05 00.2 -05 50	8.1+8.6	28.6	89
Σ642	66	05 40.3 -04 43	6.0+9.2	52.8	9

Another comes to north of primary.

Σ649		05 50.9 -08 44	7.0+8.7	21.6	72

Located in a striking row of three stars that includes λ.

CATALOG NUMBER		R.A.(1950) Dec. h m ° '	Mags.	Sep. "	P.A. °
Σ830		06 00.3 27 39	8.2+8.7	12.0	254
OΣ134		06 60.2 +24 26	7.0+8.3	31.0	188

Located on northeast edge of open cluster M35.

Σ897		06 19.2 +26 42	8.2+8.5	18.0	348
	Mu	06 19.9 +22 33	3.0+9.5	122.0	141
Hh 223	15	06 24.8 +20 49	7.0+9.0	27.1	204

ν in same field. Nice sight.

OΣΣ77	Nu (18)	06 26.0 +20 15	4.2+8.0	113.0	329

Each star is a close pair.

Σ924	20	06 29.4 +17 49	6.0+6.9	20.0	210
Hh 246	Epsilon	06 40.8 +25 11	3.0+9.0	110.0	94
Σ962		06 45.1 +26 46	8.5+8.5	25.7	241
Σ982	38	06 51.8 +13 15	5.4+7.7	7.0	151

Binary with long period. Slowly increasing.

OΣΣ80		06 55.3 +14 18	7.0+7.0	100.0	-
			+8.0	60.0	-
			+9.5	70.0	-

Striking group. Data are estimates.

Σ1000		06 56.3 +25 18	7.7+8.7	22.3	67
OΣΣ81	Zeta	07 01.2 +20 39	var+8.0	96.5	350

Primary is a Cepheid variable (mag. 3.7-4.1; period 10.2 days).

Σ1012		07 01.8 +28 12	8.2+8.7	12.7	167
Σ1023		07 05.4 +25 04	8.0+8.5	24.7	102
Σ1035		07 09.0 +22 22	7.4+7.4	8.7	41
Σ1054		07 24.8 +35 03	7.3+8.5	18.6	291
			+9.0	79.4	268
Σ1083		07 22.6 +20 36	6.8+7.8	6.4	44
Σ1088		07 23.2 +14 12	7.0+9.0	11.1	195

An 8th mag. star, located 113" away, is the primary to Σ1087. Its 11.5 mag. partner is too faint for small instruments.

Σ1089		07 23.4 +14 57	8.5+8.5	7.2	8
Σ1090		07 23.6 +18 37	7.0+7.8	60.8	97
			+9.5		

The 9.5 mag. star is 19.9" (p.a. 320°) from the primary.

CATALOG NUMBER		R.A.(1950)Dec. h m ° '		Mags.	Sep. "	P.A. °

GEMINI (Continued)

CATALOG NUMBER		R.A.(1950)Dec. h m ° '		Mags.	Sep.	P.A.
S548		07 24.7	+22 15	7.5+9.5	35.6	276

Primary has decided yellowish cast.

pair		07 26.4	+14 29	7.0+7.5	40.0	345

Situated about 45' southeast of Σ1089.
Striking twosome.

Σ1106		07 28.5	+16 25	8.7+8.7	10.6	32
Σ1108		07 29.8	+23 00	6.7+8.5	11.5	178
Σ1110	Alpha	07 31.4	+32 00	2.0+2.9	2.3	98

Castor. Currently difficult for small telescopes, this grand binary will widen to a
comfortable 4.0" by the end of the century.
Sep. and p.a. given are for 1980. A 9th
magnitude star (p.a. 164°; sep. 72.5") is a
physical member of the system.

Σ1124		07 38.8	+21 55	8.2+8.4	19.4	326

Has two comites, each about 9.5 mag.

Σ1129		07 38.8	+18 10	8.2+8.7	21.7	64
		07 45.5	+18 28	6.8+8.5	6.3	273

HERCULES

CATALOG NUMBER		R.A.(1950)Dec.		Mags.	Sep.	P.A.
Σ2010	Kappa (7)	16 06.8	+17 11	5.0+6.0	28.2	12
Σ2017		16 09.9	+14 41	7.7+8.4	27.7	254
Σ2021		16 11.0	+13 40	6.7+6.9	4.0	347
Hh 506	Gamma	16 19.7	+19 16	3.5+9.5	41.6	233

Optical. Little change.

Σ2051		16 27.0	+10 42	7.1+8.6	13.7	19
Σ2063		16 30.3	+45 42	5.7+8.2	16.4	195
Σ2065		16 31.0	+40 07	8.0+8.7	31.2	217

Attractively positioned between a 6th mag.
star and a row of 8th mag. stars.

125	Pi	16 33.2	+17 10	6.2+7.5	156.2	359
Σ2079		16 37.5	+23 06	7.1+7.9	16.8	91
ΣI 31	36, 37	16 38.2	+04 19	6.0+6.5	69.8	230

Beautiful low power pair. Both white.

Σ2085		16 40.3	+21 41	7.3+8.8	6.1	309
Σ2083		16 40.4	+13 42	8.3+8.8	12.7	335
Σ2098		16 43.8	+30 06	8.0+9.0	14.3	146
				+8.0	64.2	140
				+9.7	63.7	17

Stiking sight!

Σ2104		16 46.9	+36 00	6.2+8.0	5.8	19
ΣI 32		16 56.5	+47 26	7.5+7.5	114.0	263

CATALOG NUMBER		R.A.(1950)Dec., h m ° '	Mags.	Sep. "	P.A. °
Σ2120		17 02.8 +28 09	6.4+9.2	16.8	234

Optical. Distance increasing.

Σ2131		17 07.8 +30 26	7.5+8.5	24.3	179
Σ2135		17 10.0 +21 17	7.1+8.4	7.9	187
Σ2140	Alpha	17 12.4 +14 27	var+5.4	4.6	110

Ras Algethi. Grand, close pair for small telescopes. Main star is a red supergiant that varies in brightness from mag. 3.1 to 3.9 every 3 months.

Σ3127	Delta	17 13.0 +24 54	3.0+8.1	8.8	241

Sarin. Optical. Distance increasing. Difficult.

Σ2161	Rho	17 22.0 +37 11	4.0+5.1	4.1	317

Fine pair, both white. OΣ329 in same field.

OΣ329		17 22.6 +37 01	7.0+8.5	32.4	13
Σ2165		17 24.3 +29 30	7.0+8.5	9.4	59
			+8.8	98.1	252
Σ2178		17 27.7 +34 59	7.0+8.6	10.7	130
Σ2189		17 31.5 +47 55	8.0+10.0	21.0	100
			+8.5	65.1	360
Σ2194		17 39.0 +24 32	6.2+8.5	16.3	8
Σ2214		17 41.3 +43 46	8.5+8.8	19.4	212

Followed closely by a nice row of 9th mag. stars.

Σ2213		17 43.0 +31 09	7.5+8.0	4.5	329
OΣ335		17 43.8 +21 55	7.3+8.3	25.0	140

Has 10th mag. partner about 100" away.

Σ2220	Mu	17 44.5 +27 45	3.8+9.5	34.0	247
Σ2232		17 48.2 +25 18	7.0+8.5	6.4	141
Σ2245		17 54.2 +18 20	7.0+7.0	2.4	294
Σ2259		17 57.2 +30 03	7.0+8.0	19.6	278

Easily found in field with ν.

Σ2264	95	17 59.4 +21 36	4.9+4.9	6.3	258

Beautiful pair. The colors, described by one 19th century observer as "apple green and cherry red," are subject to debate. While some astronomers see these contrasting colors, others see both stars as white, or slightly yellowish. Here is a classic example of the difficulty with which star colors are perceived.

CATALOG NUMBER	R.A.(1950)Dec. h m ° '	Mags.	Sep. "	P.A. °

HERCULES (Continued)

CATALOG NUMBER	R.A. / Dec.	Mags.	Sep.	P.A.
Σ2268	18 01.2 +25 22	8.0+9.0	21.0	210

Distance slowly increasing.

Σ2277	18 01.8 +48 28	6.3+8.2	27.0	125
		+9.9	94.0	292

Both companions are optical.

OΣ341	18 03.7 +21 26	7.0+9.0	28.2	172
		+9.0	38.4	100
		+9.0	62.8	38

Primary forms wide double with 7th mag.
star, about 120" away. Nice group.

Σ2280 100	18 05.8 +26 06	5.9+5.9	14.2	183

A Beautiful twin double. Both white.

Σ2291	18 08.4 +34 00	8.5+9.0	27.2	340

Distance increasing.

triple	18 12.5 +23 33	8.5+9.0	40.0	270
		+10.0	90.0	290

In field southwest of 2301.

Σ2301	18 13.8 +23 58	8.5+9.0	22.7	123
Σ2317	18 23.3 +26 03	8.0+10.0	24.8	224
		+9.5	44.6	190
Σ2319	18 25.6 +19 16	7.2+7.6	5.4	191

A beauty! 10th mag. companion at 41",
278°.

Σ2330	18 28.9 +13 09	8.0+9.0	17.6	169
Σ2401	18 46.8 +21 07	7.0+8.6	4.3	38
Σ2399	18 46.8 +13 09	8.2+8.8	15.8	119
		+10.0	31.5	48

HYDRA

h99	08 35.4 -06 38	6.3+7.5	61.0	202
Σ1255	08 37.0 +05 57	7.0+8.0	26.6	31

Easily found just west of .

Hh 303 F	08 41.2 -07 13	5.5+8.1	78.1	309

Yellowish primary. Formerly 31
Monocetotis.

Σ1270	08 42.8 -02 25	6.6+7.6	4.7	262

CATALOG NUMBER		R.A.(1950)Dec. h m ° '		Mags.	Sep. "	P.A. °

HYDRA (Continued)

Σ1281		08 45.0	+00 11	7.8+8.9	35.4	319

Rapidly widening. Most likely optical.

Σ1295	17	08 53.0	-07 47	7.2+7.3	4.3	359
Σ1309		09 04.0	+03 01	8.0+8.3	11.5	273
Wei 21		09 12.4	-08 33	7.5+9.0	25.8	14

Easily found 1/2° west of 24 Hya.

Σ1329		09 13.2	-01 02	8.3+8.5	14.5	253

Optical. Closing.

Sh 105	27	09 18.0	-09 20	5.0+7.0	119.0	211

Secondary has a 9th mag. companion at 9.6", 196°.

Σ1347		09 20.7	+03 43	6.7+8.0	21.1	311
Σ1072		10 01.7	-17 51	6.0+7.0	21.0	274
Σ1416		10 09.9	-15 50	6.7+8.5	11.5	277
Σ1473		10 45.2	-15 20	8.0+8.9	30.7	10

Nicely grouped with Σ1474, which is 20' south

Σ1474		10 45.2	-15 00	6.9+7.5 +7.5	69.4	25

The 7.5 mag. stars are just 6.7" apart in p.a. 196°. Beautiful triple.

Hh 376	N	11 29.8	-28 59	6.0+6.0	9.1	210

Formerly 17 Crateris.

h4465		11 39.2	-32 13	5.5+7.5	67.0	44

Orange-yellow primary.

Σ116		11 54.2	-31 59	7.0+7.0	19.6	263
S651		13 34.0	-26 14	5.0+7.0	10.9	192
Hh 449	54	14 43.1	-25 14	5.2+7.1	8.8	126

LACERTA

| h1735 | | 22 07.2 | +44 36 | 7.0+8.5 | 27.1 | 110 |
| Σ2890 | | 22 13.2 | +49 38 | 8.5+8.7
+9.5 | 9.4
73.0 | 11
278 |

Located in the open cluster NGC 7243.

| Σ2891 | | 22 14.4 | +47 44 | 8.2+9.2 | 13.0 | 309 |
| Σ2894 | | 22 16.7 | +37 31 | 6.0+8.2 | 15.8 | 194 |

CATALOG NUMBER		R.A.(1950) Dec. h m ° '	Mags.	Sep. "	P.A. °

LACERTA (Continued)

| Σ2902 | | 22 21.4   +45 06 | 7.1+8.0 | 6.4 | 90 |

Beautiful sight. Nice double in same field to the northwest (7.5+9; 35"; 360°).

| OΣΣ234 | 380 | 22 24.9   +49 27 | 7.5+8.0 | 36.2 | 135 |

Visible in same 1/2° field as 4 Lac, and located between 4 and .

| Σ2916 pair | | 22 29.1   +40 57 22 32.3   +40 32 | 7.3+8.8 7.0+9.0 | 44.8 40.0 | 336 250 |

Data are author's estimates.

| Arg 44 Σ2922 | 8 | 22 32.3   +50 07 22 33.6   +39 23 | 8.0+8.0 6.0+6.5 +9.5 | 7.2 22.3 81.1 | 169 186 145 |

Multiple system with several components too faint for small telescopes.

| Σ2926 | | 22 35.3   +38 38 | 8.5+8.5 | 20.8 | 336 |

In same field with 10 Lac.

| S813 h1823 | 10 | 22 37.0   +38 48 22 49.5   +41 03 | 5.5+9.0 6.3+7.3 +7.5 | 62.1 82.2 119.0 | 49 338 263 |

Striking group.

| OΣΣ239 | h975 16 | 22 53.4   +36 05 22 54.1   +41 20 | 6.0+8.5 5.0+9.0 | 51.0 62.7 | 243 48 |

Also attended by a star of 9.5 mag., 100" away.

LEO

| Σ1360 Σ1364 OΣΣ101 | 6 | 09 27.8   +10 49 09 29.2   +20 16 09 29.3   +09 56 | 7.4+7.7 7.7+9.2 6.0+9.0 | 14.2 16.9 37.4 | 242 155 75 |

Optical. Orange primary.

	7	09 33.2 +14 36	6.5+8.5	41.2	80
Σ1399		09 54.3 +20 00	6.8+7.8	30.8	175
ΣII 6	Alpha	10 05.7 +12 13	1.4+7.9	177.0	307

Regulus. Both stars share the same proper motion.

| ΣI 18 | Zeta | 10 13.9   +23 40 | 3.8+6.0 | 314.4 | 343 |

Optical. Separating. Unspectacular pair.

CATALOG NUMBER		R.A.(1950)Dec. h m ° '		Mags.	Sep. "	P.A. °
ΣI424	Gamma	10 17.2	+20 06	2.6+3.8	4.3	123

Slow-moving binary. Grand double star for any size telescope. Primary is rich golden yellow.

Σ1442		10 29.2	+22 18	7.2+7.8	13.3	155
Σ1448		10 31.7	+21 54	7.5+9.0	11.0	259
pair		10 33.5	+11 53	8.0+9.0	55.6	337
Σ1477		10 47.0	+13 11	8.3+8.8	17.6	276
Σ1487	54	10 52.9	+25 01	5.0+7.0	6.5	110
Σ1521		11 12.7	+27 51	7.0+7.5	3.7	96
Σ1529		11 16.8	-01 23	7.0+8.0	9.4	253
Σ1540	83	11 24.3	+03 17	6.3+7.3	28.9	150

Both stars of spectral class K. Some observers see the brighter star as yellowish and the companion as reddish. τ in field.

ΣI 19	Tau	11 25.4	+03 08	5.5+7.0	91.1	176

Slight decrease in distance.

Σ1547	88	11 29.2	+14 39	6.4+8.4	15.4	326
Σ1552	90	11 32.1	+17 04	6.0+7.3	3.4	209
				+9.0	63.1	235
Σ1558		11 34.1	+21 45	8.5+8.5	43.6	276
Σ1565		11 37.0	+19 16	7.0+8.0	21.6	305
ΣII 7	93	11 45.4	+20 30	4.7+8.4	74.3	355

Forms an interesting "double-double" with wide, faint pair in field.

Σ1582		11 53.4	+22 16	7.5+9.0	12.3	76

_____ LEO MINOR

Σ1449		10 32.3	+35 24	8.5+8.7	37.8	290

Optical pair with increasing separation. Located just east of 34 LMi.

Σ1458		10 36.7	+31 55	8.0+8.2	17.7	215

37 LMi acts as the guide star for this pretty pair, found just 20' to the southeast.

_____ LEPUS

Σ314		04 56.8	-16 27	6.5+8.2	52.9	34

9th mag. pair about 20' south.

CATALOG NUMBER		R.A.(1950) Dec. h m ° '		Mags.	Sep. "	P.A. °
		LEPUS (Continued)				
S476		05 17.1	-18 34	6.5+6.5	39.2	18

The more southerly of a wide pair of 6th mag. stars. Faint comes (9.5 mag.) 80" away.

h3752		05 19.8	-24 49	5.5+6.5	3.1	97
				+9.0	58.8	106
Σ710		05 22.9	-11 21	8.2+8.3	10.8	195
h3759		05 23.9	-19 44	6.5+8.0	27.1	318

Pretty row of 9-10 mag. stars 1/4° north and slightly east.

h3780		05 37.1	-17 53	7.0+9.0	89.1	137
				+8.0	76.0	7
				+8.5	129.0	299

A beautiful multiple star, catalogued in the NGC as a cluster (NGC 2017). To find it, sweep the skies 2° east of α.

| Hd 78 | | 05 37.6 | -20 28 | 7.5+8.5 | 11.8 | 124 |
| Hh 199 | Gamma | 05 42.4 | -22 28 | 3.6+6.2 | 94.9 | 351 |

Colors seem to be yellowish and slightly reddish.

		LIBRA				
Σ225		14 22.6	-19 44	6.0+6.5	35.0	295
Σ106	Mu	14 46.6	-13 57	5.5+6.3	1.8	355

All too rare is the evening when sky conditions permit the resolution of close pairs like this.

| | Alpha | 14 48.1 | -15 50 | 3.0+6.0 | 231 | 314 |

Yellowish and blue-white.

| Hh 457 | | 14 54.5 | -21 11 | 6.0+8.0 | 21.8 | 302 |

Both stars are traveling in the same direction, but the brighter star is moving faster, leaving its partner behind.

| | 17, 18 | 14 55.8 | -10 57 | 6.0+6.5 | - | - |

Wide pair, about 10' apart. 18, the brighter of the two, has a 10th mag. partner 19.6" away, at p.a. 39°.

Σ1899		14 59.0	-02 58	7.0+9.5	28.2	67
Hh 465	Iota	15 09.4	-19 36	4,5+9.5	58.6	111
Hh 467	Shj 195	15 11.6	-18 15	6.9+7.7	47.4	140
Li 123		15 30.2	-24 19	7.0+7.0	9.3	301

CATALOG NUMBER		R.A.(1950)Dec. h m ° '	Mags.	Sep. "	P.A. °
LIBRA (Continued)					
Σ1962		15 36.0 -08 38	6.3+6.4	11.8	189

To me, both stars seemed greenish or slightly bluish. A fine pair.

Σ1966		15 39.3 -10 59	9.0+9.0	23.2	233
LUPUS					
Δ192		15 43.9 -35 22	7.0+7.5	34.8	144
Δ196	Xi	15 53.7 -33 49	5.2+5.5	10.6	49

Were this pretty double located at a more northerly declination, it would receive the attention it so richly deserves.

h4821		15 54.7 -31 49	8.5+8.5	19.3	145

Requires skies that are clear all the way to the horizon.

LYNX					
5		06 22.4 +58 27	6.0+8.5	96.0	272

Two 7th mag. stars in immediate field.

8, 10		06 33.3 +61 33	6.5+7.0	360.0	

Wide pair with 9th mag. star between.

Σ948	12	06 41.8 +59 30	5.2+6.1	1.8	101
			+7.4	8.5	308

A grand triple, but slight atmospheric turbulence will merge the images of the close pair, which is a binary.

Σ958		06 44.0 +55 46	6.0+6.0	4.9	257

A beautiful pair, typical of the many that are found in this region. A test for 1-inch telescopes.

Σ960		06 45.6 +53 05	7.3+9.2	22.0	67

Σ968 found just over 1/2° east and slightly south.

Σ968		06 48.9 +52 45	8.0+9.0	20.7	288
Σ1001		06 59.1 +54 15	7.1+8.7	9.0	66
Σ1002		07 00.0 +56 31	8.5+9.0	30.3	317
Σ1009		07 01.7 +52 50	6.7+6.8	3.9	150

It is hard to look at this pair and not be touched by its delicate beauty.

CATALOG NUMBER		R.A.(1950)Dec. h m ° '	Mags.	Sep. "	P.A. °
	LYNX (Continued)				
Σ1025		07 08.8 +55 53	7.5+7.8	25.6	133

Distance slowly increasing.

| Σ1044 | | 07 12.7   +47 44 | 8.5+8.7 | 12.2 | 168 |
| Σ1050 | | 07 15.8   +55 01 | 7.3+8.0 | 20.2 | 20 |

Shares a 1° field with 19 Lyn, which is
to the northeast.

| Σ1065 | 20 | 07 18.4   +50 15 | 6.6+6.8 | 15.1 | 254 |
| Σ1062 | 19 | 07 18.8   +55 23 | 5.3+6.6 | 14.7 | 315 |

Color of the fainter star varies with
observer. Greenish to me--blue, lilac,
and plum-colored to others.

| OΣΣ87 | | 07 35.1   +42 35 | 7.5+8.0 | 64.4 | 178 |

Forms long isoceles triangle with 8th
mag. star.

h2405	24	07 38.8 +58 50	5.0+9.0	54.8	320
Σ1200		08 12.3 +49 56	8.5+8.5	8.2	360
pair		08 19.9 +45 11	8.5+8.5	40.0	-

Just northwest of Σ1217. P.a. 160° or 340°

1217		08 20.8 +45 07	7.0+8.5	29.0	241
OΣ93		08 21.4 +42 11	6.0+8.0	77.4	168
Σ1234		08 29.2 +55 32	7.0+8.3	23.5	67

Yellowish primary.

| Σ1274 | | 08 45.8   +38 32 | 7.0+8.7 | 8.9 | 42 |

Companion can be quite elusive!

| Σ1282 | | 08 47.6   +35 15 | 7.0+7.0 | 3.7 | 278 |

A beauty!

| Σ1334 | 38 | 09 15.8   +37 01 | 4.0+6.7 | 2.9 | 228 |

Well seen in the clear skies of early
spring.

| 40 | Alpha | 09 17.9   +34 37 | 4.0+8.6 | 200.0 | |

Yellow and deep blue. Separation is
estimated. Faint star is Σ1342. (8.5+11.0;
17.1"; 320°),

| Σ1369 | | 09 32.3   +40 11 | 7.0+8.0 | 24.7 | 149 |
| | | | +8.0 | 118.0 | 325 |

Stiking group.

CATALOG NUMBER		R.A.(1950) Dec. h m ° '		Mags.	Sep. "	P.A. °
Σ2333		18 29.2	+32 13	7.5+8.0	6.4	334

A little gem!

Σ2351		18 34.6	+41 14	7.4+7.4	5.1	340
Σ2367		18 39.4	+30 15	7.0+8.4	14.3	193
Σ2371		18 40.2	+27 36	8.5+8.5	9.7	56
Σ2372		18 40.3	+34 42	6.7+8.2	25.1	83
Σ2380		18 41.4	+44 52	6.7+8.2	25.6	9
Σ2376		18 41.8	+30 21	7.7+8.4	22.3	64
Σ2382	Epsilon	18 42.7	+39 37	5.1+6.0	2.8	359
Σ2383	Epsilon	18 42.7	+39 37	5.1+5.4	2.2	98

Epsilon[1] and Epsilon[2] form the fine binocular pair I 37 (mags 5+5; 208"; 173°). A good telescope at 100x will show all four components of this grand "double-double."

ΣI 38	Zeta	18 43.0	+37 33	4.2+5.5	43.7	150
Σ2392		18 43.5	+39 10	8.2+9.3	23.4	175

Located 1/2° south of Epsilon [1,2].

Σ2390		18 44.0	+34 28	7.3+8.7	4.2	158

Don't try this one unless skies are steady.

h1347		18 45.7	+28 22	8.0+8.5	18.4	275
				+8.2	75.3	164

A beautiful sight.

ΣI 39	Beta	18 48.2	+33 18	var+6.7	46.6	149
				+9.0	68.6	318
				+9.0	85.7	19

Primary is an eclipsing binary, mag. 3.4-4.3; period 12.9 days. Fine multiple.

	Delta	18 52.2	+36 54	4.5+5.5	500.0	-

Brighter star (δ^2) is reddish orange; its partner is bluish.

OΣ525		18 53.0	+33 54	5.1+7.1	45.2	350

Yellow and blue. Σ2421 in field to southeast.

Σ2421		18 54.1	+33 44	8.0+8.7	22.6	64

CATALOG NUMBER		R.A.(1950) h m	Dec. ° '	Mags.	Sep. "	P.A. °
	LYRA (Continued)					
Σ2458		19 05.0	+27 41	8.5+9.0	11.9	227
				+9.0	70.2	63
Σ2472		19 06.8	+37 50	7.5+9.0	20.9	338
				+9.0	75.4	346

Nicely aligned triple. Furthest member is the close pair Σ2473.

| Σ2470 | | 19 06.9 | +34 42 | 6.7+8.2 | 13.5 | 271 |

Σ2474 in field forms a beautiful "double-double" that rivals Epsilon[1,2] in splendor.

Σ2474		19 07.2	+34 31	6.7+8.0	16.7	262
Σ2483		19 10.4	+30 16	7.2+8.3	9.7	318
				+8.5	71.0	236
Σ2487	Eta	19 12.0	+39 03	4.0+8.1	28.2	83

Optical.

| OΣ366 | | 19 12.4 | +34 08 | 7.0+10.0 | 21.8 | 230 |

With OΣ367 in the same field to the north, forms yet another "double-double" for Lyra.

OΣ367		19 12.6	+34 28	7.0+9.5	33.4	228
OΣ371		19 13.9	+27 22	6.8+9.0	47.4	268
Hh 608	Theta	19 14.6	+38 03	5.0+8.0	99.8	71
	MONOCEROS					
Σ869		06 08.4	-09 50	7.5+8.5	24.3	279
Σ900	Epsilon (8)	06 21.1	+04 37	4.0+8.7	13.2	27
Σ911		06 24.2	+04 06	8.5+8.5	13.0	156
Σ914		06 24.3	-07 29	6.7+9.0	20.9	298

Bluish primary. β is a degree northeast.

| Σ919 | Beta (11) | 06 26.4 | -07 00 | 5.0+5.5 | 7.4 | 132 |
| | | | | +6.0 | | |

Perhaps the finest triple star in the heavens for the small telescope. The 6.0 mag. star is 2.8" from the 5.5 mag. member, in p.a. 105°. All three stars are white. Beautiful sight!

| Σ921 | | 06 28.4 | +11 17 | 6.0+8.2 | 16.3 | 3 |
| Σ926 | | 06 29.0 | +05 48 | 7.3+8.7 | 11.7 | 289 |

Beautiful open cluster NGC 2244 just 1° south.

| Σ939 | | 06 33.3 | +05 22 | 8.1+8.7 | 29.8 | 106 |
| | | | | +9.0 | 39.8 | 49 |

CATALOG NUMBER		R.A.(1950) h m	Dec. ° '	Mags.	Sep. "	P.A. °

MONOCEROS (Continued)

Σ953		06 38.4	+09 02	7.0+7.5	7.0	330

Easily located just south of S (15) Mon.

Σ952		06 38.5	+09 57	9.0+9.0	13.6	295

To locate this faint pair, just train your
telescope on S Mon and study the field
immediately east. You should find Σ952,
plus two wider pairs that form a striking
slanted row. S is the primary star of the
open cluster NGC 2264.

Σ1010		06 59.0	-03 03	7.8+8.8	23.1	6

We can appreciate the keen eyesight of the
great double star observers when we
realize that Aitken discovered, just 2.7"
from the primary, a companion of mag.
15.5!

Σ1030		07 06.4	-08 36	8.0+9.2	15.8	43

1° east of open cluster M50.

Σ1052		07 12.2	-10 11	8.5+8.7	20.0	20

Found in the coarse open cluster NGC 2353.

Σ1111		07 29.6	-08 35	8.2+8.7	20.0	220
pair		07 39.6	-03 41	9.0+9.5	30.0	45

In the same field, to the south, as Σ1132.

Σ1132		07 39.7	-03 24	8.1+8.7	19.7	235
Σ1183		08 04.0	-09 06	5.5+7.8	30.9	326
	Zeta (29)	08 06.1	-02 50	6.0+8.5	66.4	245

Yellowish primary.

CATALOG NUMBER	R.A.(1950) Dec. h m ° '		Mags.	Sep. "	P.A. °
OPHIUCHUS					
Hh 512 Rho	16 22.6	-23 20	5.7+6.4	3.1	223
			+8.0	152.0	360
			+8.0	156.0	253
Σ2096 96	16 44.6	+02 09	6.0+9.3	23.2	89
Σ2105	16 48.8	+01 15	8.0+9.5	29.1	130

So close to 21 Oph that it's nearly drowned by the light.

Sh 240 Pi (236)	16 54.1	-19 28	6.3+8.0	4.5	232
Σ2122	17 04.3	-01 35	6.5+8.7	20.4	280
Σ2123	11 04.6	+06 57	8.5+8.5	19.3	218
h589	17 07.7	-14 53	7.5+7.8	10.0	304
Sh 243 36	17 12.3	-26 30	5.6+5.7	4.4	163

A 7th mag. star, located 732" away, at p.a. 74°, is a physical member of the system.

Hh 534 39	17 15.0	-24 14	5.5+6.0	10.8	355

Nice color contrast between the yellowish primary and its blue or green companion.

Σ2159	17 22.6	+13 22	7.4+8.1	26.3	326

Found almost dead center between α Her and α Oph.

Σ2166	17 25.5	+11 26	5.6+7.4	27.4	283
ΣI 34 53	17 32.2	+09 37	5.6+7.3	41.3	191
Σ2185	17 32.4	+06 03	7.0+10.0	27.7	5
			+8.0	80.0	225
			+9.0	89.6	202

The 9th mag. star is close enough to the 8th mag. component as to be rather difficult to see.

Σ2191	17 37.1	-04 57	7.0+8.0	36.4	267
Σ2202 61	17 42.0	+02 36	6.2+6.6	20.6	93
Σ2223	17 46.5	+04 59	7.5+8.5	18.3	211

Σ2227 in field to north. Both pairs lie a degree to the southeast of the large open cluster IC 4665.

Σ2227	17 47.6	+05 21	8.8+8.8	19.6	297
S694	17 49.5	+01 08	6.5+7.0	81.8	237

Yellowish-orange 6th mag. star in field.

Σ2235	17 50.4	-02 15	7.5+9.1	19.5	124

Slowly widening. Faint triple 1/4° west.

Hh 551 67	17 58.1	+02 56	4.0+9.0	54.6	142

CATALOG NUMBER		R.A.(1950)Dec. h m ° '	Mags.	Sep. "	P.A. °
OPHIUCHUS (Continued)					
Σ2262	Tau	18 00.4 -08 22	5.3+6.0	1.8	277

Binary. Period 280 years. Though gradually closing, this pair should be visible in a good 3-inch telescope the rest of this century.

OΣΣ164		18 00.9 +07 55	7.3+8.2	49.8	3
Σ2265		18 01.7 +06 27	8.4+9.4	14.5	183

Interesting field.

Σ2272	70	18 02.9 +02 32	4.3+6.0	2.2	322

A binary star whose position angle is currently going through a rapid change (decreasing). The separation will decrease to 1.5" in 1990, thereafter increasing rapidly to 3.0" by the end of the century. A pair to watch closely!

Σ2276		18 03.4 +12 00	6.0+7.0	7.1	258

Beautiful double.

HV 74		18 05.5 +13 04	6.0+9.0	42.3	138
OΣ355		18 31.0 +08 14	6.0+9.5	38.7	248
Σ2346		18 34.8 +07 29	7.5+9.0	23.6	292

An optical pair. Increasing separation.

ORION					
OΣΣ55		04 46.5 +05 07	8.0+8.8	37.7	16

1/2° west of π^4.

Σ612		04 51.6 +07 18	7.6+7.9	16.7	198
OΣΣ58		04 56.2 +14 28	5.0+6.5	39.4	305
			+9.0	54.4	89
Σ627		04 57.8 +03 33	6.3+7.0	21.0	260
Σ630		04 59.4 +01 32	6.8+8.0	14.4	50
J307		05 01.2 -02 36	7.0+8.0	52.2	322
Σ654	Rho	05 10.7 +02 48	4.7+8.5	7.0	63

Difficult because of the nearness of the faint star to the primary.

Σ668	Beta	05 12.1 -08 15	0.1+6.7	9.4	202

Rigel. To split this pair with a 3-inch telescope is quite an accomplishment. The companion seems bluish, compared to the white primary.

Σ664		05 12.4 +08 23	7.5+8.0	5.0	172
Σ688		05 17.0 -10 48	7.0+7.4	10.3	273

CATALOG NUMBER		R.A.(1950)Dec. h m ° '		Mags.	Sep. "	P.A. °

| Σ692 | | 05 18.0 | -08 05 | 7.8+8.8 | 35.1 | 4 |

This faint pair is easily located one third of the way from 29 Ori to Rigel.

| | 22 | 05 19.0 | -00 25 | 4.7+5.2 | 250.0 | - |

This fine binocular pair seems to have been overlooked by the major observer's guides.

Σ696	23	05 20.2	+03 30	5.0+7.0	32.0	28
Σ697		05 20.6	+16 00	7.2+8.2	26.0	285
Σ701		05 20.9	-08 28	6.7+8.5	6.0	141
A 847		05 21.3	-00 55	6.5+6.8	2.7	160

Also listed as Winnecke 2. Lies just west of 27 Ori. Separation is increasing.

h702		05 25.9	-02 00	8.3+8.6	24.1	148
Σ721		05 26.9	+03 07	7.0+9.0	24.7	149
ΣI 14	Delta	05 29.4	-00 20	2.0+6.8	52.8	360

Mintaka.

| Σ734 | | 05 30.6 | -01 45 | 7.0+8.6 | 29.7 | 243 |

Each component is a close pair.

| Σ745 | | 05 32.3 | -06 02 | 8.5+8.7 | 28.6 | 347 |

Nicely grouped with ι and Σ747.

Σ738	Lambda	05 32.4	+09 54	4.0+6.0	4.4	44
Σ747		05 32.6	-06 02	5.6+6.5	36.0	223
	Theta	05 32.8	-05 25	5.4+6.3	13.3	61
				+6.8	12.9	311
				+7.7	16.8	342

The "Trapezium." Located in the heart of the Orion Nebula. Easily the loveliest multiple star in the heavens for the small telescope. The two faintest members are eclipsing binaries.

| | Theta | 05 32.9 | -05 27 | 5.0+6.5 | 52.5 | 92 |
| | | | | +8.5 | 129.0 | 97 |

Also immersed in the nebulosity of M42. Amid the splendor of this region, θ^2 is hardly noticed. In a barren part of the sky, it would be a striking object.

| Σ750 | | 05 33.0 | -04 24 | 6.0+8.0 | 4.3 | 60 |

CATALOG NUMBER		R.A.(1950)Dec., h m ° '		Mags.	Sep. "	P.A. °

ORION (Continued)

| Σ752 | Iota | 05 33.0 | -05 56 | 3.2+7.3 | 11.4 | 141 |

Can be difficult. A 1/2° field includes θ¹, θ², Σ745, and Σ747.

| Σ751 | | 05 33.2 | -01 01 | 8.0+8.7 | 15.6 | 123 |

Easily found in the same field as ε.

| Σ762 | Sigma | 05 36.2 | -02 38 | 4.1+7.5 | 12.9 | 84 |
| | | | | +7.0 | 42.0 | 61 |

A multiple star for larger telescopes.

| Σ766 | | 05 37.4 | +15 20 | 6.8+8.0 | 10.0 | 276 |
| | Zeta | 05 38.2 | -01 58 | 1.9+10.0 | 57.6 | 10 |

Alnitak.

| Σ789 | | 05 42.4 | +09 59 | 7.0+8.5 | 16.0 | 150 |
| Σ792 | | 05 44.3 | -03 167 | 8.2+8.7 | 24.9 | 134 |

Forms a triangle with 790 (7+9; 7", 88°) and another star.

| Σ798 | | 05 45.8 | -08 24 | 7.2+9.2 | 20.7 | 181 |
| Σ809 | | 05 48.1 | 0-01 27 | 7.7+8.8 | 24.6 | 97 |

Another pair nearby (7+9; 25"; 80° -- author's estimates).

| Σ817 | | 05 52.2 | +07 02 | 8.2+8.3 | 18.4 | 73 |
| S503 | | 05 53.2 | +13 56 | 7.0+9.0 | 26.9 | 326 |

Optical.

| | 59 | 05 55.8 | +01 50 | 6.0+9.5 | 36.5 | 204 |

Another 6th mag. star, about 200" away. Nice sight.

Σ838		06 02.8	+00 52	7.0+9.0	40.0	327
Σ840		06 03.7	+10 45	6.2+8.3	21.7	248
Σ848		06 05.7	+13 59	7.5+8.0	28.4	121
				+9.0	43.3	183

Part of the open cluster NGC 2169, located a degree south and slightly east of .

| Σ853 | | 06 06.4 | +11 40 | 7.8+8.3 | 33.2 | 1 |

Optical pair whose distance is increasing.

| Σ855 | | 06 06.4 | +02 31 | 5.8+6.8 | 29.4 | 114 |

Also attended by an 8th mag. star.

CATALOG NUMBER	R.A.(1950) Dec. h m ° '	Mags.	Sep. "	P.A. °

Σ859	06 06.9 +05 41	8.0+8.5	36.8	247

Optical and widening. The two stars are in line with a third 8th mag. star, located 4' away.

Σ877	06 11.8 +14 36	7.2+7.7	5.6	263

Part of a beautiful chain of stars.

75	06 14.4 +09 58	6.0+10.0	62.7	258
		+8.5	117.0	159

9th mag. star 110" away, at p.a. 330°.

Σ901	06 22.2 +10 33	7.5+9.5	20.0	248

PEGASUS

ΣII 11 1	21 19.8 +19 35	4.5+8.6	36.3	312
OΣ443	21 35.1 +06 29	8.0+8.3	8.3	349

Found just north of 3 Peg.

ΣI 56 3	21 35.2 +06 24	6.5+8.5	39.2	349

Interesting field.

Epsilon	21 41.7 + 09 39	2.5+8 8	143.0	321

Enif. Optical. Primary golden yellow. Interesting, because it exhibits a "pendulum-like oscillation of a small star in the same vertical with a large one, when the telescope is swung from side to side." -- Webb. Will work with similar wide, unequal pairs.

Ho 465	21 44.1 +21 57	7.0+9.0	42.6	246

Followed by a 7th mag. star, 1/4° away.

Σ2828	21 47.0 +03 10	8.0+9.0	30.8	141
Σ2829	21 47.2 +30 31	8.2+8.9	17.4	16
Σ2841	21 52.0 +19 29	6.5+8.0	22.7	110
Σ2848	21 55.5 +05 42	7.2+7.5	10.8	56
h1721	22 03.5 +29 39	7.5+8.5	10.6	270
Σ2861	22 03.6 +20 33	7.7+8.2	7.1	113
Pi , Pi (270)	22 07.0 +33 00	5.0+4.0	600.0	270

Data are author's estimates. Pi[1] Peg in Norton's Star Atlas.

Σ2867	22 07.6 +07 42	7.9+9.0	10.5	209
OΣ469	22 18.3 +34 52	7.0+8.5	28.7	45

Optical. Distance decreasing.

CATALOG NUMBER		R.A.(1950)Dec. h m ° '		Mags.	Sep. "	P.A. °
PEGASUS (Continued)						
Ho 615	32	22 19.0	+28 05	5.0+9.3	72.5	127
	33	22 21.3	+20 36	6.0+7.9	78.4	312

Optical. Rapidly separating.

| Σ2908 | | 22 25.8 | +17 00 | 7.0+8.7 | 9.0 | 116 |
| Σ2915 | | 22 30.1 | +07 09 | 8.5+8.7 | 13.7 | 134 |

Distance slowly increasing; p.a.
decreasing.

h1779		22 30.3	+33 58	8.0+9.0	22.5	216
Σ2920		22 32.0	+03 58	7.1+8.2	13.7	144
	Eta	22 40.6	+29 58	3.0+9.0	91.0	339

Primary quite yellowish.

Ho 482		22 49.0	+26 08	6.5+9.0	51.1	198
Σ2954		22 52.3	+14 54	9.0+9.0	36.7	29
Σ2978		23 05.1	+32 33	6.8+8.0	8.4	145
Σ2982	57	23 07.0	+08 24	5.9+10.2	32.9	198
Σ2986		23 07.5	+14 09	7.5+9.5	31.4	271

Very isolated in field.

h5532		23 07.9	+32 13	7.0+9.0	57.9	77
Σ2991		23 10.9	+10 48	6.0+10.0	33.6	359
Σ2997		23 14.5	+21 07	8.5+9.0	24.4	223
Σ3018		23 27.9	+30 34	8.0+9.5	18.9	203
Σ3021		23 28.9	+15 57	7.7+8.9	8.6	308
				+10.5	119.0	24
h3176		23 40.4	+12 16	9.0+9.0	26.8	165
Σ3041		23 45.3	+16 47	7.3+8.1	61.0	352

Gradually closing. 8th mag. component has
a partner of similar magnitude just 3.4"
away.

| Σ3044 | | 23 50.4 | +11 39 | 6.9+7.3 | 17.8 | 282 |

An attractive sight.

3048		23 55.5	+24 04	7.7+8.8	8.8	313
Σ3061		00 03.2	+17 34	8.5+8.5	7.6	146
PERSEUS						
Σ162		01 46.2	+47 39	7.0+9.7	20.7	178
Σ230		02 11.4	+58 15	8.0+9.0	24.1	258
Σ270		02 27.3	+55 20	7.5+9.5	21.5	304
				+10.5	38.3	338
h2143		02 29.9	+57 19	8.0+8.5	23.4	19

In field with open cluster NGC 957.

CATALOG NUMBER		R.A.(1950)Dec. h m ° '		Mags.	Sep. "	P.A. °

h1123

02 38.7 +42 35   8.5+8.5   20.0   248

Beautifully placed amid the swarm of suns that makes up M34.

Σ292

02 39.3 +40 03   7.5+8.2   22.8   212

Conveniently located near 12 Persei.

Theta (13)

02 40.7 +49 01   4.2+9.6   75.4   228

Optical, rapidly widening. A 10th mag. star, located 18" from the primary, orbits this star every 27 centuries. This system is Σ296.

Σ297

02 41.8 +56 21   8.0+8.3   15.7   278

Σ301

02 44.0 +53 44   7.3+8.3   8.1   16

One of Perseus' finest offerings.

Σ304

02 45.4 +48 59   7.5+9.0   24.9   290

Σ307   Eta

02 47.0 +55 41   4.0+8.5   28.4   301

Yellow and Blue. 10th mag. comes 66" away.

Σ316

02 48.9 +37 05   8.5+8.7   14.3   135

Σ325

02 52.7 +34 17   8.0+9.5   15.0   160

Optical. Distance increasing.

Σ331

02 57.2 +52 09   5.3+6.7   12.2   86

Fine pair. One of the easiest Struve doubles to locate--found midway and slightly south of a line joining γ and τ Persei.

Σ336

02 58.4 +31 13   6.5+8.0   8.5   8

Yellow and blue.

Σ364

03 10.4 +38 47   8.5+8.5   11.9   311

S430

03 34.8 +44 39   8.0+8.0   41.1   95

Σ426

03 37.5 +38 57   7.0+8.5   19.8   342

In low power field with Σ434.

Σ431   40

03 39.2 +33 48   4.2+9.5   20.0   238

Difficult if skies are even slightly hazy.

OΣΣ37

03 40.4 +44 39   6.2+6.5   41.2   95

Σ434

03 40.7 +38 13   7.0+7.8   31.8   85

Primary shows strong yellow color.

CATALOG NUMBER		R.A.(1950) h m	Dec. ° '	Mags.	Sep. "	P.A. °
Σ439		03 41.4	+32 00	8.0+9.2	23.8	39

In field with *o* Persei.

Σ443		03 43.5	+41 19	8.2+8.8	8.0	50
Σ446		03 45.7	+52 30	7.0+9.2	8.5	255
				+10.5	8.5	255
Σ447		03 50.8	+38 12	7.8+9.0	28.0	168

A 1° line drawn from the primary of Σ434 through its companion will lead to this pair.

| | Zeta | 03 51.0 | +31 44 | 2.7+9.3 | 94.2 | 195 |
| | | | | +10.0 | 119.0 | 185 |

A 9.3 mag. star, 13" from the primary, forms Σ464. Interesting sight.

| Σ471 | Epsilon | 03 54.5 | +39 52 | 3.1+8.3 | 8.8 | 9 |

Requires good seeing.

| Σ476 | | 03 58.2 | +38 32 | 7.5+8.7 | 21.8 | 287 |

Slowly widening.

| pair | | 04 03.8 | +43 04 | 6.5+6.5 | 167.7 | 286 |
| OΣΣ44 | | 04 13.7 | +46 06 | 6.2+7.2 | 58.4 | 321 |

OΣΣ47 in same field.

| OΣΣ47 | | 04 17.2 | +50 08 | 6.5+7.2 | 72.6 | 327 |

Yellow and blue.

| Σ533 | | 04 21.2 | +34 12 | 6.0+7.5 | 19.6 | 61 |

Part of a beautiful 0.5° chain of stars that includes 56 and 55 Persei.

Σ552		04 28.0	+39 54	6.3+6.5	9.1	115
Σ551		04 28.3	+52 06	8.5+9.0	13.7	126
OΣΣ50	57	04 29.9	+42 58	5.2+6.2	115.0	199
S451		04 32.6	+47 15	7.5+7.5	58.4	199

PISCES

Σ3009		23 21.7	+03 26	6.8+8.8	7.1	230
	Kappa	23 24.3	+00 59	5.0+6.0	600.0	150
Σ3019		23 28.1	+04 58	7.1+8.1	11.0	185
Σ3031		23 38.6	+05 59	7.5+8.5	14.3	311
Σ3054		00 00.6	+07 59	7.5+8.5	33.7	182

Just 1/4° southeast of 32 Psc.

CATALOG NUMBER		R.A.(1950) Dec h m ° '		Mags	Sep. "	P.A. °

PISCES (Continued)

Σ8		00 09.0	-03 21	7.5+8.5	7.8	291
Σ12	35	00 12.4	+08 33	6.2+7.8	11.8	149
Σ20		00 14.8	+16 14	8.0+9.0	11.6	232
Σ22	38	00 14.8	+08 36	7.0+8.0	4.3	237

Requires excellent seeing and high power.

Σ36	51	00 29.8	+06 41	5.0+9.0	27.7	83
Σ46	55	00 37.3	+21 10	5.0+8.2	6.6	193

A challenge for small telescopes.

Σ61	65	00 47.2	+27 26	6.0+6.0	4.5	297

At the theoretical limit of resolution for a 1-inch telescope. Beautiful object.

Σ88	Psi	01 03.0	+21 13	4.9+5.0	30.0	160
Σ90	77	01 03.2	+04 39	5.9+6.8	32.9	83
Σ98		01 10.1	+31 50	7.0+8.0	19.6	249
Σ100	Zeta	01 11.1	+07 19	4.2+5.3	23.6	63

Spectacular pair.

OΣΣ19		01 25.8	+07 42	7.3+7.8	68.4	100
Σ136	100	01 32.2	+12 18	6.9+8.0	15.6	78
Σ142		01 37.2	+15 00	8.2+8.4	26.1	312
Σ146		01 38.6	+09 52	8.3+8.3	24.1	306
Σ155		01 41.6	+09 14	7.5+7.9	5.0	326

Less than 0.5° northwest of o Psc.

Σ202	Alpha	01 59.4	+02 31	4.3+5.2	1.7	281

Alrisha. Binary. Separation will be 1.5" by the end of the century and will continue to close to about 1.0" in 2074.

PISCIS AUSTRINUS

Σ240	Beta	22 28.7	-32 36	4.4+7.8	30.4	172
h5356		22 37.0	-28 36	6.5+7.0	86.6	160

PUPPIS

	32	06 40.6	-38 20	6.3+7.7	8.2	277
h3966		07 23.0	-37 12	7.0+7.0	7.0	142
h3969		07 25.2	-34 13	7.0+7.5	17.4	227

Nice sight, with wide pair (6+8; 60"; 200°) to the north.

	49	07 26.9	-31 45	6.5+7.0	9.0	52
j3973		07 29.7	-20 48	7.5+8.5	9.7	35
Hh 269	n	07 32.2	-23 22	6.0+6.0	9.6	114

CATALOG NUMBER	R.A.(1950)Dec. h m ° '	Mags.	Sep. "	P.A. °

PUPPIS (Continued)

p (h3982)	07 33.4 -28 15	5.0+9.5	38.4	156
Σ1121	07 34.3 -14 22	7.2+7.5	7.4	304

A gem, surrounded by sparkling suns of the open cluster NGC 2422. Just to its west is Σ1120 (6.5+9.5; 20.0; 35°).

1 (h273)	07 36.8 -26 41	4.5+4.6	9.8	318

The finest pair in Puppis.

pair	07 39.9 -18 05	9.0+9.0	30.0	-

The above coordinates are for the bright planetary NGC 2440 (listed as magnitude 11.5 by the RNGC, but definitely visible in a 3-inch scope. Look just east to find this pair, whose stars are oriented in a north-south direction.

2 (Σ1138)	07 43.2 -14 34	6.2+7.0	16.9	340

Viewed through the finder, forms a nice pair with 4 Pup.

pair	07 45.4 -15 51	6.4+6.4	128.0	311
h4009	07 48.4 -32 02	8.0+8.5	9.7	322
h4035	08 01.1 -32 19	6.0+8.0	34.8	134
h4093	08 24.5 -38 54	7.0+7.5	8.2	124

PYXIS

h4166	09 01.2 -33 24	6.5+7.5	13.7	153

SAGITTA

Σ139	19 10.3 +16 46	6.5+7.5	113.0	285
Σ2504	19 18.8 +19 03	6.1+8.1	9.0	285
2,3	19 22.2 +16 50	5.9+6.7	360.0	70
Epsilon (O 185)	19 35.0 +16 21	5.7+7.7	89.2	81

Optical. Distance decreasing.

Hh 630	19 37.2 +16 27	6.5+8.6	28.4	301

Primary shows striking reddish color. Several aint pairs in field.

Zeta (2585)	19 46.8 +19 01	5.7+8.8	8.4	311
Eta	20 02.8 +19 53	-	-	-

Webb notes that several pairs may be found within a 30' to 40' radius of this star. 0.5° east is a pair of 8th mag. stars, separated by about 30". 20' south is a mag. 8 + 8.5 pair with a 40" gap between.

CATALOG NUMBER		R.A.(1950)Dec. h m ° '	Mags.	Sep. "	P.A. °

SAGITTA (Continued)

| Σ2637 | Theta | 20 07.7 +20 46 | 6.0+8.3 | 11.9 | 325 |
| | | | +7.1 | 83.9 | 223 |

The 6th and 7th mag. components are optical and are separating.

SAGITTARIUS

| Σ219 | | 17 55.5 -36 51 | 5.5+8.5 | 50.1 | 259 |
| h5003 | | 17 55.9 -30 15 | 6.0+7.0 | | |

Primary shows reddish hue.

| HN 40 | | 17 59.3 -23 02 | 7.0+8.0 | 10.6 | 212 |

Found in the Trifid Nebula (M20).

h2822	Mu	18 10.8 -21 05	3.5+9.5	47.4	312
			+9.5	50.6	115
Σ299	Sh 263	18 14.9 -18 50	6.5+9.5	54.4	13

Σ639 located 1/4° to the northeast. Both are part of the Small Sagittarius Star Cloud (M24).

| Σ639 | | 18 15.7 -18 39 | 7.0+8.0 | 17.6 | 52 |

A pretty object, easily found in M24.

| pair | | 18 25.0 -26 48 | 7.0+9.0 | 45.0 | 160 |

"About 1-1/4° south of Lambda (Sgr) ... is a fine 7th mag. triangle with comites to the southern and following (eastern) stars....."--Webb. Beautiful group. This pair is the southerly star in the triangle. Data are author's estimates.

| pair | | 18 25.7 -26 36 | 7.0+8.5 | 35.0 | 200 |

The easterly star in Webb's triangle. Data are author's estimates.

| | Nu | 18 51.5 -22 45 | 4.8+5.0 | 900.0 | 70 |

Included for historical importance, rather than visual appeal. It is this pair that Ptolemy referred to when he coined the term "double star."

HN 129		19 01.2 -22 58	7.5+8.5	7.8	308
S 711		19 05.0 -26 55	7.0+8.5	45.5	124
h5094		19 09.5 -33 57	7.5+7.5	23.6	191
S 715		19 14.8 -16 04	7.5+8.0	8.2	15

Very pretty object. S 716 (8+8-1/2, 5."0, 196°) located just 8' eastward.

CATALOG NUMBER		R.A.(1950) h m	Dec. ° '	Mags.	Sep. "	P.A. °
h2866		19 20.5	-18 06	8.0+8.3 +8.6	23.4 23.9	53 137

Located just east of Rho[1] and Rho[2] Sgr, forming a near equilateral triangle with them. A ghostly triple star.

Hh 619	HN 119	19 26.8	-27 05	6.0+8.2	7.5	142
S 722		19 36.3	-17 02	8.0+8.5	10.0	236
h599	54	19 37.9	-16 25	5.5+8.5	45.6	42

Bright component shows almost ruddy hue.

h5188		20 17.4	-29 21	6.5+8.0	27.4	322

SCORPIUS

Σ1998	Xi	16 01.6	-11 14	4.9+7.2	7.4	53

Elacrab. Bright component is circled by a 5.1 mag. star every 45.7 years. Widest separation was in 1976 (1.25"). Closing to 0.2" by 1997. The 7th mag. star circles these two in a retrograde direction every thousand years. Σ1999, located just 5' southward, shares Xi's proper motion.

Σ1999		16 01.7	-11 18	7.8+8.1	11.4	100

With Xi, forms an attractive sight.

Hh 497	Beta	16 02.5	-10 49	2.6+4.9	13.7	23

One of the finest doubles for small telescopes. Primary white, companion seems deep blue-green.

	Omega	16 40.0	-20 40	4.0+4.3	-	-

15' separates this rather unspectacular pair.

Σ199		16 05.1	-38 57	6.5+7.0	44.3	185
L6706	Brs 11	16 06.3	-32 32	6.3+7.0	7.8	85
Hh 497	Nu	16 09.1	-19 21	4.1+7.0	41.4	336

Each component is again doubled in large telescopes.

Σ2019		16 11.5	-101 7	8.0+9.5	22.2	154
Brs 12	55G	16 16.4	-30 47	5.5+6.5	23.0	319
Hh 503	Sh 225	16 17.2	-19 56	7.0+8.5	47.1	333
Hh 504	Sh 226	16 17.5	-20 00	7.5+8.0	12.7	22
Hh 505	Sigma	16 18.1	-25 29	3.0+9.0	20.0	273
H4848		16 20.7	-33 05	7.0+7.5 +9.0	6.3 92.0	154 357

CATALOG NUMBER		R.A.(1950) h m	Dec. ° '	Mags.	Sep. "	P.A. °

_____ SCORPIUS (Continued) _____

| H4850 | | 16 21.5 | -29 35 | 6.5+7.0 | 5.4 | 354 |

Distance has been slowly decreasing.

| | 22 | 1627.2 | -24 57 | 6.0+8.0 | 200.0 | 250 |
| | | | | +8.5 | 500.0 | 330 |

Mentioned by Serviss in his classic
Astronomy With An Opera Glass. Data are
author's estimates.

| Σ209 | | 16 44.9 | -36 48 | 7.5+8.5 | 23.4 | 141 |
| | Mu | 16 48.5 | -38 00 | 3.0+3.6 | - | - |

About 6' apart. Both white, Beautiful in
finder.

| WNO 5 | | 17 02.1 | -33 42 | 8.0+8.5 | 17.6 | 296 |

Optical, distance increasing.

| Stn 37 | | 17 48.0 | -30 33 | 6.5+7.5 | 9.9 | 190 |

Preceded about 20' by a 6th mag. star.

_____ SCULPTOR _____

h 3216	Delta	23 46.3	-28 24	4.5+9.5	74.3	297
Σ253		23 51.8	-27 19	6.0+7.0	6.8	269
h1991		00 36.4	-25 22	6.5+8.5	46.5	93
h3542		01 37.5	-37 44	7.0+8.5	20.5	276

_____ SCUTUM _____

Σ2306		18 19.4	-15 07	7.2+7.9	10.2	220
Σ2313		18 22.0	-06 38	7.2+8.5	6.1	198
Σ2325		18 28.7	-10 50	6.0+9.3	12.4	257
Σ2337		18 32.1	-14 45	7.8+8.8	16.3	297
	Delta	18 39.5	-09 06	4.5+10.0	52.5	130
Σ2373		18 43.1	-10 33	7.1+8.1	4.4	337
Σ2391		18 46.0	-06 05	6.2+9.0	38.2	333

In low-power field with the open cluster
M11.

_____ SERPENS _____

Σ1919		15 10.5	+19 28	6.1+7.0	24.0	10
Σ1931		12 16.3	+10 27	6.2+7.6	13.3	170
	5	15 16.7	+01 57	5.0+9.0	127.0	40

In field with M5. A 10th mag. star, 11.2"
from the primary, forms the double Σ1930.

| Σ1951 | | 15 29.5 | +09 50 | 7.8+9.0 | 15.9 | 222 |

CATALOG NUMBER		R.A.(1950)Dec., h m ° '	Mags.	Sep. "	P.A. °
Σ1954	Delta	15 32.4 +10 42	3.0+4.0	3.9	178

Distance slowly increasing.

	Psi	15 41.5 +02 40	6.1+9.0	108.0	108

Nice sight, with 6.5 mag. star located 400" away.

Σ1970	Beta	15 43.9 +15 35	3.0+9.2	30.8	265

Extremely difficult in small telescopes. Use averted vision.

Σ1978		15 48.6 +14 51	8.5+9.0	15.33	235
Σ1986		15 53.2 +10 15	8.2+8.8	14.4	94
Σ1985		15 53.3 -02 03	7.0+8.1	5.8	347
Σ1987		15 54.8 +03 33	7.2+8.7	10.4	322
Σ1990		15 56.8 +22 56	8.0+8.0	56.2	59

Medium-sized telescopes split the northeast component (8.5+8.5; 3.8").

Σ1993		15 57.6 +17 31	8.2+8.2	24.5	40

Closing from a separation of 34.0" in 1783.

Σ2007		16 03.7 +13 27	6.5+8.0	36.6	323

The separation of this optical pair is increasing.

Σ2031		16 13.8 -01 32	7.5+9.5	21.1	230
Σ2033		16 15.6 -02 09	8.5+8.7	10.7	174
Hh 535	Nu	17 18.0 -12 48	4.5+8.5	46.3	28
Σ2204		17 43.5 -13 18	7.0+7.2	14.5	24
h2814		17 53.4 -15 49	6.5+9.0	20.8	157
Σ2316	59	18 24.6 +00 10	5.5+7.8	3.9	318

Requires high power and excellent seeing.

Σ2342		18 33.2 +04 54	6.5+8.5	30.5	5

Distance increasing. Rich field.

AG 224		18 37.6 +03 19	9.0+10.0	22.2	348

Found 1/4° north of Σ2361. Both pairs are faint but form a nice sight.

Σ2361		18 38.1 +03 02	8.3+8.8	25.1	211
OΣ361		18 41.3 +05 35	7.5+8.2	22.7	173
Σ2375		18 43.0 +05 27	6.2+6.6	2.4	116

A truly incredible sight! For delicate beauty this pair has few equals.

CATALOG NUMBER		R.A.(1950) Dec. h m ° '		Mags.	Sep. "	P.A. °

_____SERPENS (Continued)_____

| Σ2417 | Theta | 18 53.8 | +04 08 | 4.0+4.2 | 22.2 | 103 |

The tail of the Serpent. A showpiece
double for small telescopes. Both white.

_____SEXTANS_____

| S 605 | 9 | 09 51.5 | +05 11 | 6.7+9.0 | 51.0 | 291 |

Bright component has yellowish tint.

| Σ1456 | | 10 35.7 | +01 30 | 8.0+9.5 | 13.6 | 46 |
| Σ1466 | 35 | 10 40.7 | +05 01 | 6.1+7.2 | 6.4 | 236 |

_____TAURUS_____

| ΣI 7 | | 03 28.0 | +27 33 | 6.9+7.4 | 44.0 | 233 |

Σ401 just 10' south. Nice sight.

| Σ406 | | 03 28.2 | +04 59 | 7.0+9.0 | 9.4 | 124 |

Part of a nice row of 6th mag. stars.

| Σ401 | | 03 28.3 | +27 24 | 6.5+7.0 | 11.0 | 270 |
| Σ4124 | | 03 31.6 | +18 38 | 8.0+8.0 | 7.4 | 185 |

Closely followed by Σ416. Attractive
double header!

| Σ416 | | 03 32.1 | +19 38 | 8.5+9.7 | 26.4 | 57 |
| Σ422 | | 03 34.2 | +00 26 | 6.0+8.2 | 6.2 | 260 |

Easily found near 10 Tau. Not so easily
split.

Σ427		03 37.6	+28 37	6.6+7.4	6.9	209
Σ430		03 37.8	+04 58	6.0+9.0	26.1	55
				+9.8	37.0	301

Viewed with a 3-inch reflector, the
companions are visible with averted vision
only. They immediately disappear when the
eye falls on the primary. An interesting
triple.

Σ435		03 40.1	+25 31	7.5+8.5	13.0	2
Σ1041		03 41.6	+27 45	6.2+6.3	127.0	43
h4351	19	03 42.3	+24 18	4.3+10.0	69.0	330

In the Pleiades. 21, 22 in 0.5° field.

| | 21, 22 | 03 42.9 | +24 23 | 5.6+6.4 | 168.0 | - |

Asterope I and II.

CATALOG NUMBER		R.A.(1950)Dec., h m ° '	Mags.	Sep. "	P.A. °
TAURUS (Continued)					
Σ536		03 43.3 +24 02	8.5+8.0	39.1	208

Distance increasing. A pretty sight in the "bowl" formed by Pleiades stars 17, 20, 23, and 25. Alcyone in 1/2° field.

ΣI 18	Eta (25)	03 44.5 +23 57	2.9+8.1	117.2	289
			+8.1	180.8	312
			+8.7	190.5	295

Alcyone. The 8th mag. stars form a lovely triangle that precedes Eta.

	27, 28	03 46.2 +23 55	3.6+5.1	300.0	-

Would be much more striking were it isolated indthe sky. OΣΣ40 located 1/4° to the north.

OΣΣ40		03 46.4 +24 14	6.6+8.1	87.1	308
OΣ64		03 47.0 23 42	7.0+9.0	10.1	234
Σ479		03 58.0 +23 04	7.0+7.9	7.2	128
			+9.7	58.3	241
Σ481		03 59.2 +27 59	7.5+9.5	15.5	326
Σ494		04 05.9 +22 58	7.7+7.7	5.3	187
HVI 98		04 12.8 +06 04	6.5+7.0	65.5	315
OΣΣ48	Phi	04 17.3 +27 14	5.0+8.0	52.1	250

Optical. Slowly closing.

Σ528	Chi	04 19.5 +25 31	5.7+7.8	19.5	25
Σ534	62	04 21.0 +24 11	6.2+8.0	29.0	290
I 9	Kappa	04 22.4 +22 08	5.0+6.0	339.0	173
Kui 17	68	04 22.6 +17 48	4.5+9.0	77.1	233
Σ545		04 24.2 +18 06	7.5+9.3	18.8	57

In field with 68 Tauri.

Σ548		04 25.7 +30 15	6.0+8.0	14.6	36
ΣI 10	Theta	04 25.8 +15 46	3.4+3.8	337.0	346

In the Hyades. Best seen in the finder.

OΣ84		04 28.4 +06 41	7.5+8.0	9.5	254
Σ559		04 30.6 +17 55	7.0+7.0	3.1	276
OΣΣ52	88	04 32.9 +10 04	4.5+8.0	69.7	299
Σ569		04 33.5 +09 07	8.2+8.7	8.2	133
Σ572		04 35.4 +26 51	6.5+6.5	3.9	194

A gem made all the more spectacular by its relative isolation.

ΣI 11	Sigma	04 36.4 +15 45	4.7+5.1	431.0	193

In the Hyades. A finder pair.

CATALOG NUMBER		R.A.(1950)Dec. h m ° '		Mags.	Sep. "	P.A. °

TAURUS (Continued)

OΣΣ54	Tau	04 39.2	+22 52	4.0+9.0	62.9	212
Σ623		04 56.8	+27 15	6.8+8.3	20.7	204
ΣI 12		04 58.6	+26 36	7.0+8.5	78.7	159
	103	05 05.1	+24 12	5.5+9.0	35.3	197
Σ645		05 06.6	+27 58	6.2+8.2	11.9	27
Σ686		05 17.9	+23 59	7.9+8.1	9.3	223

On the faint side, but a beauty, anyway.

| Hh 166 | 111 | 05 21.5 | +17 20 | 5.0+8.0 | 90.0 | 270 |

Data are author's estimates.

Σ716	118	05 26.2	+25 07	5.8+6.6	5.1	204
OΣΣ64		05 26.9	+18 24	7.2+7.7	54.2	21
Σ730		05 29.3	+17 01	6.5+7.0	9.8	141
Σ742		05 33.4	+21 58	7.2+7.8	3.6	268
Σ740		05 33.4	+21 09	8.2+9.0	21.7	119

Pretty; located 1/4° east of ζ Tauri.

Σ785		05 42.8	+25 54	6.7+7.7	14.2	348
OΣ118		05 45.5	+20 51	6.0+7.7	75.5	161
Σ805		05 48.6	+28 27	7.7+8.4	12.2	49

TRIANGULUM

| Σ143 | | 01 37.6 | +34 06 | 7.7+9.0 | 37.8 | 319 |
| | | | | +9.9 | 70.8 | 137 |

Optical system. The separation of the closer pair is increasing.

Σ197		01 58.1	+35 05	7.3+8.3	28.1	234
Σ219		02 07.3	+33 08	8.2+9.0	11.6	183
Σ227	Iota (6)	02 09.5	+30 04	5.0+6.4	3.8	72

Σ232 in same field. Beautiful sight.

Σ232		02 11.8	+30 10	7.5+7.5	6.5	246
Σ239		02 14.5	+28 31	7.0+8.0	14.0	211
Σ246		02 15.6	+34 16	7.3+8.5	9.2	123

Easily located less than 1/2° northeast of γ Tri.

URSA MAJOR

Σ1193		08 15.2	+72 34	6.0+9.0	43.1	87
Σ1232		08 31.0	+66 27	8.0+8.5	31.1	350
Σ1250		08 36.0	+51 59	8.8+8.8	21.7	167
Σ1248		08 37.9	+62 13	8.3+8.8	18.1	209

Conveniently situated inside a triangle formed by ο, π², and 5 UMa.

CATALOG NUMBER	R.A.(1950)Dec. h m ° '	Mags.	Sep. "	P.A. °

URSA MAJOR (Continued)

| Σ1256 | 08 39.5 | +49 29 | 7.8+9.3 | 25.5 | 212 |

Σ1258 in same 1/2° field.

| Σ1258 | 08 39.9 | +49 03 | 7.1+7.4 | 9.7 | 331 |
| Σ1293 | 08 55.9 | +54 10 | 7.8+9.0 | 18.6 | 92 |

Flanked by two brighter stars.

| Sigma² | 09 60.0 | +67 20 | 5.0+9.5 | 205.0 | 148 |

The primary is joined by an 8.3 magnitude star to form the binary system 1306. The two are currently about 4" apart--a bit too close for small telescopes. They are slowly widening.

Σ1312	09 60.8	+52 35	7.7+8.2	4.5-	149
Σ1315	09 08.8	+61 53	7.0+7.2	24.8	27
Σ1321	09 11.4	+52 55	7.4+7.4	18.1	82
Σ1340	09 19.2	+49 46	6.5+8.3	6.2	319

Σ1341 is just 1° to the north.

| Σ1341 | 09 19.2 | +50 50 | 8.5+8.5 | 21.1 | 267 |

The galaxy NGC 2841 is in the same 1/2° field.

21 (1346)	09 22.1	+54 15	7.0+8.0	5.7	311
OΣΣ99	09 25.4	+45 50	5.5+7.0	77.3	162
Σ1349	09 26.9	+67 46	6.8+8.0	19.2	166
23 (1351)	09 27.6	+63 17	3.8+9.0	23.0	271

Save this one for a clear night.

Σ1358	09 27.7	+44 54	7.3+8.8	23.5	164
Σ1350	09 30.2	+67 01	7.2+7.3	10.4	248
			+9.0	130.0	214
Σ1402	10 01.6	+55 44	8.0+9.5	27.2	102

Optical. Distance increasing.

Σ1415	10 13.9	+71 18	6.1+7.0	16.7	167
Σ1427	10 19.0	+44 09	7.2+7.7	9.4	213
Σ1486	10 52.1	+52 24	7.5+8.8	28.3	103
Σ1495	10 57.0	+59 11	6.0+8.3	34.3	37

Easily found midway between Dubhe (α) and Merak (β).

| Alpha | 11 00.7 | +62 01 | 1.8+7.0 | 378.0 | 204 |

Despite their wide separation, these two stars share the same common proper motion.

Σ1512	11 06.2	+62 46	8.0+8.5	9.9	52
OΣ231	11 08.3	+30 43	8.0+9.0	35.0	264
			+9.0	174.0	332

CATALOG NUMBER	R.A.(1950)Dec. h m ° '	Mags.	Sep. "	P.A. °
Σ1520	11 13.2 +53 03	6.5+7.8	12.6	344
Xi (Σ1523)	11 15.5 +31 49·	4.4+4.8	2.9	105

URSA MAJOR (Continued)

An interesting binary pair that is currently
undergoing.great orbital changes. Closing to
0.9" by 1992, after which the two will rapidly
widen. A beautiful object.

Σ1533	11 19.5 +37 22	8.2+8.4	23.1	173
Σ1544	11 28.5 +59 59	7.0+8.0	12.3	91
Σ1553	11 33.9 +56 25	7.3_7.8	6.0	168

A pretty pair, located right in the bowl of
the Dipper.

Σ1561	11 36.1 +45 23	5.9+8.0	9.7	253
		+9.5	_121.0	90
65	11 52.5 +46 45	6.0+6.5	63.1	114
Σ1600	12 03.0 +52 13	7.0+8.0	7.5	92
Σ1603	12 05.6 +55 45	6.9+7.3	22.3	82

Positioned midway between γ and δ.

Σ1608	12 09.0 +53 42	7.5+7.7	12.7	221

A true gem! Well-seen at 30x.

Winnecke 4	12 20.0 +58 22	9.0+9.3	49.0	83

Messier 40. Amazingly enough, this double is a
Messier object! Searching for a nebulosity
reported to be in the area, Messier could find
only this pair. It became the 40th object in
his catalog. Easily found by extending a line
from δ to 70 0.5° beyond.

Σ1692	12 52.8 +58 26	8.2+9.0	18.8	277
Zeta (Σ1744)	13 21.9 +55 11	2.4+4.0	14.4	151

Mizar. One of the finest doubles in the
heavens, and, as the middle star in the Dipper's
handle, the easiest to find. This was the first
double discovered with a telescope. 12' eastward
is Alcor (mag. 4.0), which shares Mizar's
proper motion. A grand group.

S 649	13 27.0 +60 11	5.5+8.5	182	111

URSA MINOR

Alpha (93)	01 48.8 +89 02	2.0+8.8	18.4	218

Polaris. A classic small-telescope test. When
seeing is average, the companion is invisible in
a 3-inch telescope. Primary is yellowish-white.

CATALOG NUMBER		R.A.(1950) Dec. h m ° '	Mags.	Sep. "	P.A. °
Σ1583		11 57.8 +87 18	7.5+8.5	11.1	285
OΣ262		13 08.9 +74 15	7.3+8.2	28.0	183
Σ1761		13 30.8 +71 59	8.5+9.0	20.1	72

URSA MINOR (Continued)

Like Σ1583, situated near a 7th mag. star.

h2682		13 40.2 +77 05	7.0+10.0	26.1	280
			+9.5	45.9	316
Σ1840		14 18.9 +68 01	6.5+9.0	27.0	222

Easy averted vision pair. Forms nice wide double with nearby 6th mag. star.

Σ1972	Pi	15 32.0 +80 37	6.1+7.0	31.1	80
OΣ340		17 14.9 +86 58	7.8+8.3	31.5	229

Easily found by sweeping the skies 0.5° north of ϵ UMi.

VIRGO

Σ1575		11 49.4 +09 07	7.0+8.0	30.4	210
Σ1591		11 58.9 -00 11	8.0+8.0	51.7	352

Gradually closing.

Σ1605		12 07.9 -01 58	8.0+8.5	23.7	278
Σ1618		12 12.5 +10 16	8.5+8.5	26.3	245

Located 0.5° east of 12 Vir.

Σ1619		12 12.6 -06 58	7.5+7.8	7.2	273
Σ1627		12 15.6 -03 41	5.9+6.4	19.9	196
Σ1628		12 16.2 +12 04	8.5+8.7	9.8	239
Σ1635		12 18.6 -11 11	7.7+8.7	13.3	173

Faint comes precedes.

Σ1636	17	12 20.0 +05 36	6.2+9.0	19.6	337

Companion requires averted vision.

A2583	Sh 146	12 28.6 +01 36	8.0+8.5	50.0	290
Σ1649		12 29.0 -10 48	7.2+8.0	15.4	194
Σ1664		12 35.8 -11 12	7.7+8.8	26.3	237

Forms nice group with two other 8th mag. stars.

Σ1670	Gamma	12 39.1 -01 11	3.6+3.6	3.9	297

A beautiful twin binary that is steadily closing. Minimum separation will be 0.4" in 2008.

Σ1677		12 42.7 -03 37	7.0+8.0	16.2	348

CATALOG NUMBER		R.A.(1950)Dec. h m ° '		Mags.	Sep. "	P.A. °

_____VIRGO_(Continued)

| Σ1681 | | 12 47.0 | +04 06 | 8.5+8.5 | 8.7 | 197 |
| Σ1682 | | 12 48.8 | -10 04 | 6.7+9.0 | 30.8 | 301 |

Optical. Slowly closing.

Σ1689		12 53.0	+11 46	6.7+9.0	28.6	211
Σ1701		12 56.8	+06 47	7.5+9.5	21.6	306
Σ1719		13 04.8	+00 51	7.3+7.8	7.5	1

A beauty!

| Hh 412 | 54 | 13 10.8 | -18 34 | 7.0+7.2 | 5.3 | 34 |
| Σ434 | | 13 12.3 | -11 06 | 7.0+8.0 | 71.2 | 40 |

Optical. Widening.   P.a. is author's estimate.

Σ1740		13 21.1	+02 59	7.1+7.2	26.5	75
Σ1764		13 35.2	+02 38	7.0+8.7	15.7	32
Σ1775		13 40.9	-04 02	7.0+9.7	27.7	336
Σ1788		13 52.4	-07 49	6.7+7.9	3.3	91

A tough customer unless skies are steady.

| Hh 432 | Tau | 13 59.1 | +01 47 | 4.0+9.0 | 80.1 | 290 |

Optical. Slight distance increase.

| Σ1807 | | 14 08.7 | -03 06 | 7.8+8.0 | 6.9 | 29 |

Followed by 6th mag. field star.

| Σ1833 | | 14 20.0 | -07 33 | 7.0+7.0 | 5.7 | 172 |

Very lovely little pair.

| Σ1852 | | 14 27.4 | -04 01 | 7.0+10.0 | 25.0 | 267 |
| Σ1869 | | 14 40.1 | -05 45 | 8.0+9.0 | 26.0 | 133 |

Beautiful sight just south of μ Vir.

| Σ1904 | | 15 01.7 | +05 41 | 7.0+7.0 | 9.9 | 347 |

_____VULPECULA

Σ2445		19 02.5	+23 15	6.3+8.0	12.4	263
Σ2455		19 04.8	+22 06	7.3+8.3	6.6	40
ΣI 42	Alpha (6, 8)	19 26.7	+24 38	4.0+5.0	413.7	40

Southerly component is 6 (a Vul). 7'
northwest of this star is a faint pair
(9+9.5; 20"; 160°). A second pair
(9.5+9.5; 40"; 60° or 240°) is just 2'
east of 6.

| Σ2655 | | 20 11.9 | +22 04 | 7.5+7.5 | 6.2 | 3 |
| Σ2769 | | 21 08.3 | +22 15 | 6.5+7.5 | 17.9 | 300 |

Fig. 3-1. **Algol in Perseus**

3

Variable Stars

David H. Levy

Not all stars shine with constant light. Temperamental stars, those that alter their brightnesses, lie in every constellation. Some of these variable stars, like Mira in Cetus, display slow, stately rhythms, while others show deep and complex changes. Still others brighten in violent and unpredictable explosions. What are these variable stars? Can we observe many of them with small telescopes?

In this section we'll look at the history, nature, and observation of variable stars. This is a growing field for backyard astronomers, one in which amateurs can make significant contributions. The work is not exceptionally difficult. It involves comparing the brightness of a variable star to that of nearby stars of known fixed brightnesses. Anyone seriously interested in observing variable stars should contact the American Association of Variable Star Observers (AAVSO), 187 Concord Avenue, Cambridge, Massachusetts 02138. The AAVSO is the clearinghouse for variable star observations and provides excellent finder charts like the ones reproduced in this chapter.

Watching variables can turn into a lifelong interest. I've been a variable star observer for over 15 years, and yet there are areas in which I'm still a beginner. I could not have written these pages without the help of several people who have contributed to my knowledge of variable star observing: Dave Eicher, whose vision set the stage for this project: Janet Mattei, director of the AAVSO, who has listened patiently to my observational questions; Isabel Williamson, who helped me become interested in variables; and Judy Stowell, my secretary, who probably now knows more about variable stars than I do. And I must mention the late Leslie C. Peltier, whose experience and gentle manner helped me begin my voyage into the world of variable star astronomy.

David H. Levy

Tucson, Arizona

About the Author: David H. Levy is an avid amateur observer of variable stars, planets, deep-sky objects, and comets. He has written two books about astronomy, The Joy of Gazing and The Universe for Children. Levy has discovered four comets, including Comet Levy-Rudenko (1984t) and Comet Levy (1987a). He is a frequent contributor to Astronomy and Sky and Telescope magazines, and a Senior Contributing Editor of Deep Sky. When he isn't involved with comet hunting or writing about astronomy, Levy works as a professional astronomer at the University of Arizona's Lunar and Planetary Laboratory studying Comet Halley and various asteroids.

HISTORICAL BACKGROUND

Quite possibly, ancient peoples were the first to identify stars that varied. They probably noticed that the star Algol in Perseus changed in brightness by a factor of five from time to time; this "Demon Star" in the winter River of Heaven--the Milky Way--probably got its reputation as an oddity early on. But it wasn't until 1572, when Danish astronomer Tycho Brahe made careful observations of the "new star" in Cassiopeia that astronomers realized points of light in the sky--other than the planets--changed. In 1596, David Fabricius, a German theologian and astronomer, discovered a new second-magnitude star in the constellation Cetus. In 1609 he noticed it again, and confirmed that it was a regularly varying star with a period of 11 months and a range of six or seven magnitudes. He nicknamed the star Mira, which means "the Wonderful."

As more variable stars were discovered, astronomers were confronted with the task of inventing some kind of a naming scheme to classify and identify them. The existing system of lettering stars--created by German amateur astronomer Johann Bayer--utilized Greek letters and lower-case letters in order of brightness (i.e., the brightest star in a constellation was known as Alpha, the second brightest Beta, and so on). How to identify variable stars? Friederich Wilhelm Argelander, a German amateur who became director of the Bonn Observatory, proposed using an upper-case "R" as the first variable discovered in a constellation, since Bayer's system ran out at lower-case "q." Argelander was rather proud of his system, and couldn't really conceive of more than nine variables in a given constellation.

This led to a rather confused system of designations as astronomers found more and more variables. A constellation's 10th variable became RR, and more would be lettered through RZ, then SS through SZ, then TT through TZ. Then what? The discovery process ground relentlessly and astronomers went back to the beginning of the alphabet. Making the most out of a bad situation, astronomers referred to the 55th variable star in a constellation as AA. Additional variables would proceed through AZ, then BB through BZ, and so on, forgetting J and ending with 10 variables running from QQ to QZ. This muddled system allows for 334 variable stars in any constellation.

When still more variables inconveniently showed up, astronomers decided they'd had enough of the letters and went to using numbers. Thus the 335th variable star in a constellation--the one directly following QZ--is known as V335. Although this system is still in use, it is one of the oddest uses of nomenclature in all of science! In the late 1800s, astronomers at Harvard College Observatory began anew with a more convenient system. Known as the 1900 designation, this six-digit number displays the star's hours and minutes in 1900 coordinates--the first four digits--and its declination in 1900 coordinates--the last two digits. If the star is south of the celestial equator, its declination designation is underlined.

In the first half of this century, knowledge of variable stars rapidly developed as new odd classes and subclasses of stars were discovered. The center of activity was Harvard College Observatory where Henrietta Swan Leavitt, working on the Small Magellanic Cloud in 1912, discovered a period-luminosity relationship in certain variables, the Cepheids (named after Delta [δ] Cephei, the prototype). Once the periods of variation and the intrinsic brightnesses of these stars were known, astronomers could measure the distances to clusters and galaxies. This was one of the fundamental scientific discoveries of the 20th century.

Around the time of the discovery of Cepheid variables and their behavior, amateur and professional astronomers founded an organization to serve as a clearinghouse for observations of variable stars, the American Association of Variable Star Observers. There are so many types of variables, and so many examples of each type, that professional astronomers rely on the AAVSO and its backyard observers to supply them with data about what certain stars are doing. Seventy years ago, when the AAVSO began, a handful of stars needed watching. Now, half a million observations later, AAVSO members watch tens of thousands of stars and contribute data for scheduling the Einstein Observatory (HEAO-2), an orbiting X-ray telescope, and other vital programs of research.

THE NATURE OF VARIABLE STARS

The great variable star observer Leslie C. Peltier once said, "A variable star isn't just there, it's happening!" This provides an enticing reason for backyard astronomers to hunt them: they are not static, but rather you can see them change. Go out under the stars and ask yourself, "What has changed since last night?" At first you may see nothing, but upon closer inspection you'll see that a lot changes. You might see that R Coronae Borealis, an irregular variable, was bright last night but has since dropped by two magnitudes by tonight. You might see that R Leonis--a long-period variable--is taking a nap two-thirds of the way toward its maximum light. You might see SS Cygni, a miniature nova, leaping three magnitudes in a single night as it throws its bimonthly temper tantrum. You might think about GK Persei, a nova that every so often rolls over in bed, making us suspect that it might erupt again. Or you might look at V Cephei, a star which may have varied in brightness long ago. You'll see that many stars are "happening." But why do they vary? What makes them undergo such energetic pulses in brightness?

The answer is complicated, since there are many types of stars that vary their energy output for different reasons. Long-period variables (LPVs) or Mira stars, for the prototype in Cetus, are relatively steady variables. These are old stars that vary because of instability due to a lack of hydrogen, most of which they've burned up. They have periods from about 80 days to well over 600, and often vary over a wide range of magnitudes (Chi [χ] Cygni, for example, spans 11 magnitudes in its 407-day ritual.) These late-type giants are rather stately in their fluctuations, and have mean absolute magnitudes of +2 to -2. Their periods are not absolutely constant (as are those of the Cepheids), and often these stars are red. They are ubiquitous, and a good number are always visible to small-telescope observers.

The semi-regular variables are also old stars--late-type giants and supergiants--whose periods are ill-defined, usually falling between 20 and 100 days. Because they usually don't vary by much, their entire cycles can be viewed with small telescopes. They seem to be ideal stars for observing, but sometimes they aren't: since many of them are red, they show the Perkinje effect. When you stare at a red star, light builds up on your retina, changing the estimation of its brightness. Be careful to use quick glances when observing these red stars.

Eclipsing variables owe their changes to their unique orientation with respect to the Earth--each member of these binary systems alternately blocks out the other. There are three types of eclipsing variables, all of whose periods are well known. The first is the Algol type, named for the bright eclipsing star in Perseus. This system is composed of a faint star eclipsing a bright one for a few hours during each orbit. Algol is at maximum most of the time. The second type is the Beta [β] Lyrae type, whose components are so close that their gravity deforms them into ellipsoidal shapes. The Beta Lyrae system undergoes some eclipsing almost constantly, and is easy to monitor with small telescopes. The third type of eclipsing variable is the W Ursae Majoris type, composed of dwarf stars almost in contact. These stars have a period of less than one day.

Short-period variables are pulsating stars that are not physically blocked by an object but rather, like the LPVs and SRVs, intrinsically vary in light output. There are six types of short-period variables, some of which are rare and difficult to observe. The classical Cepheids--named after Delta [δ] Cephei--are those well-defined stars that enable us to measure the distance scale of the universe. They have periods of 3 to 50 days, and are F- to G-type supergiant and

superluminous stars with absolute magnitudes of -1.5 to -5. Polaris
(Alpha [α] Ursae Minoris), the North Star, is a classical Cepheid.
Another type is the W Virginis class, also known as Type II Cepheid
stars. These are like the classical Cepheids but are intrinsically
fainter, with absolute magnitudes of 0 to -3.5. The RR Lyrae type
stars--formerly called cluster Cepheids--are A- to F- type giant stars
in the initial stage of helium burning. These are old stars and are most
often found in globular clusters. They don't vary by more than two
magnitudes, and have periods from about 0.05 to 1.2 days. The Beta [β]
Cephei short-period variables are B-type giants with periods of less
than 0.5 days and don't vary by more than three-tenths of a magnitude.
Needless to say, these stars are not easily observed with backyard gear.
The fifth type of short-period variable is the Delta [δ] Scuti type,
F-type subgiant stars with periods of less than one day and variances of
about the same as δ Cephei types. They are not well observed with
amateur telescopes. The last type of short-period star is the magnetic
or spectrum variable, with a small variance in brightness and powerful
variable magnetic fields.

    The RV Tauri class of variables is characterized by pulsating G-
and K-type giant stars. They show alternate deep and shallow minima, and
occasional irregularity. About 100 are known, the brightest being R
Scuti. Pulsation apparently drives off material from the outer layers of
these stars, encapsulating them in a shell of gas and dust that emits
strongly in the infrared.

    There are several types of eruptive or cataclysmic variables, the
best known of which are the SS Cygni or U Geminorum type. These are
known as the dwarf novae, binary systems composed of a main sequence
dwarf coupled with a white dwarf. These stars normally remain at
minimum, but occasionally and irregularly increase by several
magnitudes. They have periods of 20 to over 600 days, their outburst
caused by instabilities in a ring of hydrogen-rich material pulled from
the main-sequence companion. The prototype, SS Cygni, has a period of 50
days; most of the time it is in a state of 12th magnitude sleep, but
without warning, it jumps to 8th magnitude in seven hours. Cousins of
the SS Cygni stars, the Z Camelopardalis systems, are similar but
undergo standstills where they apparently freeze their light output for
several months, sometimes longer. The cause of these standstills is not
known. Flare stars, or UV Ceti-type variables, are M-type dwarf stars
whose reddish light brightens by several magnitudes in only a few
minutes! This is apparently caused by localized flares on the stellar
surfaces--triggered perhaps by gigantic sunspot systems. P Cygni-type
stars are intensely luminous ones which are enshrouded in a shell of
expanding gas; they are erratic, hard-to-predict variables. Another type
of eruptive variable is the Z Andromedae type, or the symbiotic stars.
These show normal semi-regular characteristics most of the time, but at
long intervals flare up and show a P Cygni-type shell spectrum, leading
astronomers to believe that they are composed of a low temperature red
giant and a hot blue star. They are quite mysterious. The last type of
eruptive variable is the recurrent nova or T Coronae Borealis-type;
these stars suffer a series of nova-like outbursts in intervals of 15 to
80 years. They may hold some link between novae and normal stars.

    Irregular variables are generally late-type red giant stars that
pulsate in irregular ways. This class includes the nebular variables (or
T Tauri-type), which are F-, G-, or K-type giant stars surrounded by
clouds of gas and dust. These are some of the most complex variable
stars in the sky, sometimes changing within minutes as they flicker from
behind curtains of matter. Their variation is due to pulsation and
blockage from the hydrogen gas that surrounds them.

    R Coronae Borealis stars are F- to K-type supergiants which are low in hydrogen but relatively rich in carbon. These are rare stars which most of the time stay at maximum but suffers from sudden drops in brightness. They act like novae in reverse, perhaps because of carbon soot accumulating in their atmospheres and causing a minimum, soon blown away and resulting in the star's return to normal brightness.

A strange class of stars are the secular variables, stars whose brightness has apparently sometimes changed in historical times but has stayed constant in recent times. Centuries ago astronomer Claudius Ptolemy ranked Beta [β] Leonis and Theta [θ] Eridani right up with the first magnitude stars, but today they shine respectively at second and third magnitude. Could these stars have resumed a normal steady life, or should we suspect the observations of our early astronomers?

Novae--from Latin for "new star"--appear to be solitary exploding stars that suddenly erupt from anonymity to become some of the brighter stars in the sky. They are thought to be binary systems with, however, one star in a late stage of its life. Nuclear reactions from hydrogen-rich material falling onto the small white dwarf (which has spent all of its fuel) get out of control and blow off the accumulated matter. These stars remain bright for days or weeks and then fade into oblivion. Ten to 15 novae probably occur in our galaxy each year, some hidden by the thick clouds of gas and dust that obscure the galactic center. The last bright nova was V1500 Cygni; for a short time in 1975 a dim star near Deneb (Alpha [α] Cygni) increased its light output by 19 magnitudes to shine at magnitude 1.8.

Supernovae are a bit like novae but on a larger scale: they are exploding stars that temporarily brighten to absolute magnitude -15 or brighter, over a hundred times brighter than a nova outburst. Supernovae explosions come in two varieties, Type I and Type II. Type I supernovae occur in elliptical and spiral galaxies and have absolute magnitudes of -19. The cause may be a white dwarf accreting matter from a large companion. Type II supernovae occur only in arms of spiral galaxies and are the result of supermassive stars collapsing because they cannot burn their iron cores. They have absolute magnitudes of -16 or -17. Supernovae are relatively rare happenings: we've observed only four in our galaxy since historical times began--ones in A.D. 1006 in Lupus, A.D. 1054 in Taurus (creating the Crab Nebula), A.D. 1572 in Cassiopeia, and A.D. 1604 in Ophiuchus. The fact that a supernova hasn't appeared in our galaxy since 1604 suggests that we might be about due for one.

BEGINNING TO OBSERVE

Variable star observing is easy--its principles are simple and its techniques basic. It involves gauging the brightnesses of known variables against nearby stars of fixed brightness and like magnitude. Many variables can be watched simply with binoculars, and several hundred can be observed with a small telescope. The catalog section that ends this chapter contains a list of 110 of the best variables for small telescopes. Before you begin observing, however, you must realize that variable star watching depends critically on three factors--the sky, the telescope, and the observer--which all must work together.

The sky at your observing site must be dark enough and steady enough so that you can observe relatively faint variables, and small changes in brightness, with ease. If you go out to view and see that many stars are apparently twinkling, indicative of a turbulent atmosphere, you'll want to forgo estimating magnitudes until a crisper night comes along. Make sure that your telescope is one that fills your needs; it should be of a size you can easily work with and transport, and should probably be some type of reflector. Refractors pose a potential problem with variables because they show different relative brightnesses for red and blue stars unless their color correction is absolutely perfect. Schmidt-Cassegrains pose a problem because they are not easily used with the standard AAVSO estimating charts, which are essential tools for variable observers. My preference for variable stars is the good, old, standard Newtonian reflector. If I've had a bad day, I try to avoid watching variables: comfort is a must, as tired or strained eyes yield many observations useless.

A good first star to set your scope on is Delta [δ] Cephei, a simple variable with a period of about a week which offers slightly different brightnesses every night. Begin by looking at the chart showing Delta and Mu [μ] Cephei; Delta's two neighbors, Zeta [ζ] and Epsilon [ε] serve as excellent comparison stars. Every 5.37 days Delta fluctuates between magnitude 3.6 and 4.4, and Zeta and Epsilon bracket this range fairly well at 3.6 and 4.2, respectively. Out under the stars, find the field using an atlas like Sky Atlas 2000.0 and center Delta in your eyepiece. Now, assign that star Zeta a value of 1 and nearby Epsilon a value of 5. With binoculars or our small scope, compare the three stars back and forth and see if Delta is closer to Zeta or Epsilon in brightness. Give Delta a "1" rating if it is as bright as Zeta; "2" if slightly fainter than Zeta; "3" if midway between Zeta and Epsilon; "4" if slightly brighter than Epsilon; or "5" if as faint as Epsilon. Try estimating this triangle of stars until you are confident that you can pinpoint Delta's brightness. Then practice with increments of 10 rather than 5--you will be estimating to one-tenth of one magnitude.

After you've mastered the five- and ten-step methods with a few variables (try it with the charts in this section), you're ready to target more difficult stars. Look carefully at the chart for R Scuti; the circle-and-dot mark the location of the variable, and numbers like 61, 67, and 71 mark the brightnesses of nearby stars with the decimal omitted to avoid confusion with stars. Thus the star marked 67 is a magnitude 6.7 object. With binoculars or a small telescope, scan and find the area with a star chart. Is R brighter than 67 but fainter than 61? Perhaps it falls between 61 and 67: if so, follow the same procedure but use magnitudes instead of arbitrary numbers. If R is as bright as 61, it is at magnitude 6.1. If it is just slightly fainter it must be magnitude 6.2. Now be very careful: if it is about midway between the two but ever so slightly closer to 61, it is magnitude 6.3. If it is midway between it is 6.4 magnitude, and so on.

It is almost as simple as that. Congratulations! You have just made a variable star estimate in the tradition of the four million observations that have been sent to the AAVSO since its founding in 1911. But if you had problems--and I say this delicately because after I first estimated a star I resolved never to do it again--do not despair. It could have been the Perkinje effect. To avoid this problem when looking at red stars, try using quick glances instead of long, soulful looks. Averted vision also helps, looking sideward to use the rods in your eyes which are sensitive to faint variations in light. You may also slightly defocus your telescope, as a soft ball of light is often easier to compare in brightness than a sharp point.

Once you find a variable, estimating is usually not difficult. It is locating the object which most often deters prospective variable star hunters. A good atlas will help you find your stars with relative ease every time. You must be a good map reader, and find your way around without road signs.

Another interesting star you should watch early on is Mira (Omicron [o] Ceti) in the constellation Cetus. It is plotted on every star atlas and is pretty easy to find. Look for Mira in your finder scope; chances are its 11 month period of magnitude 3.4 to 9.5 variation will allow you to see it in binoculars or your finder. Follow the same procedure as with R Scuti, and if it's too faint for binoculars, use a low-power telescopic field. Estimating Mira's brightness once every two weeks should allow you to produce an interesting light curve.

As you expand your program, you may want to do two things: first, observe different types of variables like eclipsing stars, dwarf novae, or nebular variables. You'll also want to record your work in some sort of observing logbook. I usually write down the name of each star I observe on an index card along with my estimate and notes if I wish to make them. I keep the cards arranged in order of 1900 designations (you might want to keep them arranged by constellation). I leave the cards inside so they don't blow about in the wind, and so they don't influence my judgement at the telescope. At the end of a month, I take the cards and transfer their information onto an AAVSO standard report form (available from that organization), which is not time-consuming since the stars are listed there by designation and date of observation. Those of you with home computers can maintain a lightning-fast update on your variable star estimates.

ADVANCED OBSERVING TECHNIQUES

As you get more advanced as a variable star observer, you can estimate more difficult and unusual stars. Data and charts on such stars can be obtained from the AAVSO (its address appears at the beginning of this chapter). One of the most promising types of stars for backyard observers is the dwarf nova, the recurring eruptive star that--without warning--rises from its sleep and bursts into activity. These stars are being watched from time to time by large Earth-based telescopes and the orbiting Einstein Observatory satellite, but amateur observers are needed to monitor potential outbursts in these systems. One such easy-to-observe star is SS Cygni, but estimates must be made nightly to look out for a rapid climb in brightness.

Amateurs can also help greatly in another area--observing faint Mira stars. The AAVSO annually publishes a list of these stars--some of which have minima of 10th and 11th magnitude--and includes it as a privilege of membership. The AAVSO files also contain gaps where stars begin to set early or rise late. Catching stars at off-season times is another way to provide valuable data. Some lesser-known stars with preliminary charts are not yet widely observed. You may wish to contact the AAVSO and obtain information on them. This group includes newly discovered novae, faint unusual stars, and stars about which little is known.

The field of variable star observing is wide open, and its procedures are simple. If you're looking for a challenge, you'll find it in following the behavior of stars. Your success as an observer will depend on how you think of the relationship between you, your telescope, and the sky--a communion with the universe around you.

The following is a list of 114 of the best variable stars for small telescope observing. The first column gives their standard 1900 epoch designation; the second column provides their epoch 1950.0 coordinates. Also given are the stars' magnitude range of variation, period in days, and type-- RV = regular variable, SRV = semi-regular variable, EV = eclipsing variable, LPV = long period variable, CV = Cepheid variable, CCV = cataclysmic variable, NV = nebular variable, and N = nova.

DESIGNATION	R.A.(1950)Dec., h m ° '	Mag. Range	Period days	Type
_____ANDROMEDA				
001838 R And	00 21.4 +38 17	5.3-15.1	409	LPV
With an AAVSO chart, use M31, the Andromeda Galaxy, to find this star.				
005840 RX And	01 01.7 +41 02	10.3-13.6	Irr	CCV
Lies near the 6th mag. star 39 Andromedae.				
232848 Z And	23 31.2 +48 32	8.0-11.5	Irr	SRV
Symbiotic star.				
_____AQUARIUS				
233815 R Aqr	23 41.2 -15 34	5.9-11.4	386	LPV
Symbiotic star. Easy to find.				
_____AQUILA				
184300 V603 Aql	18 46.4 +00 31	-1.4-12.0	Irr	N
Nova Aquilae 1918. On June 8, 1918, this star erupted in a violent nova explosion, increasing its light by a factor of 100,000 in only 6 days! For a brief time it shone as the brightest star in northern skies, but has since dimmed to 12th mag.				
190108 R Aql	19 04.0 +08 09	5.3-12.0	300	LPV
191007 W Aql	19 12.7 -07 08	7.5-13.9	487	LPV
200715 S Aql	20 09.3 +15 28	8.4-12.1	147	LPV
_____ARIES				
024217 T Ari	02 45.5 +17 18	7.4-11.0	314	LPV
5th mag. star Pi [π] Arietis lies nearby.				
_____AURIGA				
050953 R Aur	05 13.2 +53 32	6.8-13.2	459	LPV
052034 S Aur	05 23.8 +34 06	8.3-12.2	590	SRV
Difficult to locate in a rich Milky Way field.				
062938 UU Aur	06 33.1 +38 29	5.1-6.8	235	SRV

DESIGNATION	R.A.(1950)Dec. h m ° '	Mag. Range	Period days	Type

_____BOOTES

| 141954 S Boo | 14 21.2 +54 02 | 8.0-13.7 | 271 | LPV |

Use mag. 4.4 Kappa [κ] Boo as a guide star.

| 142539 V Boo | 14 27.7 +39 05 | 7.0-11.3 | 258 | LPV |
| 143227 R Boo | 14 35.0 +26 57 | 6.7-12.8 | 223 | LPV |

Difficult to find when at minimum.

_____CAMELOPARDALIS

| 043065 T Cam | 04 35.2 +66 03 | 7.2-14.1 | 374 | LPV |

Use mag. 4.4 Alpha [α] Cam as a guide star.

043274 X Cam	04 39.2 +75 01	7.4-13.6	143	LPV
052372 RR Cam	05 29.4 +72 26	9.6-11.3	124	SRV
071082 VZ Cam	07 20.8 +82 31	4.7-5.2	237	SRV

Fine semi-regular visible in binoculars.

| 081473 Z Cam | 08 19.7 +73 17 | 9.9-14.3 | Irr | CCV |

Excellent eruptive variable star.

_____CANCER

| 081112 R Cnc | 08 13.8 +11 53 | 6.1-11.5 | 362 | LPV |
| 084917 X Cnc | 08 52.6 +17 25 | 6.2-7.5 | 170 | SRV |

Located close to M44, the Beehive Cluster.

| 085518 SY Cnc | 08 58.2 +18 05 | 9.5-14.0 | Irr | CCV |

An eruptive variable much like Z Cam.

_____CASSIOPEIA

| 005060 γ Cas | 00 53.7 +60 27 | 1.6-3.0 | Irr | IV |

An erratic variable easily visible in binoculars. One night in 1936, famed variable star observer Leslie Peltier watched this star climb a magnitude and a half until it rivaled Deneb in Cygnus!

| 235350 R Cas | 23 55.9 +51 07 | 5.4-13.0 | 431 | LPV |

Difficult to find at minimum because of a rich star field.

| 235659 WZ Cas | 23 58.7 +60 05 | 7.4-10.0 | 186 | SRV |

_____CEPHEUS

| 210868 T Cep | 21 08.9 +68 17 | 5.3-10.9 | 390 | LPV |
| 213678 S Cep | 21 35.9 +78 24 | 7.4-12.9 | 487 | LPV |

A very red star.

DESIGNATION	R.A.(1950)Dec. h m ° '	Mag. Range	Period days	Type

_____CETUS_____

| 021403 o Cet | 02 16.8 -03 12 | 3.4-9.5 | 331 | LPV |

Mira, the prototype long period variable star. Over a period of months, watch this bright naked eye star fade until you need binoculars or a telescope to spot it. Nicknamed "the Wonderful."

| 022813 U Cet | 02 31.3 -13 22 | 6.8-13.4 | 235 | LPV |
| 031401 X Cet | 03 16.9 -01 15 | 8.4-12.5 | 177 | LPV |

Use 94 and 95 Cet as guide stars.

_____CORONA BOREALIS_____

| 151731 S Cor Bor | 15 19.4 +31 33 | 6.0-14.0 | 360 | LPV |

Its period of almost exactly a year is helpful in keeping a regular observing schedule.

| 154428 R Cor Bor | 15 46.5 +28 19 | 5.6-14.8 | Irr | N |

A recurrent nova in reverse; stays at maximum for several years, then dramatically and unexpectedly drops for several weeks.

| 154639 V Cor Bor | 15 47.7 +39 43 | 6.9-12.5 | 358 | LPV |
| 155526 T Cor Bor | 15 57.4 +26 04 | 2.3-10.0 | Irr | N |

Recurrent nova. Erupted in 1866 and 1946; it is difficult to tell when T Cor Bor may erupt again.

| 161138 W Cor Bor | 16 13.6 +37 54 | 7.9-14.3 | 238 | LPV |

_____CYGNUS_____

192150 CH Cyg	19 23.2 +50 08	6.8-8.0	97	SRV
192745 AF Cyg	19 28.7 +46 03	6.4-8.4	94	SRV
193449 R Cyg	19 35.5 +50 05	6.6-14.1	426	LPV
194048 RT Cyg	19 42.2 +48 39	6.5-12.6	190	LPV
194632 X Cyg	19 48.6 +32 47	3.6-14.2	407	LPV

Famous long period variable that is hard to find when at minimum.

| 195849 Z Cyg | 20 00.0 +49 54 | 7.6-14.0 | 264 | LPV |

The bright nearby double 26 Cyg serves as a guide star.

| 200938 RS Cyg | 20 11.6 +38 35 | 6.6-9.4 | 417 | SRV |
| 210847 V1500 Cyg | 21 09.9 +47 57 | 1.8-21.0 | Irr | N |

Nova Cygni 1975. Then at 2nd mag., now at 15th.

| 213244 W Cyg | 21 34.1 +45 09 | 5.0-7.6 | 131 | SRV |

DESIGNATION	R.A.(1950)Dec. h m ° '	Mag. Range	Period days	Type
_____DELPHINUS				
201008 R Del	20 12.5 +08 56	7.6-13.7	284	LPV
_____DRACO				
163266 R Dra	16 32.5 +66 51	7.1-13.0	246	LPV
Use 5th mag. 18 Dra as a guide star.				
175458 T Dra	17 55.7 +58 14	7.2-13.0	422	LPV
Use 3.9 mag. ξ Dra as a guide star.				
_____GEMINI				
064030 X Gem	06 43.9 +30 20	7.9-13.4	263	LPV
Use 5.5 mag. 28 Gem as a guide star and beware of the rich Milky Way field!				
074922 U Gem	07 52.1 +22 08	8.9-14.0	Irr	CCV
Peculiar nova-like variable; stays at minimum but occasionally bursts to 9th mag.				
_____HERCULES				
160325 SX Her	16 05.3 +25 03	7.8-9.5	103	SRV
Use 6th mag. 10 Her as a guide star.				
160625 RU Her	16 08.2 +25 12	7.0-14.0	484	LPV
162807 SS Her	16 30.5 +06 58	8.6-12.5	107	LPV
Use 5.6 mag. 28 Her as a guide star.				
163137 W Her	16 33.4 +37 27	7.7-14.0	280	LPV
Located near globular cluster M13.				
_____HYDRA				
085005 T Hyd	08 53.2 -08 57	7.2-13.1	288	LPV
Use 6th mag. 17 Hyd as a guide star.				
_____LEO				
094211 R Leo	09 44.9 +11 40	5.2-10.5	312	LPV
A standard long period variable. A fiery red giant.				
095814 RY Leo	10 01.6 +14 14	8.5-11.0	155	SRV
_____LEO MINOR				
093934 R LMi	09 42.6 +34 45	6.3-13.0	372	LPV
094735 S LMi	09 50.8 +35 10	8.0-13.5	234	LPV

DESIGNATION	R.A.(1950)Dec. h m ° '	Mag. Range	Period days	Type
LEPUS				
045514 R Lep	04 57.3 -14 53	5.9-11.0	432	LPV

Hind's Crimson Star. One of the reddest stars in the sky; avoid staring because of the Perkinje effect.

LIBRA				
151520 S Lib	15 18.5 -20 13	8.0-13.0	193	LPV
151822 RS Lib	15 21.4 -22 44	7.0-12.5	217	LPV
LYRA				
181136 W Lyr	18 13.2 +36 39	7.5-13.0	196	LPV

Use 4th mag. κ Lyr as a guide star.

181631 TU Lyr	18 18.6 +31 44	9.5-11.0	Irr	IV

A slowly fluctuating irregular; estimate once a month.

183439 XY Lyr	18 36.5 +39 37	6.1-6.7	Irr	IV

Bright enough to estimate with binoculars.

184134 RY Lyr	18 43.1 +34 37	9.1-15.0	326	LPV
185243 R Lyr	18 53.8 +43 53	4.1-5.0	46	SRV

Be careful when comparing with Eta [η] and Theta [θ] Lyr; they are listed as the same brightness, but one is clearly brighter than the other.

MONOCEROS				
063308 R Mon	06 36.4 +08 47	10.0-12.0	Irr	IV

Nucleus of NGC 2261, Hubble's Variable Nebula, which fluctuates in brightness with the star.

OPHIUCHUS				
162112 V Oph	16 23.9 -12 19	7.3-11.5	298	LPV

Globular cluster NGC 6171 lies nearby.

170215 R Oph	17 04.9 -16 02	7.0-13.6	302	LPV

Eta [η] Oph (2.6 mag.) lies less than 1° northeast. Hard to identify when faint due to rich field.

172809 RU Oph	17 30.5 +09 27	8.5-14.2	202	LPV

Mag. 5.8 53 Oph lies half a degree away.

174406 RS Oph	17 47.5 -06 42	4.0-12.0	Irr	N

Recurring nova. Outbursts in 1898, 1933, 1958, and 1967.

181103 RY Oph	18 14.1 +03 40	7.6-13.8	150	LPV

DESIGNATION	R.A.(1950)Dec., h m ° '	Mag. Range	Period days	Type
OPHIUCHUS (Continued)				
183308 X Oph	18 36.0 +08 47	6.0-9.3	334	LPV
ORION				
050001 W Ori	05 02.8 +01 07	6.5-10.0	210	SRV
054907 α Ori	05 52.5 +07 24	0.4-1.3	2070	SRV

Betelgeuse. Fun to watch in binoculars, but avoid a buildup of red light.

054920 U Ori	05 52.9 +20 10	5.4-12.5	373	LPV
PEGASUS				
220133 RZ Peg	22 03.7 +33 16	7.7-13.5	439	LPV
220412 T Peg	22 06.5 +12 18	8.5-14.0	374	LPV
220912 RU Peg	22 11.6 +12 27	9.7-13.0	Irr	N

Irregular recurrent nova.

230110 R Peg	23 04.1 +10 16	7.2-13.6	378	LPV
PERSEUS				
015254 U Per	01 56.2 +54 35	7.7-12.0	321	LPV

Mag. 5 stars 1 Per and 4 Per serve as guide stars.

021558 S Per	02 19.3 +58 22	7.3-11.0	810	SRV

A member of the Double Cluster.

032043 Y Per	03 24.3 +44 00	8.1-10.9	252	LPV

Nearby lies GK Per.

032443 GK Per	03 27.8 +43 44	0.2-14.0	Irr	N

Nova Persei 1901. Flared by a factor of 6 in brightness in February 1901, then faded to 14th mag. Illuminates a faint nebula.

PUPPIS				
071044 L Pup	07 12.0 -44 33	3.0-6.0	141	SRV

Good semi-regular variable for binoculars.

SAGITTARIUS				
190819 RW Sgr	19 11.0 -18 57	9.0-11.6	190	LPV

Use 5th mag. 43 Sgr as a guide star.

190818 RX Sgr	19 11.6 -18 54	9.4-14.0	334	LPV
191033 RY Sgr	19 13.3 -33 37	6.5-14.0	Irr	IV

R Cor Bor type irregular variable.

DESIGNATION	R.A.(1950) Dec. h m ° '	Mag. Range	Period days	Type

SCORPIUS

155823 RZ Sco	16 01.6 -23 58	8.2-12.8	160	LPV

Use Delta [δ] and Pi [π] Sco as guide stars.

| 165030 RR Sco | 16 53.4   -30 30 | 5.1-12.3 | 279 | LPV |

Located close to globular cluster M62.

SCUTUM

| 184205 R Sct | 18 44.8   -05 46 | 4.9-8.2 | 140 | SRV |

Reddish pulsating star 1° northwest of the bright open cluster M11.

TAURUS

| 041619 T Tau | 04 19.1   +17 27 | 9.4-13.0 | Irr | NV |

Unusual nebular variable embedded in the variable nebulosity NGC 1555 (Hind's Variable Nebula).

URSA MAJOR

| 103769 R UMa | 10 41.2   +69 02 | 6.7-13.4 | 302 | LPV |
| 105270 VW UMa | 10 55.6   +70 16 | 6.9-7.8 | 125 | SRV |

Fun to estimate with binoculars.

| 112245 ST UMa | 11 25.1   +45 28 | 6.7-7.9 | 81 | SRV |

A good binocular semi-regular star.

115158 Z UMa	11 53.9 +58 09	6.8-9.2	196	SRV
123160 T UMa	12 34.1 +59 46	6.5-13.0	257	LPV
123459 RS UMa	12 36.7 +58 46	8.4-14.0	260	LPV
123961 S UMa	12 41.8 +61 22	7.4-12.4	226	LPV

A very red star.

URSA MINOR

| 153378 S UMi | 15 31.4   +78 48 | 7.8-12.7 | 327 | LPV |

An easy variable to observe, using Theta [θ] and Xi [ξ] UMi as guide stars.

| 163172 R UMi | 16 30.6   +72 23 | 8.7-11.0 | 324 | LPV |

VIRGO

| 122001 SS Vir | 12 22.7   +01 03 | 6.0-9.6 | 355 | LPV |

Less than 2° southwest of quasar 3C-273.

| 123307 R Vir | 12 36.0   +07 16 | 6.2-12.1 | 146 | LPV |

Use 5.5 mag. 31 Vir as a guide star.

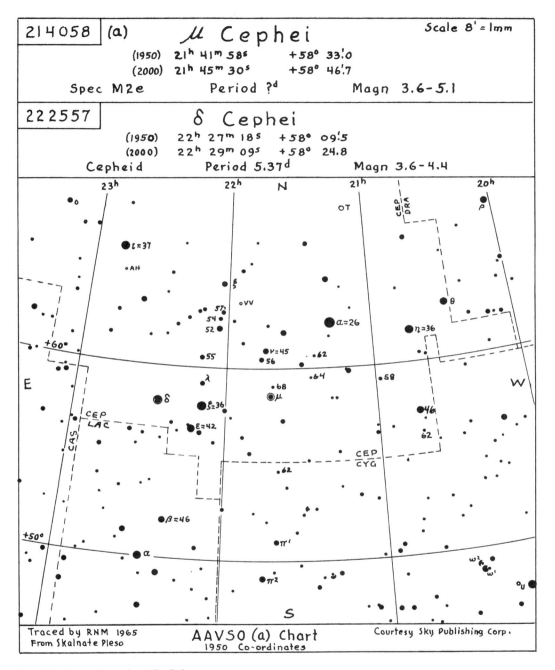

| 214058 | (a) | μ Cephei | | Scale 8' = 1mm |

μ Cephei

(1950) 21ʰ 41ᵐ 58ˢ   +58° 33'.0
(2000) 21ʰ 45ᵐ 30ˢ   +58° 46'.7

Spec M2e   Period ?ᵈ   Magn 3.6−5.1

222557

δ Cephei

(1950) 22ʰ 27ᵐ 18ˢ   +58° 09'.5
(2000) 22ʰ 29ᵐ 09ˢ   +58° 24.8

Cepheid   Period 5.37ᵈ   Magn 3.6−4.4

Traced by RNM 1965
From Skalnate Pleso

AAVSO (a) Chart
1950 Co-ordinates

Courtesy Sky Publishing Corp.

Fig. 3-2. **Finder Chart for** δ **Cephei**

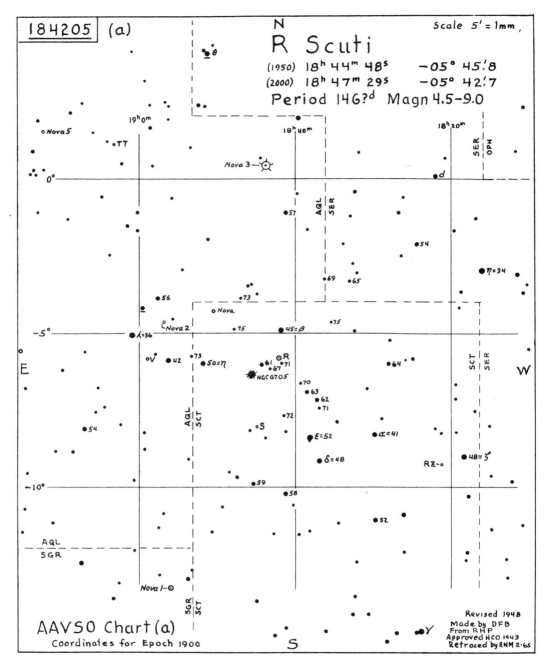

Fig. 3-3. **Finder Chart for R Scuti**

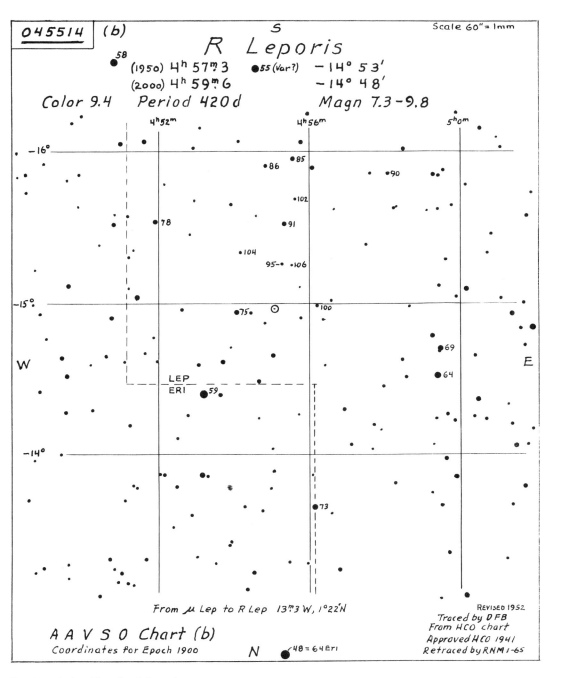

Fig. 3-4. **Finder Chart for R Leporis**

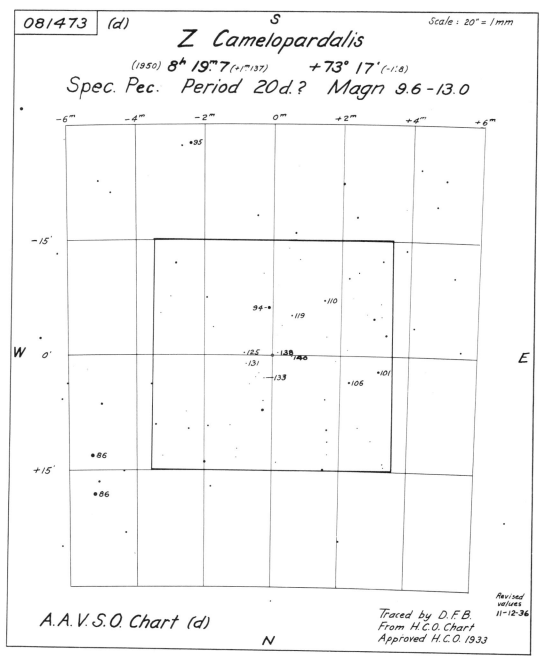

Fig. 3-5. **Finder Chart for Z Camelopardalis**

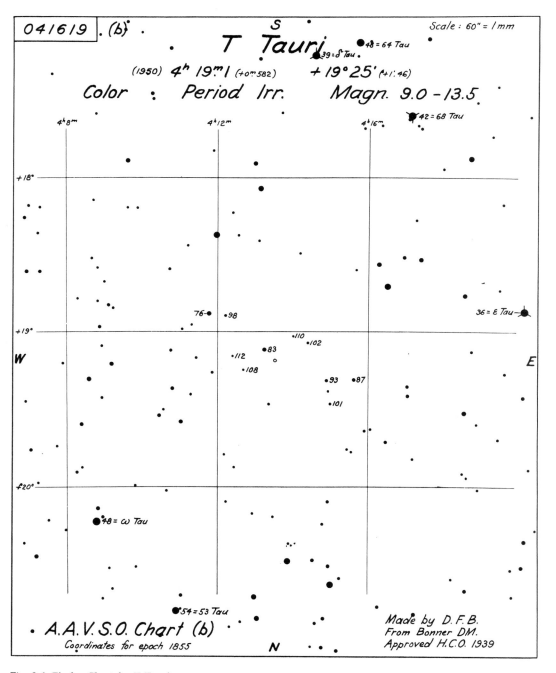

Fig. 3-6. **Finder Chart for T Tauri**

Fig. 4-1. **Star Cloud Messier 24**

4

Open
Star Clusters

David J. Eicher

Shortly after I became interested in astronomy, I started using an old pair of 7x50 binoculars to gaze at the stars. I knew nothing of the sky, nothing of the stars and clusters that peppered the Milky Way, and each night out was a marvelous adventure of discovery. One night in the spring of 1976 my Dad, who often accompanied me out to the end of the driveway where no trees blocked the sky, pointed out a fuzzy patch hanging low in the west. He excitedly asked what it was. "I don't know; let me check the star chart!" A few seconds later we found the misty patch of light was the Pleiades star cluster in Taurus, one of the closest and brightest open clusters in the sky. The binoculars confirmed a loose, dipper-shaped assemblage of bright and faint blue-white stars. Ever after when the subject of star clusters came up at the dinner table, my Dad proudly proclaimed that regardless of who saw it first, he had independently discovered the Pleiades.

Open star clusters, loose groups of young stars scattered throughout the disk of our Galaxy, offer a great deal of fun and discovery for users of binoculars and small telescopes. There are dozens of bright open clusters visible in a 2-inch telescope, and a 6-inch instrument shows several hundred such star groups, many composed of numerous faint stars that together provide a pale, ghostly, unresolved glow. Under a dark sky, several like the Pleiades--among them the Double Cluster in Perseus, M6 and M7 in Scorpius, and the Beehive in Cancer--are plainly visible as fuzzy patches to the naked eye.

In this chapter we'll discover the history of open cluster research, the nature of open clusters, and survey the best and most challenging examples of these star groups for your small telescope. Why do open clusters exist? Open clusters are young stars that form from clouds of hydrogen gas and revolve about the Milky Way's center during the early stages of their lives. Often the gravitational forces acting on a cluster, whose stars stay together by their mutual gravitational attraction, eventually tear the stars apart and distribute them in various parts of the Galaxy. The Sun most likely formed in an open cluster that has long since dissipated.

Because open clusters give astronomers a look at a stage in stars' lives immediately following star birth, these clusters are valuable for discovering much about the way stars evolve and are distributed in galaxies. After reading about the nature of these plentiful groups of stars, taking your telescope out under the sky and finding a number of these clusters will give you quite an impressive view of a highly important stage in the lives of all stars, one that is inextricably linked to all types of objects in the universe.

David J. Eicher

Brookfield, Wisconsin

David J. Eicher became interested in astronomy as a high school student in 1976. A year later he founded the magazine Deep Sky Monthly," a journal for backyard observers of star clusters, nebulae, and galaxies. In 1982 the rapid growth and success of this magazine led AstroMedia Corp. to acquire Deep Sky Monthly, begin publishing it as a quarterly magazine called Deep Sky, and hire Eicher as editor of Deep Sky and assistant editor of Astronomy magazine.

Fig. 4-2. **The Pleiades**

Fig. 4-3. **The Beehive Cluster in Cancer**

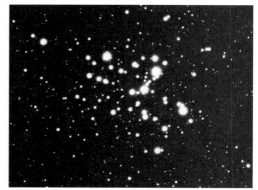

Fig. 4-4. **M6 in Scorpius**

An expert deep-sky observer and authority on deep-sky objects, Eicher enjoys sketching galaxies and nebulae and frequently gives talks at amateur meetings. He has worked as an assistant at Lowell Observatory in Flagstaff, Arizona. In 1987 Eicher was awarded the Lone Stargazer Award from the Texas Star Party and the Caroline Herschel Astronomy Project Award from the Western Amateur Astronomers. In addition to astronomy, Eicher is interested in U.S. history, especially Lincolniana and the Civil War period.

HISTORICAL BACKGROUND

The history of the development of man's knowledge of open star clusters is an immense story resulting in some of the fundamental breakthroughs in astronomical research. The term open star cluster dates back only 200 years to the English observer William Herschel, but the existence of open clusters was known long before Herschel's time and their importance to our understanding of the cosmos blossomed long after his death.

Although the nature of open star clusters remained unknown until Galileo's telescopic observations in 1610, ancient observers knew about many open clusters because they were bright enough to see with the naked eye. These naked-eye open clusters appeared to the ancients as "little clouds" or "misty patches," since they couldn't be resolved into stars with the eye alone. There were six exceptions including the bright Pleiades star cluster in Taurus, large enough to appear stellar to the naked eye, but enveloped in a cloud of misty light caused by multitudes of unresolved stars. Because these nebulous or partially nebulous objects--including both star clusters and nebulae --were "not dissolvable" to the naked eye, they were regarded with much fascination and held by ancient astrologers as being evil and associated with eye sickness and death.

One of the earliest recorders of celestial sights was Claudius Ptolemaeus Pelusiniensis, or Ptolemy, who lived approximately between A.D. 83-161 and is known to have observed from Alexandria between A.D. 127 and 151. He authored a famous star catalogue which, when translated in Baghdad in the ninth century, acquired the title Al-megisti, or "the greatest" of Ptolemy's many works. This star catalogue has since become known as the Almagest. Included in this catalogue are four objects now known to be open star clusters, the Coma Berenices star cluster, the Double Cluster in Perseus, M7 in Scorpius, and the Beehive Cluster in Cancer.

Ptolemy's descriptions of the mistiness of these regions provide a good indication of what such early observers were looking for. Ptolemy described the Coma star cluster as the "most northerly part of the cloudy convolutions which are called Coma Berenices, between the borders of Leo and Ursa [Major]." The description for the Double Cluster reads: "at the tip of the right hand of [Perseus] and is misty." That for the cluster M7 in Scorpius is as follows: "Following the sting [of Scorpius] and is misty." The description for the Beehive Cluster reads: "Centre of the cloud-shaped convolutions in the breast [of Cancer], called Praesepe." Clearly Ptolemy's criterion for inclusion was any suspiciously nebulous sky objects. His catalogue was a revision of the one prepared by Hipparchus 250 years earlier, which included the Beehive and Double clusters.

By the tenth century A.D. the descriptions of such nebulous objects had progressed somewhat in clarity. The Persian astronomer Al-Sufi lived between A.D. 903 and 986, and described eight nebulous objects in his work The Book of the Fixed Stars. Al-Sufi mentioned the Double Cluster by stating the "the first star [in Perseus] is the little cloud...it is situated on the right hand." His description of the Beehive Cluster was the first to provide any detail: "The first of the stars [in Cancer] is the little patch which resembles a small cloud surrounded by four stars which are found--the patch being in the middle--two in front and two behind." Al-Sufi is also the first to assign a magnitude to M7: "the first of the stars external to the figure [of Scorpius] is the cloudiness following the sting; mag. 4.5."

A number of observers including the Arab Ulugh Begh (1394-1449), the Danish observer Tycho Brahe (1546-1601), and the German mapmaker Johann Bayer (1572-1625), compiled catalogues of nebulous objects mentioning star clusters, but none until Galileo made any significant progress toward better describing them. However, when Galileo turned his primitive telescope skyward in 1610, the world of observational astronomy rocketed ahead and the understanding of nebulous patches of light in the sky dramatically changed almost in an instant.

Galileo published a work called the Sidereal Messenger in 1610 and his descriptions of star clusters included in it are fascinating in their freshness and excitement. Of Theta Orionis and the surrounding group of stars, the cluster at the center of the Orion Nebula, Galileo wrote: "I have selected three stars in Orion's Belt and six in his Sword which have been long well-known groups and I have added eighty other stars recently discovered in their vicinity and I have preserved as accurately as possible the intervals between them." Another passage describes the Pleiades Cluster in Taurus. "As a second example I have depicted the six stars of the constellation Taurus, called the Pleiades, (I say six intentionally since the seventh is scarcely ever visible), a group of stars which is enclosed in the heavens within very narrow precincts. Near these lie more than forty others invisible to the naked eye, no one of which is more than half a degree off any of the aforesaid six; of these I have noted only thirty-six on my diagram."

The Beehive Cluster in Cancer was a prime example of one of the sky's nebulous patches. Galileo's observations solved the mystery of the Beehive Cluster with the following passage: "A cluster which contains the nebula called Praesepe which is not one star only but a mass of more than forty small stars. I have noted thirty-six stars besides [Delta and Gamma Cancri]. From these observations of large groups of cleanly resolved stars, Galileo drew a powerful conclusion about the "misty clouds" in the sky. "The stars," he wrote, "which have been called by every one of the astronomers up to this day, nebulous, are groups of small stars set thick together in a wonderful way and although each one of them, on account of its smallness, or its immense distance from us, escapes our sight, from the commingling or their rays, there arises that brightness which has hitherto been believed to be the denser part of the heavens and able to reflect the rays of the stars or the Sun."

Only after a few nights' observing in 1610, Galileo had positively identified that some nebulae were actually groups of stars that appeared nebulous because of their "smallness or immense distance from us," in Galileo's words. For some years after Galileo's first observations, few star clusters were known. (And Galileo himself was having too many problems in convincing people of his fundamental observations, such as the proposal that not all in the heavens revolved around Earth, to pursue cataloguing of star clusters.) As more and more telescopes were produced and more and more people turned to telescopically looking at the heavens, the task now turned toward discovery and cataloguing previously unknown objects in the sky.

One of the early discoverers was the German astronomer Gottfried Kirch (1639-1710), an observer at the Berlin Observatory. In the appendix of the 1682 edition of his annual Ephemerides, Kirch announced his discovery of the "nebulous star" in Scutum, then called Ganymede. "Although early astronomers have listed several nebulous stars in the heavens," wrote Kirch, "nevertheless, in the place of the so-called nebulous stars, the telescope shows us clusters of minute bright stars. Only three true nebulae have been discovered by star-lovers: the

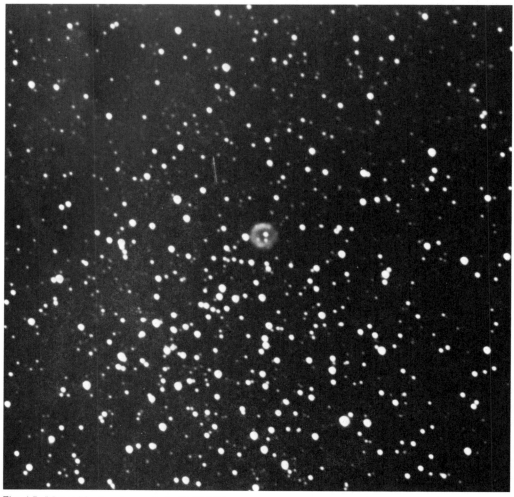

Fig. 4-5. **M46 with planetary nebula NGC 2438**

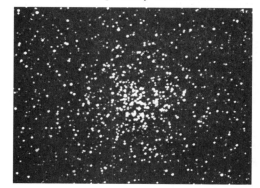

Fig. 4-6. **M37 in Auriga**

Fig. 4-7. **Large cluster M39 in Cygnus**

first, in Andromeda's girdle, first noticed by Simon Marius, the second
in Orion's sword, found by Christian Huyghens in the telescope in
1656 and a third in Sagittarius which John Abraham Ihle discovered
in 1665; afterwards, however, we established that it had been reported
a little earlier by John Hevelius."

"However, on the evening of Sept. 1st, 1681," he continued, "I
observed another nebulous star, which, as far as I know, no one has
observed before, close to the northern foot of Ganymede. Its shape
was not unlike that of the comet which I found in the telescope at
0 degrees M on the morning of Nov. 4th, 1680, and therefore I was
at first uncertain whether the phenonmenon was a comet or a nebulous
star. When, for successive days its form and position remained
unchanged it was easy to decide that it was not a comet but most
certainly a nebulous star."

Kirch had discovered the open cluster that would later be called
M11, the Wild Duck Cluster in Scutum. Of the mysterious "nebulous
star" Kirch concluded by writing, "Whether it will always be thought
truly stellar or whether, on the other hand, it will appear more like
the Andromeda Nebula, experience will tell." Kirch would probably
be quite happy that indeed his discovery turned out to be a genuine
star cluster.

Other observers continued the tradition of observation for
discovery, and continued to record their discoveries in carefully-minded
catalogues. John Flamsteed (1646-1719), Britain's first Astronomer
Royal, found the clusters M41 in Canis Major, NGC 2244 in Monoceros
(the cluster enveloped by a bright nebula called the Rosette), and
the open cluster NGC 6530 in Sagittarius (surrounded by the Lagoon
Nebula). The Frenchman Philippe Loys de Cheseaux (1718-1751) discovered
five open clusters, M6 in Scorpius, IC 4665 and NGC 6633 in Ophiuchus,
M25 in Sagittarius, and M35 in Gemini. Another French observer,
Guillaume-Joseph-Hyacinthe-Jean-Baptiste Le Gentil (1725-1792) found
the clusters M36 and M38 in Auriga. The Abbe Nicholas-Louis de la
Caille (1713-1762) located a number of open clusters in the southern
sky, including IC 2602, NGC 4755, NGC 2516, and NGC 2477. Clearly,
the era of telescopic discovery in the eighteenth century belonged
to the French.

But the great numbers of discovery brought about by rigorous,
systematic means came with the association of two French comet hunters
in the late 1700s. The catalogue of nebulous objects compiled by
Charles Messier (1730-1817) is the most famous list of such objects
ever compiled. Deep-sky objects are still referred to with "M numbers"
given before anything else. Messier compiled his catalogue not because
he wanted to search for nebulae or star clusters but because he wanted
their positions recorded to avoid confusion with comets, his chief
passion. Messier discovered a number of comets, but is ironically
remembered today for his catalogue of objects that rather than study,
he wanted to avoid.

Messier was an assistant to an observer named J.N. Deslile at
a small observatory located in Paris on the tower of the Hotel de
Cluny. His first catalogue was published in 1771 and contained
descriptions of 45 objects. In 1780 he extended that list to contain
70 objects, and with the additions and consultation provided by his
friend Pierre Mechain (1744-1804) he published a list totaling 103
objects in 1784. Messier found 40 new objects altogether. Included
in his discoveries are star clusters M18, M21, and M23 in Sagittarius,
M26 in Scutum, M29 and M39 in Cygnus, M34 in Perseus, M37 in Auriga,
M46, M47, and M93 in Puppis, M48 in Hydra, and M52 in Cassiopeia.
Pierre Mechain's discoveries included open cluster M103 in Cassiopeia.

Although Messier and Mechain were effective discoverers of dozens
of bright nebulous objects, their telescopes were, like all typical
telescopes in the eighteenth century, rather limited for finding faint
objects. The French discoveries would serve as a prelude to a truly
amazing system of discovery undertaken by the English observer William
Herschel, who would become almost universally accepted as the greatest
sky observer of all time.

Freidrich Wilhelm Herschel (1738-1822), always known as William
Herschel, was born in Hanover, Germany, and became a musician early
in life. He acquired the hobby of making telescope mirrors and
eventually moved to Slough, England. In 1781 Herschel became famous
overnight by discovering Uranus from his garden in Slough. He received
instant worldwide acclaim and became intensely interested in observing
the sky more than ever. In 1786 Herschel provided a reasonably accurate
account of the shape of the Milky Way Galaxy. By 1789 he had finished
a 49-inch telescope with a 40-foot focal length that was the largest
telescope in the world at the time. With it, and assisted by his
sister Caroline (who became a famous observer and comet discoverer
in her own right), he began making systematic discoveries of double
stars, clusters, and nebulae.

From 1789 until he was unable to observe due to frail health,
Herschel scoured the sky and placed his observations into accurate
notebooks for later study. Herschel catalogued the positions of 2,500
nebulae and gave brief descriptions of their appearances. Years later
his son, John Frederick William Herschel (1792-1871) took a large
telescope to the Cape of Good Hope and conducted a similar survey
of the southern sky, discovering 3,347 double stars and 525 nebulae
visible from that location. Together the Herschels completed the
first systematic study of the sky seen from Earth. Their results
were compiled into the General Catalogue, which John published in
1864. This work contained information for 5,079 objects.

In 1888 the Danish astronomer J.L.E. Dreyer (1852-1926) published
a revision of the Herschel's work entitled the New General Catalogue
of Nebulae and Clusters of Stars. This publication contained positions
and brief descriptions for 7,840 star clusters and nebulae. The
additional objects were those listed in other sources as nebulae and
star clusters up to 1888. In 1973 the American astronomers Jack W.
Sulentic and William G. Tifft published the Revised New General
Catalogue of Nonstellar Astronomical Objects, an updated and corrected
version of the Herschels' and Dryer's work. These books are the basic
reference sources for bright clusters and nebulae.

So goes the story of the discovery and cataloguing of open star
clusters. After the mid-nineteenth century the work of astronomers
interested in star clusters gave way from cataloguing to astrophysical
investigation. The new tools of photography and spectroscopy would
allow astronomers to do much more than sort and classify; it would
open doors to the real understanding of what star clusters are and
how they fit into the grand scheme of the universe.

THE NATURE OF OPEN STAR CLUSTERS

What is an open star cluster? Why do stars exist in groups? How far away are these groups of stars? These questions weighed heavily upon the minds of astronomers in the mid-nineteenth century. Forging a basic understanding of the role of open clusters in the Milky Way Galaxy and in the evolution of stars would require a great deal of research over many decades.

Astronomers of long ago observed two types of star clusters. One type appeared as a circular nebulosity with few faint stars resolved at the edges, and many stars tightly packed toward the center. These are globular star clusters, ancient spheres of thousands of stars orbiting the Milky Way in the Galaxy's so-called halo. A second distinct type of cluster consisted of a loose, scattered group of between a dozen and several hundred stars without any symmetrical arrangement. These clusters are open star clusters, groups of young stars lying within the Milky Way's disk.

Two important new tools adapted for astronomical use in the mid-nineteenth century helped astronomers begin to understand open star clusters, as they did with all astronomical objects. Photography, invented in the 1830s, had been unable to record faint light until about 1850. During that year astronomers at Harvard College Observatory in Massachusetts made the first photograph of a star, one that faintly captured the image of Vega. Eight years later emulsions had gained enough speed to enable astronomers to make the first photograph of a comet. The Civil War helped to popularize photography and accelerate the quality of emulsions and ease of the photographic method such that by 1882 astronomers could use photography as a reliable means of recording images of stars for later study.

Even more powerful than astronomical photography was a new method of research called spectroscopy. Pioneered in astronomical research by the Englishman William Huggins (1824-1910), spectroscopy involved recording the spectra of stars--the wavelengths of light composing their image. By inspecting the intensities of various components of the stars' light, astronomers could determine the temperatures of stars and their chemical compositions and ages.

Astronomers found, not too surprisingly, that many of the stars in open clusters appeared to be very similar in age and chemical composition. The open clusters appeared to be distributed almost without exception throughout the plane of the Milky Way, along with many hundreds of gas clouds called bright nebulae and patches of dust called dark nebulae. A link between open clusters and nebulous gas clouds seemed to be likely. Before investigating that relationship closely, let's look at the various types of stars in the Galaxy and the types contained within open clusters.

What exactly is a star? A star is a self-luminous sphere of hot gas held together by its own gravity. Stars come in many sizes and temperatures; from enormous, cool red stars to small, intensely hot blue stars. The Sun is a relatively average-sized star, measuring some 1.4 million kilometers in diameter. Fortunately for us the Sun lies at a distance of 150 million kilometers and produces a comfortable amount of light and heat to sustain life on Earth. The Sun is known as a spectral type G2 yellow dwarf star, and it has undergone nuclear reactions for some 4.6 billion years.

There are two distinct stellar populations of objects known to astronomers, Population I and Population II. The distinction between these two classes is made on the basis of age and chemical composition, and was proposed by the American astronomer Walter Baade (1893-1959) in 1944. Baade suggested that objects in the Milky Way could be divided on the basis that some objects are found in the Galaxy's disk and are young, highly luminous and metal-rich objects. These were called Population I objects. Population II objects are old, reddish stars that are metal poor and are located outside the Galaxy's disk, in the galactic halo. In this system, the Sun would be a Population I object (as would members of open clusters), and stars in globular clusters, for example, would be classed as Population II objects.

More recently astronomers have found that Baade's system of two stellar populations was oversimplified. There are now five types of stellar populations: extreme population I, older population I, disk population, intermediate population II, and halo population II. Extreme population I objects include interstellar gas, dust, HII regions, T Tauri stars, OB associations, O and B stars, supergiants, young open clusters, and classical Cepheid variable stars. Older population I objects include the Sun, A stars, Me dwarf stars, giants, and older open clusters. Disk population objects include planetary nebulae, the components of the galactic bulge, novae, and RR Lyrae stars. Intermediate population II objects include high-velocity stars and long-period variables. Halo population II objects include globular star clusters, subdwarf stars, RR Lyrae stars, and Type II Cepheid variables.

Together, the objects mentioned as examples of the five population classes make up the Milky Way Galaxy. To understand the structure of the Galaxy and how open clusters fit into the scheme, astronomers first need to understand types of stars in the Galaxy. As astronomers began using spectroscopy, they started classifying stars by their spectral types.

In the 1860s the Italian astronomer Angelo Secchi (1818-1878) visually observed stars and placed them into four classes based on spectral types. Some thirty years later astronomers at Harvard College Observatory used the more powerful technique of photographic spectroscopy to create the Harvard system of classification. At the turn of the century astronomers at Harvard including Edward C. Pickering (1846-1919) and later Annie Jump Cannon (1863-1941) developed the Harvard system into one resembling that which we use today.

The Harvard system was based on the strength of hydrogen absorption lines in a star's spectra called the Balmer lines. The order of stars ran from A to P, A stars having the strongest hydrogen lines in their spectra. The letters representing stars in this scheme were later juggled to create a system based on decreasing surface temperature.

There are seven basic types of stars: O,B,A,F,G,K, and M stars. O stars are intensely hot blue stars characterized by ionized helium lines and a strong ultraviolet continuum in their spectra. B stars are hot blue stars characterized by dominant neutral helium lines and no ionized helium in their spectra. A stars are blue or blue-white stars characterized by dominant hydrogen lines and ionized metal lines in their spectra. F stars are white stars with stronger metallic lines and weaker hydrogen lines than A stars. G Stars, like the Sun, are yellow stars with ionized calcium and strong metallic lines in their spectra. K stars are orange-red stars with strong neutral metallic lines and molecular bands in their spectra. M stars are cool red stars with strong molecular bands and strong neutral metallic lines in their spectra. You can remember the sequence of spectral types for stars by the cute mnemonic, "Oh Be A Fine Girl, Kiss Me!"

Fig. 4-8. **NGC 6520 in Sagittarius**

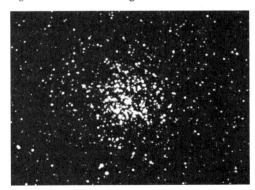

Fig. 4-9. **The Wild Duck Cluster**

Fig. 4-10. **The Owl Cluster in Cassiopeia**

Fig. 4-11. **The Double Cluster in Perseus**

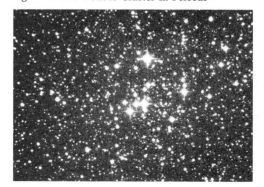

Fig. 4-12. **M47 in Puppis**

Fig. 4-13. **M41 in Canis Major**

A star's temperature and its color are related such that red stars are cool and blue ones quite hot. Thus the classification scheme for spectral types begins with hot, blue stars, runs through moderately hot white stars, average temperature yellow stars, relatively cool orange stars, and cool red stars. There are no fiercely hot red stars and no cool blue ones either.

Each class of spectral type is further divided into subclasses designated by 0 to 9 placed after the letter, simply to increase the fineness of the system. Thus, a type B5 star lies midway between B and A stars. A B5 star is hotter and bluer than an F2 star, and a K2 star is cooler and redder than a G8 star.

The Harvard system didn't solve all of the discrepancies astronomers observed between spectra of different stars, however, as far back as the 1890s astronomers noticed that stars of the same spectral types had widely differing luminosities. Thus astronomers W.W. Morgan and Philip C. Keenan at the Yerkes Observatory in Wisconsin developed a system of classifying stellar luminosities in the 1930s, calling it the Morgan-Keenan system. (It has since become simple the M-K system.) The M-K system divides stars in each spectral type into six luminosity classes designated by a Roman numeral placed after the stellar spectral type. Two of the classes have since become split into two distinctions, so that altogether eight luminosity classes exist to describe a star's characteristic luminosity.

The M-K system indicates whether a star is a bright supergiant, a supergiant, a bright giant, a giant, a subgiant, a main sequence or dwarf star, a subdwarf, or a white dwarf. Supergiants, denoted by Roman numerals Ia (bright supergiants) or Ib (supergiants), are the largest and most luminous of the stars. Although familiar examples of stars in our sky are supergiants--Betelgeuse and Rigel in Orion and Antares in Scorpius--they are quite rare types of stars. Supergiants are so bright that some of them are visible in nearby galaxies.

Giant stars are much more common. They are large, luminous stars denoted by Roman numerals II (bright giants) or III (giants). Capella in Auriga and Arcturus in Bootes are familiar examples of giant stars. These objects are highly evolved stars with little hydrogen left to burn: their energy comes from other elements burning in shells around a massive stellar core. Subgiant stars (denoted by Roman numeral IV) are small giant stars; Acrux in the southern constellation Crux is a good example.

So-called main sequence stars, or dwarfs, are stars very much like the Sun (denoted by Roman numeral V). About 90% of all stars are main-sequence stars, relatively average in mass and luminosity. Stars smaller than dwarfs are called subdwarfs (designated by Roman numeral VI); these are stars smaller than dwarfs with low luminosities. A white dwarf (designated by Roman numeral VII) is a tiny star that has undergone gravitational collapse and is dying like a cooling ember.

Just after the turn of the century astronomers found a way to statistically study stars using a simple graph. In 1905 the Danish astronomer Ejnar Hertzsprung (1873-1967) found that the widths of absorption lines in the spectra of stars are directly related to their luminosities. Hertzsprung discovered that stars with narrow absorption lines of similar spectral types have greater luminosities than those with wide absorption lines. Hertzsprung found that by using the observed spectra of various stars he could determine whether they were large or small.

Independently of Hertzsprung, the American astronomer Henry Norris Russell (1877-1957) found the same thing. Russell used stars' distances, determined by a simple geometrical method called stellar parallax. From these distances and the apparent magnitudes. of the stars, he calculated their absolute magnitudes, or intrinsic brightnesses, and plotted these against spectral classes in a graph. Russell found that stars of the same intrinsic brightnesses fell into similar spectral classes. He also found that stars in the same spectral class with narrow lines had greater luminosities than those with wide lines in their spectra.

Out of the research of Hertzsprung and Russell came the Hertzsprung-Russell diagram, a graph of spectral type on the X-axis plotted versus luminosity on the Y-axis. Rather than lying scattered all across such a plot, astronomers found that stars are clumped into distinct groups on the H-R diagrams. Almost 90 percent of all stars lie along a narrow band called the main sequence running from the upper left (blue, high-luminosity stars) to the lower right (red, low-luminosity stars) of such diagrams. White dwarf stars are rare, low-luminosity white stars lying to the lower left of an H-R diagram. Giant stars branch off of the main sequence to the upper right (most are orange or red stars of high luminosity), while supergiants are rare red and orange stars with very high luminosities.

As time passed, astronomers began using the term Color-Magnitude Diagram (CMD) to describe Hertzsprung-Russell diagrams, since after all, they plot star colors versus magnitudes, or luminosities. Color-Magnitude Diagrams are extremely important to astronomers for all sorts of facets of research. They allow astronomers to look at the overall distribution of types of stars for nearby stars, stars in a particular cluster, or stars in a particular location. In open cluster research, for example, they can be used to look at the two main types of stellar populations, Population I and Population II stars, to determine the ages of open clusters. Young open clusters contain almost no giant stars, whereas older open clusters contain a good many giants. Globular clusters contain numerous giants and supergiant stars. Color-Magnitude Diagrams are also used to determine distances of stars plotted in them, since astronomers can fit the main sequence stars onto the diagram and determine absolute magnitudes, and by apparent magnitudes, their distances.

By using Color-Magnitude Diagrams, critical photometry to measure the precise brightnesses of cluster stars, distance calculations based on apparent magnitudes and absolute magnitudes, and other tools, astronomers have gained an enormous amount of knowledge about open star clusters. It is now known that stars in the Milky Way Galaxy (and presumably throughout the universe) are born in regions of interstellar dust scattered throughout the Galaxy's disk. Interstellar dust clouds are generated by the deaths of stars in a number of ways, including powerful stellar winds, supernovae and novae explosions, planetary nebulae, and other mechanisms. Once the dust and gas from stars that could live no more scatters throughout the Galaxy, it inevitably collects into pockets of high density.

As more and more gas and dust collects in a given area, the gravitational attraction of the gas is powerful enough to draw more and more into the forming cloud. At a critical point the gas in these clouds collapses into protostars, dense collections of matter that don't have enough mass to ignite stellar furnaces and begin lives as newborn stars. Given enough time, however, these protostars do collect enough mass to "turn on," and they become infant stars. Clouds of gas typically generate more than one star, often many dozens depending on their densities and masses, and a young open star cluster

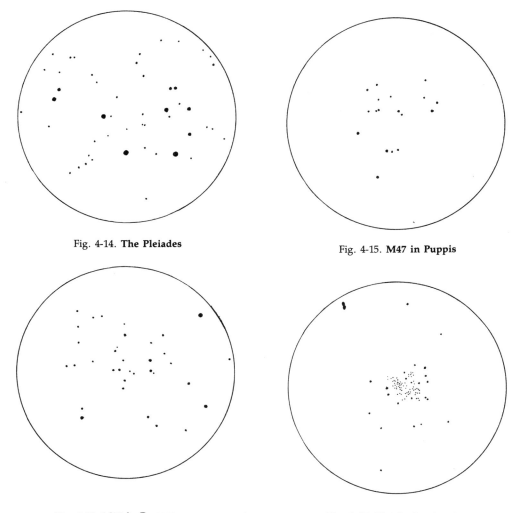

Fig. 4-14. **The Pleiades**

Fig. 4-15. **M47 in Puppis**

Fig. 4-16. **M34 in Perseus**

Fig. 4-17. **M52 in Cassiopeia**

is created as a new member of the Galaxy. Thus the cycle of star death to star birth is created: emission nebulae and dust clouds are in a very real sense immense stellar nurseries slowly recycling the stuff of the universe.

Take a careful look at some of the sky's best examples of emission nebulae on a dark night with your small telescope. If you look at the Orion Nebula, the Lagoon Nebula in Sagittarius, the Rosette Nebula in Monoceros, the Eagle Nebula in Sagittarius, or any one of several other bright examples, you'll see that each area of nebulosity is accompanied by a bright star cluster. By observing such a region, you are literally witnessing star birth shortly after the fact, at least in cosmological terms.

The stars in open clusters are held together by mutual gravitational attraction, such that members of an open cluster are physically bound and travel around the Galaxy together. Eventually, however, the gravitational tug from the center of the Galaxy and other objects orbiting it will tear an open cluster apart and disperse its members over a wide range of space. It is likely that the Sun formed as a member of an ancient open cluster that has long since vanished as a group. Most open star clusters contain between a dozen and several hundred members, but according to the American researcher Robert J. Trumpler some clusters contain as many as 2,200 members. Over 1,000 open clusters have been catalogued in the Milky Way Galaxy; about 12 are conspicuously visible to the naked eye and several hundred can be spotted with a backyard telescope.

We can put some limits on the parameters of open clusters. The closest is the Ursa Major Moving Group, a cluster so close it appears as a smattering of bright stars spread over many degrees of sky. The most distant observable open clusters in the Galaxy are about 15,000 light-years away, the distance beyond which the concentration of a cluster becomes invisible due to the rich stellar background. The ages of clusters depend critically on the balance between a group's mass and its size: some groups are just over 1 million years old--stellar infants--while others are several billion years old and still exist as groups.

A related type of object is the stellar association. An association is a loose grouping of young stars thinly spread out over a large volume of space. About 70 of these groups are known to exist, and they have relatively short lifetimes on the order of 10 million years. They are often called O-B associations because of the predominance of O and B stars contained within them.

Viewed through your telescope, you'll see that open star clusters can display many individual traits. Each will appear different and offer its own charm and beauty. In the next two sections we'll explore the possibilities of observing some of these important members of the Milky Way from your backyard, taking advantage of a chance to spy from the comforts of home a view of new objects in the universe rarely seen by inhabitants of Earth.

BEGINNING TO OBSERVE

Because the Sun lies inside the disk of the Milky Way Galaxy, the sky is filled with nearby open clusters of stars also embedded in the galactic disk. As a single class of deep-sky object, open clusters provide the greatest number of bright deep-sky objects easily visible in small telescopes. To convince yourself of this, all you need is a dark sky and the willingness to stay up an entire night under a dark sky, say in August.

As the sky darkens on your August night under the stars, you'll see a faint sprinkling of stars over the western horizon some 4° across. This is the Coma Berenices star cluster. Over the southwestern horizon in Scorpius, two faint splashes of milky light are open clusters M6 and M7. As the night grows older, the impressively bright twin glow of the Double Cluster in Perseus will come into view. As midnight passes into a new day, the Pleiades and Hyades clusters in Taurus will rise in the east. And as morning twilight approaches, the mottled glow of Cancer's Beehive cluster will show itself low in the eastern sky.

As you might guess, many more open clusters are visible using binoculars or a small telescope. In this section we'll explore a number of the brightest open clusters. These objects offer a peculiar observational advantage over nebulous objects like galaxies. Star clusters are composed of stars, so they do not suffer from low contrast problems as greatly as galaxies and nebulae when sky conditions are poor. Certainly faint open clusters become difficult to observe and faint members of bright clusters become lost in light pollution or poor sky transparency or seeing. However, open clusters are generally bright enough to be observationally satisfying even when the Moon is above the horizon or the sky is not at its best. When the sky is not good enough for spotting faint galaxies, you can always fall back on bright open clusters.

The spring evening sky offers some terrific open clusters for small telescopes. Perhaps the finest cluster visible during this season is M44 (NGC 2632), commonly called the Beehive Cluster or Praesepe. Located in central Cancer and surrounded by a trapezoid of stars formed by Delta, Gamma, Eta, and Theta Cancri, the Beehive Cluster is one of the sky's best. At magnitude 3.1, the glow produced by the Beehive's 50 stars is easily visible to the naked eye as a fuzzy patch of light twice the size of the Full Moon.

Because M44 is not visible to the naked eye on nights when the sky is somewhat hazy, the cluster was reputedly used as a weather forecaster in ancient times. The Greeks Aratus and Pliny stated that if the cluster was not visible on nights when other stars could be observed, a storm was due to approach. M44 was nicknamed the Beehive due to its naked-eye appearance long before the invention of the telescope, and many observers in antiquity referred to the group when discussing the sky. As long ago as 260 B.C. Aratus called M44 the "Little Mist." It is thought that Hipparchus called M44 the "Little Cloud" as far back as 130 B.C. With the invention of the telescope in 1610, however, the stellar nature of the Beehive Cluster was discovered and Galileo recorded 36 bright stars in the group.

The Beehive Cluster is best observed with binoculars or small telescopes using low-power eyepieces. The group's large angular diameter of 95' makes it difficult to fit into the field of view of large, long-focus telescopes. A 4-inch scope at 35x shows the Beehive as a bright splash of stars glowing at magnitudes 6.3 and fainter. The brightest stars in the cluster's center are arranged in a flattened square, around which several dozen fainter stars are scattered and appear like glistening diamonds spilled on a black velvet sky. Many of the Beehive's stars are yellowish or slightly orange in color; can you observe a range of colors in M44's brightest stars?

The constellation Coma Berenices holds another brilliant springtime cluster, this one so large that its stars actually make up much of the constellation's outline. The Coma Berenices star cluster, also known by the catalogue designation Melotte 111, is large and bright because it is one of the closest open clusters, lying at a distance of 250 light-years. The Coma Star Cluster measures 275' across, contains 80 stars, and shines at magnitude 1.8. If you go outside and look at Coma Berenices when it's high up in the sky, you'll see this clump of bright white and blue-white stars without even having to dark-adapt your eyes.

Because it's so large, the Coma Star Cluster appears at its best in binoculars, finder scopes, and small, short-focus telescopes. High magnification or a long-focal length system will show only a portion of the cluster, so that the view will look like an ordinary star field rather than a cluster. The brightest dozen stars in the Coma cluster are slightly fainter than 4th magnitude, and dozens more within the 275' diameter glow at magnitudes 5, 6, and 7. If you do explore this cluster with a telescope, you may well spot several bright galaxies in and around the area. The cluster lies in front of a rich field of galaxies spread across the constellation Coma Berenices, and the magnificent edge-on spiral NGC 4565 lies just over 1° east of the bright double star 17 Comae Berenices, one of the cluster's brightest members. The Coma Star Cluster's rich membership of bright stars and enormous size make it an attractive sight on any clear night.

During summer evenings the Milky Way stretches high overhead from Cassiopeia in the north to Sagittarius in the south, and on these evenings you'll have a field day on open clusters. Many dozens of bright clusters are visible during the summer, many of which are listed in this chapter's table. We'll investigate a few wonderful examples of these here.

Cassiopeia contains a number of bright, easily observable open clusters spread all across the familiar "W" shape of the constellation's brightest stars. Located 1° northeast of the bright star Delta Cassiopeiae is the magnitude 7.4 cluster M103 (NGC 581). The 25 members of this cluster are arranged in pretty patterns and shine at magnitude 10.6 and fainter. A bright double star located near the center of this group is not a physical member of the cluster. On the other side of Delta Cassiopeiae, just 2° southwest of the star, lies the brighter open cluster NGC 457. A group of 80 stars measuring 13' across and shining at magnitude 6.4, NGC 457 is a curious object because its stars appear to outline the form of an owl. Two bright stars are the owl's eyes, and a collection of several dozen form the body, feet, and wings extending to the north and south. I noticed this resemblance while observing one night in 1980, and this object has ever since seemed like one of the best examples of a star cluster that actually looks like an earthbound object.

Seven degrees southeast of the M103-NGC 457 area lies one of the finest open clusters in the sky. Visible to the naked eye even on marginal nights, the clusters NGC 869 and NGC 884 in Perseus lie only 30' apart and are together called the Double Cluster in Perseus. These two clusters are strikingly similar in appearance yet lie at different distances, have different ages, and are physically unconnected. NGC 869 lies 7000 light-years away and formed some 5.6 million years ago, whereas NGC 884 is 7500 light years distant and

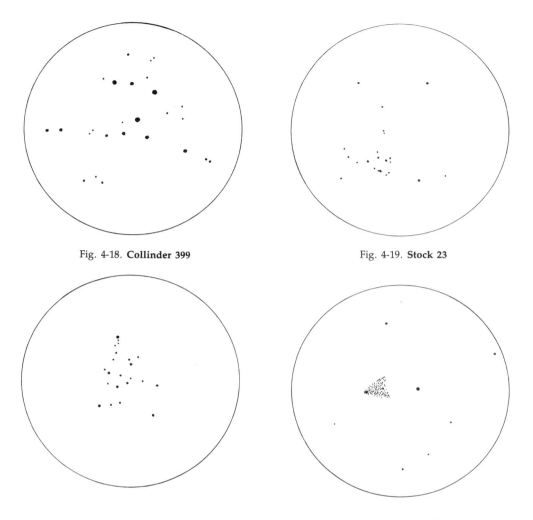

Fig. 4-18. **Collinder 399**

Fig. 4-19. **Stock 23**

Fig. 4-20. **M103 in Cassiopeia**

Fig. 4-21. **M11 in Scutum**

formed 3.2 million years ago. The fact that each measures 30' across and is slightly brighter than magnitude 4.5 is a coincidence.

Observationally the Double Cluster is a delight. Binoculars show a bright double knot of misty light seemingly almost in contact. A 2-inch refractor at low power shows both clusters within the same field and resolves them into dozens of glistening stars. A 6-inch telescope provides a wonderful view of the Double Cluster, because it shows over 100 stars in each group and reveals subtle colors in many of the stars. While most shine blue-white or white, a great many tiny points of light in each cluster are tinted slightly yellow, orange, or even faintly appear red. These ruddy M-type stars are red supergiants. In 1892 the astronomer T.E. Espin recorded that three red stars brighter than magnitude 10.5 exist in NGC 884, four lie in between the clusters, and three lie within the outlying region. Can you spot these ruddy supergiant stars in your telescope?

Also in Perseus, about 5° west-northwest of the bright variable star Algol, lies the impressive open cluster M34 (NGC 1039). This cluster is a gem in binoculars and small telescopes, containing 60 stars in an area spanning 35' across. The brightest star in M34 glows at magnitude 7.3, and the group shines with the light of a magnitude 5.2 star. On dark nights this cluster is faintly visible to the naked eye, and is clearly a large scattered group of stars in binoculars. The brightest stars in M34 form an unusual shape that resembles a distorted "X." Lying in the center of M34 is the bright double star h1123, a pair of white stars separated by 20", making them easy to see. Both stars in h1123 glow at about magnitude 8.5.

Moving back up the stretching Milky Way on our summer night, we can find one extremely bright open cluster in Cygnus. The best and brightest is M39 (NGC 7092), an enormous cluster containing 30 stars of magnitudes 6.8 and fainter. The amorphous glow of M39 is visible to the naked eye on dark nights 9° east-northeast of Deneb, the constellation's brightest star. Because M39 measures 32' across--just larger than the diameter of the Full Moon--you'll need to use low-power eyepieces to see the entire cluster. When you train binoculars or a small scope on M39 you'll see why the English astronomer Admiral Smyth called this area a "splashy field of stars." A 4-inch scope at 20x shows M39 as a bright, loose assemblage of stars scattered across an entire field of view, with the starry background of faint suns peppered across the group like a stellar backdrop. Clearly M39 is an enjoyable object for almost any instrument that can show it in entirety.

The constellation Scutum, farther south along the great arch of the Milky Way, contain's one of the loveliest open clusters in the sky. M11 (NGC 6705) lies in northeastern Scutum near the bright curve of stars that forms part of Scutum and the westernmost section of Aquila. The German astronomer Gottfried Kirch discovered M11 in 1681 and described as a "small, obscure spot with a star shining through and rendering it more luminous." With today's telescopes M11 appears considerably more spectacular than Kirch's description suggests. M11 contains several hundred stars packed into a 14' diameter with a resulting magnitude of 5.8. The brightest member of M11, an orange star located near the center, shines at 8th magnitude. The group's brightest stars are extremely luminous giants; by comparison, the Sun would feebly glow at magnitude 15 at M11's distance of 5,700 light-years.

M11 is one of the richest open clusters in the sky. Its stars are shaped in a concentrated clump that appears triangular, leading the English observer Admiral Smyth to say that M11 resembled "a flight

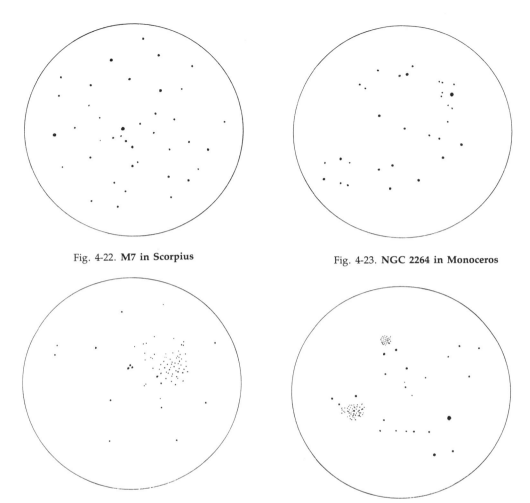

Fig. 4-22. **M7 in Scorpius**

Fig. 4-23. **NGC 2264 in Monoceros**

Fig. 4-24. **M44 in Cancer**

Fig. 4-25. **M21 and NGC 6530**

Fig. 4-26. **M35 and NGC 2158 in Gemini**

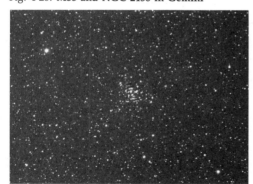

Fig. 4-27. **M36 in Auriga**

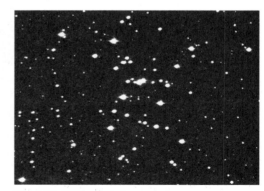

Fig. 4-28. **M7 in Scorpius**

of wild ducks." Ever since, M11 has been known as the Wild Duck Cluster. Binoculars show M11 as a fuzzy patch of light set amidst a rich star field. A 3-inch telescope at moderate magnifications resolves M11 into several dozen pinpoints of light, but a hazy background glow remains behind the stellar members. A 6-inch scope at high power cleanly resolves the group, showing well over 100 stars shining white, blue-white, yellow, and orange.

Continuing southward along the Milky Way, the teapot-shaped group of stars known as Sagittarius contains a fine collection of bright clusters. This is hardly surprising, since Sagittarius marks the direction toward the center of the Milky Way Galaxy. One of the finest open clusters in Sagittarius is NGC 6530, which lies in the bright emmission nebula M8, the Lagoon Nebula. This cluster is easy to find because its light, along with that of the Lagoon Nebula, is easily visible to the naked eye under a dark sky. The Lagoon complex lies about 5° west-northwest of Lambda Sagittarii, the star that marks the teapot's "lid."

Star clusters are created from regions of emission nebulosity, and the Lagoon complex is one of the finest examples of a stellar birthplace in the sky. NGC 6530 is a young cluster that is still forming from the Lagoon Nebula gas, so observing this object even with binoculars will show you the process of star formation in action.

Binoculars show a cluster of two dozen stars measuring 15' across and glowing at magnitude 4.6. The brightest stars in NGC 6530 shine at 7th magnitude and are surrounded by faint wisps of the nebulosity that makes up the Lagoon Nebula. The brightest section of nebulosity lies to the west of the cluster, and a fainter section of nebulosity on the eastern side of the Lagoon Nebula covers the field containing NGC 6530. Between these two sections of nebulosity lies the dark band of dust that gave rise to the name Lagoon Nebula. All of these features are visible in small telescopes. To get the best possible view of this remarkable object, observe it on clear, moonless nights when the Lagoon is relatively high in the sky. You might try using a nebula filter to enhance the contrast between the sky and the Lagoon's delicate glow.

Just 2° north of the Lagoon Nebula lies another bright open cluster, M21 (NGC 6531). This compact group contains 70 stars of magnitudes 7.3 and fainter in an area 13' across. M21 appears like a richer version of NGC 6530, and is consequently a wonderful object for binoculars. It is small enough to appear like a misty patch of nebulosity, but some of its stars bright enough to cleanly shine through to reveal its stellar nature. Binocular and Rich-Field Telescope users may fit both the Lagoon Nebula complex and M21 into the same low-power field of view, along with the faint light of the Trifid Nebula which lies 1° southwest of M21. This field is one of the prettiest in the sky, and shouldn't be passed up on clear summer evenings.

Another remarkable open cluster in Sagittarius is M25 (IC 4725), a bright, scattered group of stars located 5° north-northeast of Lamba Sagittarii. M25 is a typical loose cluster that contains 30 stars spread across an area as large as the Full Moon, and shining at magnitude 4.6. M25's brightest star shines at magnitude 6.7, making the group easily visible as a cluster in binoculars and small scopes. Near the cluster's center, between two other bright stars, lies the Cepheid variable star U Sagittarii. This star varies between magnitudes 6.3 and 7.1 over a period of 6.7 days.

Scorpius is renown for containing brilliant star clusters visible not only in small telescopes but to the naked eye. Located in Scorpius between the bright stars of Scorpius and Sagittarius is the large open cluster M7 (NGC 6475), a group of 80 stars measuring over 2° across that glows at magnitude 3.3. Easily visible to the naked eye, M7 is a spectacular sight in binoculars and small scopes. It lies in a rich star field and shows dozens of bright stars arranged in curving arcs and clumps throughout the diameter of the cluster. About 3.5° northwest of M7 lies another brilliant open cluster, M6 (NGC 6405). This group is called the Butterfly Cluster because of its distinctive shape, and is also easily visible in any telescope. M6 contains 80 stars in a diameter of 15' and shines at magnitude 4.2. The brightest star in the cluster, BM Scorpii, is an irregular variable star with a distinctly orange hue.

The winter sky also holds fine examples of open star clusters. The constellation Taurus is made up chiefly of two bright star clusters that are among the closest in the Galaxy. The Hyades cluster (Melotte 25), surrounding the bright star Aldebaran (which is not a physical member), consists of several dozen stars arranged ina giant "V" shape measuring over 5° across. Obvious and bright to the naked eye, the Hyades cluster is so large that it is best observed with the naked eye and low-power binoculars or finder scopes. The group's total magnitude is 0.5, although the members are spread out so thinly that the Hyades doesn't appear as bright as a single 0.5 magnitude star. The distance to the Hyades is known to be 150 light-years.

Some 12° northwest of the Hyades lies the Pleiades (Melotte 22), the most observed open cluster in the sky. Shining at magnitude 1.2 and measuring 110' across, the Pleiades is a striking sight even to the naked eye, appearing as a patch of hazy light with at least six distinct stars visible. Some observers can see seven or more stars distinctly without optical aid. The Pleiades is so striking that many legends associated with its rising and setting have originated in widespread cultures throughout history. The brightest stars in the cluster, called the "Seven Sisters," are Alcyone, Merope, Celaeno, Taygeta, Asterope, Electra, and Maia. The cluster contains at least 100 stars and lies 410 light-years away; the brightest Pleiades form a dipper-shaped asterism that is sometimes confused with Ursa Minor, the Little Dipper.

Observationally the Pleiades cluster is a delight. Binoculars show the dipper shape of the group's brightest stars and a smattering of several dozen fainter stars strewn across the field of view. With an age of 78 million years, the Pleiades cluster is relatively young and its stars are white and blue-white in appearance. Small telescopes with wide-field eyepieces show the entire group, including a striking, close double star in the center of the dipper's bowl. A 6-inch telescope under a very dark sky may just show some of the faint reflection nebulosity surrounding Merope, residual dust left from the star's formation.

Three bright, easily observable open clusters lie in the constellation Auriga. M36 (NGC 1960) and M38 (NGC 1912) lie within the pentagonal figure of Auriga, near the star Psi Aurigae. M38 is a cluster spanning 21' and containing 100 stars of magnitudes 9.5 and fainter, resulting in a total magnitude of 6.4. A wide field is necessary to show the full extent of this cluster and the surrounding Milky Way star field. Nearby M36 is smaller and slightly richer, containing 60 stars in an area only 12' across. The magnitudes of bright cluster members and total magnitudes of these two clusters are quite similar.

Four degrees southeast of M36 is Auriga's finest star cluster, M37 (NGC 2099). This spectacular group holds 150 stars in an area 24' across and glows at magnitude 5.6. M37 is visible to the naked eye on very dark nights and appears as a rich concentration of faint stars resembling M11 in small telescopes. The subtle yellow and orange tints of many members of M37 are visible in a 6-inch telescope, particularly if you use averted vision.

The constellation Gemini holds one of the winter sky's finest open clusters in M35 (NGC 2168). This expansive cluster lies 2.5° northwest of the bright star Eta Geminorum, one of the stars that marks the "feet" of Gemini. A large, bright group just visible to the naked eye, M35 is impressive in small scopes because it packs 100 stars into an area just smaller than that covered by the Full Moon. The brightest stars in M35 glow at magnitude 8.2, and the cluster's total magnitude is 5.1.

ADVANCED OBSERVING TECHNIQUES

The sky is full of open star clusters, especially along the Milky Way. Just as there are many bright examples of open clusters for small telescopes--some of which we investigated in the previous section--there are also numerous examples of fainter, more challenging open clusters for users of small telescopes.

The springtime sky holds a number of such challenging clusters. In Cancer, about 9° south-southeast of the Beehive cluster, lies M67 (NGC 2682). Although this cluster was bright enough to be included in the Messier catalogue, M67 offers a marked contrast to the bright, scattered group of stars composing its famous neighbor. M67 holds 200 stars in an area 30' across, and has a total magnitude of 6.9. But the brightest star in M67 glows only at 10th magnitude, and many of the dozens of stars in the cluster are significantly fainter. Thus M67 is visible as a reasonably large hazy patch in finder scopes and binoculars, but it has a faint, hazy quality something like seeing the Beehive with the naked eye.

A 6-inch telescope at moderate powers shows that many of M67's stars appear yellowish or orange. M67 is one of the oldest known open clusters, having existed for some 3.2 billion years. The stars in M67 have evolved such that many of its stars resemble those in a globular star cluster. Peculiarly, M67 lies some 1,500 light-years above the plane of the Galaxy, whereas most open clusters lie inside the Galaxy's disk.

A similar open cluster lies in the constellation Cepheus and is visible on spring night. NGC 188 is even older than M67, having existed for 5.0 billion years. This beautiful group of stars is difficult to view on nights of poor transparency because its brightest stars glow at 12th magnitude. NGC 188 contains 120 stars arrayed in a 14'-diameter, stars that combine to give the group a magnitude of 8.1. A 3-inch telescope shows NGC 188 as a patch of milky light some 5' across. A 6-inch telescope at 100x provides a much better view of this faint cluster, revealing several dozen pinpoints of light scattered through a nebulous background.

As the spring sky gives way to summer, many examples of challenging open clusters arise in the east and await inspection. As mentioned in the previous section, Sagittarius contains many open clusters because the constellation lies toward the star-crowded center of the Milky Way. Under the summer sky, look 10° north of the teapot asterism in Sagittarius and you'll see a milky patch of light some 2° by 1° across. This is M24, catalogued by Charles Messier as a "large cluster" in June 1764. M24 isn't actually a star cluster, but a star cloud--a rich concentration of stars that appears like a cloud due to perspective.

Now scan M24, also known as the Small Sagittarius Star Cloud, with binoculars or a small telescope. You may see a small concentration of light in the cloud's northern part, seemingly wedged between two 6th-magnitude double stars. This object is NGC 6603, a faint group of 100 stars compressed into an area only 5' across. NGC 6603 is difficult to see on less than perfect nights, since the group glows feebly at magnitude 11.

Also in Sagittarius, 3° north of the bright star Gamma Sagittarii and 4° south of the Lagoon Nebula, is the unusual open cluster NGC 6520. This cluster is reasonably bright, containing 60 stars of magnitudes 9 and fainter over a 6' diameter. Try observing NGC 6520

on a very dark night and use high powers with your telescope: resolving
this tight group into component stars is an interesting challenge.
Incidentally, the dark nebula Barnard 86 lies adjacent to this little
cluster to the northwest. You may spot B86 as a small patch of darkness
behind which no stars can shine through.

Also prominent in the summer sky is majestic Cygnus. Within
this constellation lies one of the most neglected of the Messier
objects, a small, poor open cluster designated M29 (NGC 6913). To
find M29, begin by aiming your finder scope toward Gamma Cygni, the
star marking the center of the bright "cross" shape of Cygnus. Move
your telescope southward by 2°, and you should see a faint hazy glow
1° west of a 5th-magnitude star. Although it is an attractive open
cluster containing 50 stars, M29 is overshadowed by the brighter or
more famous Cygnus deep-sky objects M39, NGC 6871, the North America
Nebula, and the Veil Nebula. Nonetheless, M29 is a sight worth seeing
as an example of a compact, pretty open cluster.

East of Cygnus lies the diminutive constellation Lacerta, one
that is difficult to see with the naked eye. Within this star group
is the challenging open cluster IC 1434, a 9th-magnitude group of
40 stars spanning 8'. IC 1434 is a good example of an open cluster
faint enough to have been missed by the compilers of the New General
Catalogue, and if you successfully find it you'll see why. The
brightest stars in IC 1434 glow at 12th magnitude, making the cluster
stand out only weakly from the surrounding rich Milky Way star fields.

On the other side of Cygnus the small, bright constellation Lyra
holds a fascinating example of a challenging open cluster for small
scopes. Lyra is primarily known for its famous Ring Nebula, one of
the most observed of all planetary nebulae. But it also contains
NGC 6791, a splendid example of an old, rich cluster of faint stars
somewhat like M67 in Cancer and NGC 188 in Cepheus. NGC 6791 has
existed for 6.3 billion years, placing it among the oldest known open
clusters. The group contains 300 stars in an area 16' across, yielding
a total magnitude of 9.5. The difficulty in seeing NGC 6791 as a
star cluster is that the brightest members are 13th-magnitude objects.
On very dark and transparent nights you may see NGC 6791 as a large,
milky glow of light, but it may prove difficult to resolve individual
stars in the cluster.

The autumn evening sky holds few open clusters, because during
that season we are looking above the plane of the Galaxy and beyond
into intergalactic space. One of the few challenging clusters visible
during this time is M73 (NGC 6994) in Aquarius. To find M73, start
by aiming your telescope toward the bright double star Alpha Capricorni.
Move the telescope 10° east and you should come upon two deep-sky
objects. One is the globular cluster M72, a small, relatively bright
patch of fuzzy light. The group of stars known as M73 lies about
1.5° east of the globular cluster, and will appear as a tiny knot
of four stars.

For some time astrophysicists have debated about the nature of
M73. Can a group of just four associated stars be called a true open
cluster? What are the odds of four similarly-bright stars lying so
close together in the sky but at different distances? It now appears
that M73 is an asterism, a chance grouping of four physically unrelated
stars all shining at about 10th magnitude. Thus, when you view M73
you'll be gazing not at a true open cluster, but one of the sky's
great statistical oddities.

The winter sky holds many more examples of fine open clusters,
scattered throughout the gleaming band of Milky Way that stretches

from Cassiopeia in the north to Puppis in the south. One of the best
sights in Cassiopeia is the faint open cluster NGC 7789. This cluster
is composed of very faint stars, but on dark nights is a marvelous
sight in large binoculars or small scopes. To find NGC 7789, start
at Beta Cassiopeiae and move your telescope 2.5° southwest to the
bright star Rho Cassiopeiae. The cluster lies midway between Rho
and Sigma Cassiopeiae, the apex of a triangle of bright stars 2° to
the south.

NGC 7789 contains 300 stars of 11th magnitude and fainter in
an area measuring 16' across. The cluster's total magnitude is 6.7,
but the individual stars are so faint that you may not resolve it
at low power. The group appears as a large glow of nebulosity in
binoculars and 2-inch to 3-inch telescopes. A 4-inch scope at moderate
should show some of the myriad stars composing NGC 7789, and a 6-inch
scope resolves a sprinkling of faint specks of light across the
cluster's shimmering surface.

One of the finest challenging tests of the winter sky is a small
cluster lying near M35 in Gemini, which we explored in the previous
section. Less than 1° southwest of M35's center lies the open cluster
NGC 2158, a rich grouping of faint stars tightly compressed into a
5' diameter. NGC 2158 is easy to locate because it lies in the same
low-power field as its large, bright neighbor. On transparent nights
you may see NGC 2158 as a faint glow of nebulosity in a 3-inch scope,
but none of the cluster's stars will be visible. A 6-inch telescope
at high power resolves several of NGC 2158's stars, confirming its
nature as a cluster. The M35/NGC 2158 field is an extremely lucky
one for comparison, because NGC 2158 is physically much like M35 but
lies six times farther away.

The table following this chapter provides dozens more examples
of both bright and faint open clusters of every type: some are large,
some compressed; some contain hundreds of stars, some only a dozen.
If you take the time to observe many open star clusters and see their
differences and similarities, you'll gain valuable first-hand knowledge
of the circumstances by which stars in our Galaxy (and others) are
born. This is an important first step in understanding the complex
processes that govern the lives of stars throughout the universe,
and in understanding how we came to be on our little planet circling
our star, the Sun.

The following is a catalog of 109 open star clusters visible in small telescopes. They are listed in right ascension order and grouped by constellations for easy observing. You may be able to detect many more open clusters with small telescopes, but this list represents the best and brightest such objects.

Explanation of data: The coordinates provided are for epoch 1950.0 Mag.=visual magnitude of the cluster, unless follwed by a 'p," which denotes a photographic magnitude. Mag.*=magnitude of brightest star in cluster. Size=the cluster's diameter in minutes of arc. N=number of stars in cluster.

CATALOG NUMBER	R.A.(1950)Dec. h m ° '	Mag.	Mag.*	Size '	N
ANDROMEDA					
NGC 752	01 54.7 +37 25	5.7	9.0	50	60

Large, scattered group easily visible in binoculars.

AQUARIUS					
NGC 6994	20 56.2 -12 51	8.9p	10p	3	4

M73. Asterism of four physically unrelated stars.

AURIGA					
NGC 1664	04 47.4 +43 37	7.6	10.6	18	40
NGC 1883	05 22.2 +46 30	12.0p	14p	2.5	30
NGC 1893	05 22.4 +33 21	7.5	9.3	11	60
NGC 1907	05 24.7 +35 17	8.2	11.3	7	30
NGC 1912	05 25.3 +35 48	6.4	9.5	21	100

M38. Visible in finder scopes as a hazy patch and resolvable into many stars in a 3-inch telescope.

NGC 1960	05 32.0 +34 07	6.0	8.9	12	60

M36. Magnificent cluster showing several colors of stars and lanes of bright stars branching outward from the center.

NGC 2099	05 49.0 +32 33	5.6	9.2	24	150

M37. One of the best star clusters in the sky. Rich group of over 100 faint stars together appearing like a swarm of glowing bees.

CAMELOPARDALIS					
NGC 1502	04 03.0 +62 11	5.7	6.9	8	45
IC 361	04 14.8 +58 11	11.7	14.6	6	60

CANCER					
NGC 2632	08 37.5 +19 52	3.1	6.3	95	50

M44, the Beehive Cluster. Visible to the naked

eye as a fuzzy patch of light. Telescopes show
a flattened square of four bright stars surrounded
by dozens of other bright and faint yellowish stars.

NGC 2682	08 48.3	+12 00	6.9	9.7	30	200

M67. Some 3.2 billion years old, M67 is one of
the oldest open clusters.

___CANIS MAJOR

NGC 2243	06 27.6	-31 15	9.4	11.8	5	100
NGC 2287	06 44.9	-20 42	4.5	6.9	38	80

M41. Lying 4° south of Sirius, this cluster is
easy to find and a bright binocular showpiece.

NGC 2345	07 06.0	-13 05	7.7	9.9	12	70
NGC 2354	07 12.2	-25 38	6.5	9.1	20	100
NGC 2362	07 16.6	-24 52	4.1	4.4	8	60

Cluster surrounding Tau Canis Majoris.

___CASSIOPEIA

NGC 103	00 22.6	+61 03	9.8	12.3	5	30
NGC 129	00 27.0	+59 57	6.5	8.6	21	35
NGC 133	00 28.4	+63 04	9.4p	---	7	5
NGC 136	00 28.7	+61 15	---	13p	1.2	-
NGC 146	00 30.3	+63 01	9.1	11.6	7	20
NGC 225	00 40.5	+61 31	7.0	9.3	12	15
NGC 381	01 05.2	+61 18	9.3p	10p	6	50
NGC 436	01 12.4	+58 33	8.8	11.1	6	30
NGC 457	01 15.9	+58 04	6.4	8.6	13	80

The Owl Cluster. Outline forms owl shape with two
brightest stars as eyes.

NGC 559	01 26.1	+63 02	9.5	10.9	4	60
NGC 581	01 29.9	+60 27	7.4	10.6	6	25

M103. Bright double star (not a member) lies near
the center of this group.

NGC 637	01 38.3	+63 47	8.2	10.0	4	20
NGC 654	01 40.5	+61 39	6.5	7.4	5	60
NGC 659	01 40.8	+60 28	7.9	10.4	5	40
IC 1805	02 28.7	+61 13	6.5	7.9	22	40
IC 1848	02 47.3	+60 14	6.5	7.1	12	10
NGC 7654	23 22.0	+61 20	6.9	8.2	13	100

M52. One of the richest open clusters visible
in small telescopes.

NGC 7788	23 54.2	+61 07	9.4p	---	9	20
NGC 7789	23 54.5	+56 26	6.7	10.7	16	300

A magnificent faint cloud of dim stars appearing
as a smear of hazy light in small scopes.

NGC 7790	23 54.5	+60 56	8.5	10.9	17	40

CEPHEUS

| NGC 188 | 00 39.4 | +85 03 | 8.1 | 12.1 | 14 | 120 |

Its age of 5.0 billion years makes NGC 188 one of the oldest open clusters known.

NGC 6939	20 30.4	+60 38	7.8	11.9	8	80
IC 1396	21 37.5	+57 16	3.5	3.8	50	50
NGC 7510	23 09.2	+60 18	7.9	9.7	4	60
NGC 7762	23 47.5	+67 44	10.0p	11p	11	40

COMA BERENICES

| Mel 111 | 12 22.6 | +26 24 | 1.8 | 4.4 | 275 | 80 |

The Coma Berenices Star Cluster. One of the best binocular star clusters, this enormous group of bright stars is one of the closest star clusters to us and lies in front of a field of faint galaxies.

CYGNUS

NGC 6811	19 36.7	+46 27	6.8	9.9	13	70
NGC 6819	19 39.6	+40 06	7.3	11.5	5	--
NGC 6866	20 02.1	+43 51	7.6	10.7	7	80
NGC 6871	20 04.0	+35 38	5.2	6.8	20	15
IC 1311	20 09.1	+42 01	13.1p	17p	9	60
IC 4996	20 14.6	+37 29	7.3	8.5	6	15
NGC 6910	20 21.3	+40 37	7.4	9.6	8	50
NGC 6913	20 22.2	+38 21	6.6	8.6	7	50

M29. Generally considered one of the least impressive Messier objects, M29 nonetheless appears as a fairly rich group of faint stars compressed into a small area.

| NGC 7062 | 21 21.5 | +46 10 | 8.3 | 10.1 | 7 | 30 |
| NGC 7092 | 21 30.4 | +48 13 | 4.6 | 6.8 | 32 | 30 |

M39. A large, scattered group of bright stars.

| NGC 7127 | 21 42.2 | +54 24 | 12 | --- | 2.8 | 12 |
| NGC 7128 | 21 42.4 | +53 29 | 9.7 | 11.5 | 3.1 | 35 |

GEMINI

NGC 2129	05 58.1	+23 18	6.7	7.4	7	40
IC 2157	06 01.8	+24 02	8.4	11.1	7	20
NGC 2158	06 04.3	+24 06	8.6	12.4	5	--
NGC 2168	06 05.7	+24 06	5.1	8.2	28	100

M35. Just visible to the naked eye on dark nights, this cluster is impressive in any scope. Just southwest of M35 lies the faint group NGC 2158.

| NGC 2266 | 06 40.5 | +27 02 | 9.5p | 11p | 7 | 50 |

HYDRA

| NGC 2548 | 08 11.2 | -05 38 | 5.8 | 8.2 | 54 | 80 |

M48. Rich, moderately condensed cluster.

LACERTA

NGC 7209	22 03.2	+46 15	6.7	9.0	25	25
IC 1434	22 08.6	+52 35	9.0p	12p	8	40
NGC 7243	22 13.2	+49 38	6.4	8.5	21	40
NGC 7245	22 13.6	+54 05	9.2	12.8	5	3

LYRA

NGC 6791	19 19.0	+34 40	9.5	13.0	16	300

MONOCEROS

NGC 2244	06 29.7	+04 54	4.8	5.8	24	100

Cluster embedded in the Rosette Nebula.

NGC 2264	06 38.4	+09 56	3.9	5p	20	40

Surrounds bright star S Moncerotis and is involved in bright nebulosity.

NGC 2323	07 00.5	-08 16	5.9	7.9	16	80

M50. Large, rich group of bright stars that appears circular in small scopes.

OPHIUCHUS

IC 4665	17 43.8	+05 44	4.2	6.9	41	30
NGC 6633	18 25.1	+06 32	4.6	7.6	27	30

ORION

NGC 2112	05 51.3	+00 23	9.1p	10p	11	50
NGC 2175	06 06.8	+20 20	6.8	7.6		

PERSEUS

NGC 869	02 15.5	+56 55	4.3p	6.6	30	200
NGC 884	02 18.9	+56 53	4.4p	8.1	30	150

Together NGC 869 and NGC 884 comprise the Double Cluster in Perseus. Each cluster is easily visible to the naked eye and a spectacular sight in telescopes, holding many dozens of colorful stars. Both clusters fit into a single low-power field.

NGC 1039	02 38.8	+42 34	5.2	7.3	35	60

M34. An exceptionally bright, compact cluster visible in binoculars; when viewed through a telescope, the brightest stars form a distorted "X."

NGC 1245	03 11.2	+47 03	8.4	11.2	10	200
NGC 1528	04 11.4	+51 07	6.4	8.8	24	40

PUPPIS

NGC 2422	07 34.3	-14 22	4.4	5.7	30	30

M47. Visible to the naked eye.

NGC 2437	07 39.6	-14 42	6.1	8.7	27	100

M46. Superimposed on the face of this bright open cluster is the planetary nebula NGC 2438, a foreground object.

NGC 2447	07 42.4	-23 45	6.2	8.2	22	80

M93. Telescopes show strong star colors in this group.

NGC 2477	07 50.5	-38 25	5.8	9.8	27	160

_____ SAGITTARIUS _____

NGC 6494	17 54.0	-19 01	5.5	9.2	27	150

M23. Bright cluster located in a rich star field.

NGC 6520	18 00.3	-27 54	7.6p	9p	6	60
NGC 6530	18 01.6	-24 20	4.6	6.9	15	--

Embedded in M8, the Lagoon Nebula. Both cluster and nebula are visible in binoculars, offering a wonderful contrast.

NGC 6531	18 01.8	-22 30	5.9	7.3	13	70

M21. Located just northeast of the Trifid Nebula, this is a small, compact, diamond-shaped group of stars.

NGC 6603	18 15.5	-18 27	11.1p	14p	5	100

Located in star cloud M24. NGC 6603 appears as a small knot of stars within the large mass of stars known as M24.

NGC 6613	18 17.0	-17 09	6.9	8.7	9	20

M18. Small scopes show this unconcentrated group as a nebulous glow in the Sagittarius Milky Way.

NGC 6618	18 17.9	-16 12	6.0	9.3	11	40

Embedded in M17, the Omega Nebula.

IC 4725	18 28.8	-19 17	4.6	6.7	32	30

M25. Large, rich cluster lying in a dense star field.

_____ SCORPIUS _____

NGC 6231	16 50.7	-41 43	2.6	4.7	15	--
NGC 6405	17 36.8	-32 11	4.2	6.2	15	80

M6, the Butterfly Cluster. The brightest star in M6 is BM Scorpii, a ruddy irregular variable.

NGC 6475	17 50.7	-34 48	3.3	5.6	80	80

M7. An obvious sprinkling of hazy stars to the
naked eye, M7 is one of the best telescopic clusters
in the sky.

_____SCUTUM_

| NGC 6694 | 18 42.5 | -09 27 | 8.0 | 10.3 | 15 | 30 |

M26. Fan-shaped group of 30 stars in an attractive
field.

| NGC 6704 | 18 48.2 | -05 16 | 9.2 | 12.2 | 6 | 30 |
| NGC 6705 | 18 48.4 | -06 20 | 5.8 | 8.0 | 14 | -- |

M11, the Wild Duck Cluster. Triangular and containing
a bright orange star near its center, M11 appears as
a grainy patch of light in finder scopes. Small
telescopes reveal its starry nature and show it as
one of the best small clusters in the sky.

_____SERPENS_

| NGC 6611 | 18 16.0 | -13 48 | 6.0 | 8.2 | 7 | -- |

Embedded in the Eagle Nebula, M16.

| IC 4756 | 18 36.6 | +05 26 | 5.4p | 8.7 | 52 | 80 |

_____TAURUS_

| Mel 22 | 03 43.9 | +23 58 | 1.2 | 2.9 | 110 | 100 |

The Pleiades. This large, bright, dipper-shaped group
of stars is visible as a hazy cloud with at least six
distinct stars to the naked eye. Binoculars and
wide-field scopes show its true glory.

| Mel 25 | 04 16.7 | +15 31 | 0.5 | 3.4 | 330 | --- |

The Hyades. Although bright star Aldebaran is a
foreground object, the members of this immense V-
shaped group of stars offer much for small telescopes.

NGC 1647	04 43.2	+18 59	6.4	8.6	45	200
NGC 1746	05 00.6	+23 44	6.1p	8p	42	20
NGC 1807	05 07.8	+16 28	7.0	8.6	17	20
NGC 1817	05 09.2	+16 38	7.7	11.2	16	60

_____VULPECULA_

NGC 6823	19 41.1	+23 12	7.1	8.8	12	30
NGC 6830	19 48.9	+22 58	7.9	9.9	12	20
NGC 6885	20 09.9	+26 20	5.7p	6p	7	30
NGC 6940	20 32.5	+28 08	6.3	9.3	31	60

Fig. 5-1. **The Hercules Cluster**

5 Globular Star Clusters

David H. Levy

"But what does it mean?" the young man asked his father. With the coming of warm weather, the tribe had completed the climb to a mountaintop, where they would spend the next few months. The first dark night offered a respite from the long climb, and father and son were gazing up at the sky. They noticed that almost directly over their heads was a faint, fuzzy clump of light.

The father could't explain. The fuzzy patch seemed as distant and unreachable as the stars themselves, yet he wondered why this fuzziness would be in the midst of all the sharp points of starry light.

A dozen centuries later, another young boy looked skyward with anticipation. A member of an astronomical society, this stargazer had just been invited to a public "star party" to help show selected astronomical objects to a group of 125 people. The object assigned to him was the globular star cluster M15, and he had just a few days to become familiar with it.

M15, the lad would discover, is a globular cluster in the constellation Pegasus. It is not the brightest such cluster of stars, but its location makes it a popular target for telescopes on autumnal nights. M15 is bright enough to be visible as a distinctly nonstellar patch or light in small telescopes. Even from a suburban observing location, some of the cluster's individual stars can be resolved in small aperture telescopes.

By reading about this distant and vast grouping of stars, the young stargazer came to know M15 almost like a friend. Coming into the field of view, its outer stars barely revealing themselves, M15 would give him viewing delights for many years.

Globular clusters are highly important objects for professional astronomical study. They are extremely old objects, having existed since the early stages of the universe. They were around to witness our protogalaxy form out of a cloud of hydrogen and helium. Because of their great age, astronomers can tell a great deal about the conditions that existed long ago by studying the nature of their myriad stars.

The 100 or so globulars we know of aren't randomly scattered throughout the sky, but rather are grouped together in two small locations. At least 50 globulars have been found toward the center of our Galaxy. Some 20 others inhabit the Milky Way's outer edges, in the so-called galactic halo. There are probably 100 or more undiscovered globulars lying predominantly near the galactic center, hopelessly blocked by thick clouds of obscuring dust.

Globular clusters are spherical-shaped systems containing up to a hundred thousand stars, and the most distant ones in our Galaxy are some 75,000 light-years away. M22, on the other hand, is one of the closest globulars. This cluster is a stunning sight through almost any telescope. Lying in Sagittarius, a constellation filled with deep-sky objects, this wondrous haze of stars is a highlight.

Sometime during a spring observing session you must see Omega Centauri, the biggest, brightest globular cluster of them all. This cluster is visible to the naked eye as a fuzzy patch and appears as a large, oval haze splattered with tiny stars in telescopes. At a distance of 15,000 light-years, Omega Centauri is a relatively close globular, and thus offers easy resolution of its individual member suns. Unfortunately for northern hemisphere observers, however, it lies in the southern sky and rises only a few degrees above the horizon

Fig. 5-2. **Omega Centauri**

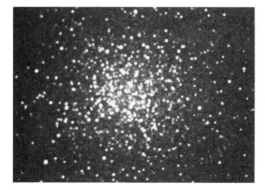

Fig. 5-3. **M55 in Sagittarius**

Fig. 5-4. **NGC 5053 in Coma Berenices**

for most skywatchers in the United States. But this shouldn't stop
you. Even if observing it means that you must make a trip to the
southern hemisphere, by all means do so. One look at Omega Centauri
will instantly show you the magnificent beauty of the globular clusters.

David H. Levy
Tucson, Arizona

HISTORICAL BACKGROUND

An early stargazer may have observed the globular cluster M13 from a mountaintop in what is now Arizona. As he looked up toward the fuzzy spot, he undoubtedly wondered about it, baffled by its different appearance from the stars. Centuries later that little spot of light would play an important role in deciphering the universe, moving its center farther away than the ancient stargazer could imagine. The process of learning about globular clusters would be slow, but unrelenting and ultimately highly successful.

In the many centuries since the ancients gazed up at the sky, other observers have asked many questions about these balls of stars, probing with every type of research they could use. Today electronic eyes attached to telescopes atop mountains point toward M13; today's astronomers know that the fuzzy light comes from a distant cluster of a hundred thousand stars, but they still possess the same basic inquisitiveness as their predecessors.

One prominent early skygazer was Abraham Ihle, who in 1665 discovered the fuzzy globular patch in Sagittarius we now call M22. Another was Edmond Halley, who in 1677 found the mighty globular cluster Omega Centauri during his vist to St. Helena. Much later, in 1714, he would be the first to record the globular we now know as M13. His primitive telescope would not show the cluster's individual stars. "This is but a little patch," wrote Halley, "but it shows itself to the naked Eye, when the Sky is clear, and the Moon absent." Halley was fascinated by these nebulous objects, and he predicted that "they cannot fail to occupy spaces immensely great, and perhaps not less than our whole Solar System."

Between 1750 and 1754 the French observer Nicholas Louis de Lacaille prepared a large catalogue of stars that included 42 nonstellar objects, some of which were globular clusters. But another Frenchman's work overshadowed Lacaille's, although it listed fuzzy patches in the sky so that comets hunters could avoid the, not sudy them. Motivated partly by his failure to be the first to recover Halley's Coment in 1759, Charles Messier was interested in finding new comets, and anything that remotely resembled a comet as seen through a telescope was an inconvenience that demanded careful recording. Like Halley, Messier was convinced that the 13th object in his list (hence the designation M13) was "A nebula which, I am sure, does not contain stars. [It is] Round and brilliant, [with a] centre brighter than the edge."

The Englishman William Herschel began his work with the opposite purpose. With a goal of cataloguing the entire northern heavens as seen through his telescopes, Herschel began a methodical sweep of the sky. He obtained semiaccurate positions by using his telescope as a transit; when a star of interest crossed a wire in the middle of his field of view, he would call to his sister Caroline, who dutifully recorded the time for later translation into astronomical coordinates. His discoveries of individual objects were not ends in themselves but means to the discovery of the shape of the entire "sidereal system." Herschel's discovery of Uranus in 1781 came as no surprise to an observer confident of the thoroughness of his observations. Five years later he would present to the Royal Society his first catalog of nebulae and star clusters. In 1789 and in 1802, two new lists appeared, totalling 2,500 nonstellar objects. These lists were not divided into types of objects, but rather into catagories of "bright," "faint," and "very faint."

Herschel's telescopes were good enough to give him a respectable hint that the nature of these fuzzy objects he saw were vastly different. In 1786 he wrote: "I have seen double and treble nebulae, variously arranged; large ones with small, seeming attendants; narrow but much extended...while others shine with a fainter mottled kind of light, which denotes their being resolvable into stars." Herschel felt that these resolvable clusters, that happened to lie near the center of the band of light called the Milky Way, actually were a part of it. He also was apparently the first to resolve M13 into what he estimated to be fourteen thousand stars.

By the late 19th century our understanding of globular clusters had matured. An 1879 astronomy text by H.W. Warren advises its readers to observe a "sprayed cluster below [the star] Eta in Hercules." Apparently these irregular clusters were different in classification from true globulars, of which Omega Centauri was listed as an example. "There are two possibilities of thought concerning these clusters," the author concluded. "Either that they belong to our stellar system, and hence the stars must be small and young, or they are another universe of millions of suns...the latter is the older and grander thought;the former the newer and better substantiated."

Early in this century, the great double star observer, S.W. Burnham found a double star near the center of M13, but remarked that in general globular clusters did not offer many close double stars.

The 20th century saw astronomers' understanding of globulars grow rapidly. A picture was becoming clear. The astronomer Solon I. Bailey studied the large collection of globular cluster plates in the collection of Harvard College Observatory. He noticed that most of the variable stars in these clusters had short periods of light fluctuation like the well-known star RR Lyrae. So many RR Lyrae variables would eventually be found in globular clusters that these stars would be called "cluster variables." M3 and Omega Centauri contain at least 100 of these variables each, although M13 itself has relatively few.

In 1912, Harvard's Miss Henrietta Leavitt examined many variable stars in globular clusters and noticed that some had longer periods than others. By plotting the average magnitudes of these longer period stars against their periods, she discovered a relation between their average magnitudes and their periods. These stars became known as Cepheid variables, after the well-known example called Delta Cephei. She also found that brighter Cepheids had longer periods. Then Miss Leavitt observed this phenomenon in a distant group of variables in the Large Magellanic Cloud; from this she deduced that by using her period-luminosity relationship she could find the distances to these stars. This method became a powerful tool in establishing the distance scale of the Galaxy.

With growing interest in these mighty clusters and the variable stars they contained, the stage was set for one of the most significant discoveries in the history of science. This would come through the efforts of a young astronomer at Mount Wilson Observatory named Harlow Shapley.

Shapley was an extraordinary man who began his career as a newspaper reporter. When he enrolled at the University of Missouri, he found so many interesting areas in which to major that he had trouble choosing. Looking through the college catalog in alphabetical order, he came across Archaeology but feared he would have trouble spelling it. Fortunately for science, he could spell astronomy, and he entered its study with a passion.

Fig. 5-5. **M22 in Sagittarius**

Fig. 5-6. **M71 in Sagitta**

Fig. 5-7. **M56 in Lyra**

After obtaining his Ph.D. from Princeton University, Shapley's first professional affiliation was with the newly formed Mt. Wilson Observatory, a remote institution in the mountains north of Los Angeles. In 1915 he started studying globular clusters and their variable stars using the observatory's 60-inch reflector. The first thing that gripped Shapley's mind was the distribution of these clusters. Although they seemed to be concentrated in the region of Scorpius and Sagittarius, they seemed also to thrive at great distances from the Galaxy's plane in a region we now call the galactic halo. Perhaps, if he could only calculate their distances, he could outline the shape of our Galaxy.

Shapley proved that globular clusters were altogether different from the smaller open clusters, and then found that the brightest stars in the clusters were red giants with such dim apparent magnitudes that they must be at great distances.

By 1917, Shapley had finally determined the distance to a nearby Cepheid variable, and then used the period-luminosity relationship developed by Leavitt to make an estimate of the size of the Milky Way. By studying Solon Bailey's variables in the globular clusters, he made the astonishing announcement that the solar system was positioned at the outskirts of the Galaxy. In Through Rugged Ways to the Stars, Shapley described his thrill at the announcement: "I stayed with the Cepheids and [globular] clusters during those early years at Mount Wilson, until I crashed through on the distances and outlined the structure of the universe."

In addition to the positions of the clusters, Shapley was interested in the variable stars within the clusters. "I plotted the clusters and locked at what I had. I found that globular clusters are mostly in the southern Milky Way and that some are bright and some faint. Those that contain Cepheid variables could be compared with those that do not. Finally I hit upon using the period-luminosity relation that had been foreshadowed by Miss Henrietta Leavitt at Harvard in a paper published in 1912. Her paper dealt with only 25 stars and did not deal with their distances at all. So I went after the distances, and that was helped by Ejnar Hertzsprung."

The young Shapley had frequently discussed his ideas with the eminent astronomer J.C. Kapteyn, and one day Shapley brought the great man results of some measurements of the globular M3. An astronomer of the old European school, Kapteyn was slow to accept the startling results. Shapley was too confident to be swayed: "There was no question about my having hit the jackpot," he later said.

In 1917 and 1918, Shapley published several revolutionary papers on globular clusters. These papers used the globulars as keys to proving that the universe was larger than had been previously thought. They included measurements of variable stars in a hundred globular clusters. Through these Shapley papers, the globulars showed that our Galaxy is huge, that its center is in the direction of Sagittarius, and not near our solar system.

Sagittarius, "home of the globular clusters," contains more of these beautiful structures than any other area of sky. Of Sagittarius, Shapley wrote: "Another part of the sky is more or less empty of globular clusters. The results could not be disproved except by claiming that the measurements were wrong or crooked. So they were accepted, except by cautious people who do not want changes."

Shapley himself would be a victim of change. In 1952, his scale had to be extensively revised due to the discovery that there are two types of Cepheid variables. The method Shapley used to arrive at distances to the globular clusters assumed that all Cepheids were the same. Also, the effect of the absorption of light by interstellar matter blocking it was not known in 1917, and this would also affect Shapley's distance estimates. One fact hasn't changed, however: Shapley removed the Sun from the position of center, just as Copernicus had done with Earth 375 years earlier.

As the 20th century marched on, many astronomers began looking for globular clusters in other galaxies, particularly the Magellanic Clouds. In 1930, Shapley had known of only two in the Small Magellanic Cloud, NGC 416 and NGC 419, and eight in the Large Cloud (NGCs 1783, 1806, 1831, 1835, 1846, 1866 and 1978). Around 1950, A.D. Thackeray discovered that the LMC's globular NGC 1866 was strange, different from those in the Milky Way in that its brightest stars were blue instead of red. Shapley noted that this cluster contained some so-called classical Cepheid variables which, unlike the cluster Cepheids, are almost unknown in globulars. In 1952, S. Gascoigne and G. Kron, at Australia's Mt. Stromlo Observatory, announced that the clusters in the Magellanic Clouds were about evenly divided between the traditional globulars with their red stars, and the new, blue ones. In 1960, H.C. Arp found that these blue clusters are poorer in heavy metals, and then concluded that the globulars in the SMC may be younger in age than those in our Galaxy.

Soon after his arrival at Mt. Wilson, Shapley's name had become synonymous with globular clusters. His work raised the importance of the globulars to such a high level that are heavily studied even today. And not only studied; one has also been talked to. On November 16, 1974, Frank Drake and other astronomers at the Arecibo Observatory in Puerto Rico used their 305 meter radio telescope to transmit a message to M13, a message that will take some 23,500 years to reach the cluster's stars.

Any recipients of this message might ponder the distant sky away from home, thinking of the incredible, unfathomable gap between their civilization and the mysterious creatures who sent them a greeting.

Fig. 5-8. **M4 in Scorpius**

Fig. 5-9. **M10 in Ophiuchus**

Fig. 5-10. **M92 in Hercules**

Fig. 5-11. **M15 in Pegasus**

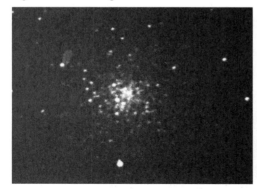

Fig. 5-12. **M72 in Aquarius**

Fig. 5-13. **M28 in Sagittarius**

THE NATURE OF GLOBULAR CLUSTERS

Most globular clusters are found in only one half of the sky and are concentrated in the region of Sagittarius. Harlow Shapley realized that by studying their distribution, he could estimate the size and shape of the Milky Way Galaxy as well as our place in it. This would not be the only important clue to the structure of the universe revealed by globulars, however. To discover more, first we must understand how globulars relate to each other.

Globular clusters are classified into a scheme that Shapley modified from his observations of open star clusters. In the scheme for open clusters, the two types of associations, field irregularities (a) and stellar associations (b) are followed by five types of open clusters ranging from very loose (c) to compact (g). Shapley felt that globular clusters had so much variety that a simple "loose, medium, compact" organization would prove insufficient for classifying them. Thus in 1927 he and Helen B. Sawyer proposed 12 classes based on decreasing density of central concentration. These follow with examples; the parenthetical numbers indicate the total number of examples he knew of at the time.

        I: highest concentration toward center: NGC 2808, 7006, (4)
       II: dense central condensation: M2. (7)
      III: strong inner core of stars: 47 Tucanae. (7)
       IV: intermediate rich concentration: M62, NGC 1866. (12)
        V: intermediate concentration: M30. (12)
       VI: M3, NGC 6752. (11)
      VII: M22. (8)
     VIII: rather loose toward center: M14, M19. (10)
       IX: M4, M12, (10)
        X: NGC 288. (9)
       XI: very loose toward center: M55. (9)
      XII: almost no concentration in center: NGC 7492. (4)

Experienced deep-sky observers know that despite their individual characteristics, globular clusters have the reputation of being a homogeneous group of objects, perhaps more so than other types of deep-sky objects. Globulars do not vary as widely as nebulae or galaxies in total brightness and size; only five magnitudes separate the brightest and faintest globulars widely observed by amateurs. (This is largely because amateur astronomers have shown little interest in observing very faint globular clusters.) Globulars average 100 light-years in diameter, and many of them can be easily resolved into constituent stars using backyard telescopes of 12-inches or more aperture.

If these clusters are similar in size and apparent magnitude, they are certainly not in chemical composition. It is difficult for astronomers to analyze any globular cluster stars save for the outermost, brightest members, and even these are very faint. To study the stars in globular clusters, astronomers take spectral plates of the entire cluster memberships, and have been able to draw some interesting conclusions. Apparently the amounts of heavy elements, or metals, in these clusters varies widely; clusters close to the center of the Galaxy tend to be metal-rich, while those farther away tend to be poor in metals.

Several globular clusters related to our Milky Way Galaxy lie at extremely large distances from the Galaxy itself and, early in the century, it appeared that they may be separate wanderers in the universe, unbounded by galactic ties. One such cluster, NGC 2419 in Lynx, is some 304,000 light-years away from the Galaxy's center; Shapley called it an "intergalactic tramp."

More recent studies show that remote clusters like NGC 2419 are most likely gravitationally bound to our Galaxy, but have wandered astray due to highly-inclined, perturbed orbits. They remain slightly puzzling nonetheless: the total mass of the Milky Way is insufficient to keep these clusters as members of the Galaxy. This "missing mass" is probably made up for by invisible dark matter in the Milky Way's extensive corona of dust, however, meaning the remote clusters will stay with us for a long time.

Astronomers have recognized another interesting difference between clusters near the center of the Galaxy and those away from its center: the outlying globulars are as much as twice as large. This is attributed to the fact that as outer globulars--whose orbits are highly inclined and tilted to the plane of the Galaxy--sweep through the plane of the Milky Way, they are disrupted by other stars and matter and consequently lose members. The galactic halo contains many stars that were once globular cluster members.

In fact, astronomers once thought that their orbits carried globular clusters close to the galactic center, the very heart of the Galaxy. Recent studies, however, indicate that this is not true.

Globular clusters contain many hundreds of thousands of stars; they are much larger and more densely packed than open star clusters. The stars in globular clusters are quite different from those in other parts of the Galaxy. The brightest stars, the ones that are visible individually in backyard telescopes, are yellowish or red giants, while the bluish stars in globulars average about three magnitudes fainter. Globular cluster stars are very old, and are thus evolved toward the later spectral classes, with little presence of early spectral types.

Globular clusters are immensely old, and many undoubtedly formed simultaneously with the Milky Way Galaxy. M13 is between 12 and 14 billion years old, three times the age of the Sun. We can get an idea of the ages of globulars by noticing that a large number of the brightest stars are of similar magnitude and color. How do we know this? Let us assume that when stars are first formed in a large group, the more massive stars and less massive stars are evenly distributed. The more massive stars will evolve faster and disappear, either as supernovae or in a more gradual process. The less massive stars would then continue to evolve in their leisurely way, and eventually many of these less massive stars will reach the upper evolutionary stage.

In the days of their formation, most of the heavier elements that are now part of newly formed stars were not present, so the cluster stars contained almost exclusively hydrogen and helium. Today, these stars have assembled a good supply of heavier elements formed in their inner cores. Cluster stars developed shells of hydrogen and helium, slowly spreading the heavier elements out toward the stellar surfaces--a process that takes several billion years to complete. However, when these shells reach the surface, their temperatures are not high enough to permit the still heavier elements to form the way they do in stars closer to our galactic neighborhood. Consequently, the elements are released into space, gently into a cluster wind, or violently in a supernova explosion. Through a technique that involves spectroscopic analysis, astronomers can detect these heavy elements.

With a large backyard telescope you may be able to follow the brightness changes of some of the bright Mira variable stars in globular clusters. About 25 Mira stars have been detected in the globular clusters, distributed mostly in the metal-rich ones. Far more numerous are RR Lyrae variables; Omega Centauri alone contains at least 137

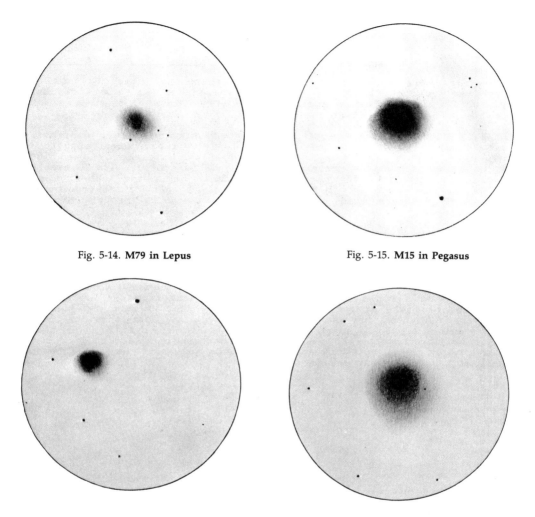

Fig. 5-14. **M79 in Lepus**

Fig. 5-15. **M15 in Pegasus**

Fig. 5-16. **M10 in Ophiuchus**

Fig. 5-17. **M53 in Coma Berenices**

RR Lyrae stars. In fact, the Canadian astronomer Helen Sawyer Hogg has recorded about 1,100 RR Lyrae stars spread between several globular clusters. The RR Lyrae variables are very large blue giant stars, mostly with periods less than a day.

To find the distance to a globular cluster using its variables, astronomers need more than a simple knowledge of the apparent magnitudes of its RR Lyrae variables. If the variables in cluster A are much fainter than those in cluster B, this may not be entirely due to greater distance, especially for clusters that we see near the center of our Galaxy. This apparent fading may be the result of absorption by interstellar material like dark nebulosity, as much as through increased distance.

Between cluster B and us lies an undetermined amount of interstellar material that absorbs light. How can astronomers find out how much absorption is interfering with the light from a cluster? By measuring the amount of reddening in a star's spectrum. Shapley was aware of this problem of interfering interstellar dust, although he may not have recognized its extent. He knew that NGC 4372 appeared to be "dimmed by one of the long dark streamers from the Coal Sack", that NGC 6144 was at the "edge of the heavy Rho Ophiuchi nebulosity", and the NGC 6569 may be partially hidden from our view by large intervening areas of dark nebulosity." Shapley didn't know this, but the information that he and his astronomical descendants have provided us makes our knowledge of globular clusters immensely beyond what it was just a few decades ago.

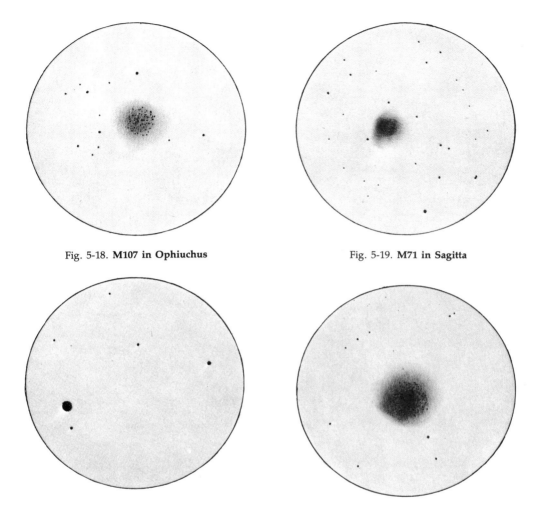

Fig. 5-18. **M107 in Ophiuchus**

Fig. 5-19. **M71 in Sagitta**

Fig. 5-20. **M30 in Capricornus**

Fig. 5-21. **M22 in Sagittarius**

Fig. 5-22. **M3 in Canes Venatici**

Fig. 5-23. **M5 in Serpens Caput**

Fig. 5-24. **M2 in Aquarius**

BEGINNING TO OBSERVE

Although they are often accused of appearing similar, bright globular clusters offer a variety of shapes, sizes, brightnesses, and degrees of resolution when viewed with small telescopes. The following is a list of some of the finest globular clusters in the sky, all accessible with backyard telescopes under moderately dark skies.

Because it is bright, large, and highly compressed (class III), many observers of the southern sky regard 47 Tucanae (NGC 104) as one of the finest globular clusters in the sky. The cluster is invisible for northern hemisphere observers, but for those who can see it offers a spectacle. The cluster measures 30.9'--a Moon diameter--across, and shines at magnitude 4.0. 47 Tucanae is easily visible to the naked eye as a tiny "star," and is seen as an unresolved disk of faint light in binoculars. A 6-inch telescopes resolves this cluster into a group of tiny pinpoint stars superimposed on a large, round glow of milky light. This cluster is 15,000 light-years away, making it slightly closer than Omega Centauri, the southern sky's other great globular.

The winter sky contains only a few bright globulars, the most outstanding example of which is M79 (NGC 1904). Besides M79, only NGC 1261 in Horologium, NGC 1851 in Columba, and NGC 2808 in Carina are brighter than magnitude 8.5. Therefore M79 is a prominent object during the winter months. M79 has a magnitude of 8.0 and measures 8.7' across. It is a class V cluster, containing stars moderately concentrated toward the cluster's center. Binoculars reveal M79 as a small, fuzzy patch, while a 6-inch telescope resolves some stars on the cluster's edge. M79 lies at a distance of 45,000 light-years.

When I first saw Omega Centauri (NGC 5139) from Peru, I was stunned. With a 6-inch telescope I could see its myriad stars covering most of a low-power field of view. the cluster has a class of VIII, meaning it is not very concentrated--it can be resolved with nearly any telescope--and its appearance is very different from most globular clusters. Omega Centauri is highly flattened, an effect caused by the cluster's rotation. This flattening is most obvious at the cluster's periphery; the core of Omega Centauri appears fairly circular.

At 5.2 kpc, Omega Centauri is one of the closest globular clusters. It measures 36.3' in diameter, making it the largest globular in the sky by a wide margin. (The three runners up are 47 Tucanae, at 30.9'; M4 in Scorpius, at 26.3'; and M22 in Sagittarius, at 24.0'.) Omega Centauri's visual magnitude is 3.7, making it the brightest globular cluster in the sky. It is easily visible as a fuzzy disk to the naked eye, and is impressive even in binoculars.

This cluster is so bright that the astronomer Ptolemy catalogued it in the 2nd century. Johannes Bayer gave it the name Omega, thinking it was a bright star, almost 500 years ago. When you see Omega Centauri you'll realize that you need not have a telescope to enjoy its appearance.

Unfortunately Omega Centauri is invisible from most of the United States, and is difficult to see from north of 38 degrees north latitude. From the southern United States Omega Centauri is visible during spring evenings, just above the southern horizon.

At magnitude 6.4, M3 (NGC 5272) is one of the best clusters in the northern sky. Visible as a small patch of nebulous light in binoculars, M3 appears as an intriguing object in small telescopes. A 3-inch scope shows a disk over 5' across. Under a dark sky, a 4-inch telescope resolves a few stars around the perimeter of this cluster. Six-inch telescopes show a sprinkling of tiny stars around the edge of M3 and reveal a few stars scattered across its face. M3 lies at a distance of 32,000 light-years.

As are most globular clusters, M3 is an extremely old object. The age of this group of stars has been estimated at 10 billion years. When you aim your telescope at one of these balls of stars, remember that the stars you are gazing at were created long before our Sun and planets.

Another fine cluster visible in the spring sky is M5 (NGC 5904) in Serpens. Lying near the bright star 5 Serpentis, M5 can be resolved in a 4-inch telescope. This cluster was noted by Shapley for its pronounced asymmetry. Star counts conducted on M5 early this century revealed that the densest part of this cluster is between 3' and 15' from the center. M5 glows at magnitude 5.8, and spans 17.4' of sky. It has an average stellar concentration, belonging to Shapley class V.

The globular cluster M80 (NGC 6093) is well-known for having an extremely densely-packed collection of stars. Although it is not the most concentrated of the globulars, it is one of the brightest highly-concentrated globulars. The field around this magnitude 7.2 cluster is striking; just east of the cluster is an extensive network of dark nebulae, called the "hole in the heavens" by Herschel.

One of the finest globulars in the summer sky is M4 (NGC 6121) in Scorpius. Walter Scott Houston, one of this century's best known deep-sky observers, once told me that there is not one M4 but several, and that the M4 that you happen to see will depend very much on the size, focal ratio, and eyepiece of your telescope. Houston's comment was driven by two factors: With a diameter of 26.3', M4 is one of the largest globulars, and it is also one of the most easily resolved. Thus in binoculars M4 appears like a faint smudge; in a 3-inch telescope at high power it looks like a large nebulosity peppered with faint stars; and a 6-inch instrument shows it as a fully resolved, bright disk of dozens of pinpoint stars. The cluster shines at magnitude 6.0, and is easy to find since it lies just over 1° west of the bright star Antares. At a distance of 7,000 light-years, M4 is one of the closest globulars.

Although it isn't as bright or large as Omega Centauri, perhaps the most observed globular cluster is M13 (NGC 6205) in Hercules. Certainly for northern sky chauvinists the Hercules Cluster is the mightiest of the globulars. Southern hemisphere observers respect this cluster too, finding its strong central condensation almost as attractive as that of 47 Tucanae.

M13 has two characteristics that make it attractive in telescopes. First, the cluster has a Shapley-Sawyer class of V, making it far more concentrated than Omega Centauri. More importantly, M13 has several "dark lanes," or low density areas, that are apparent in telescopes of 6-inch in aperture. They are much more apparent visually than in photographs. M13's diameter is 16.6', or more than 1/4 degree. Small telescopes at moderate magnifications show M13 covering 1/4 of the field of view, the brightest of its myriad stars resolved around the cluster's edges. M13 has a magnitude of 5.9, making it barely visible as a point of light to a keen-eyed viewer without optical aid. To his credit, the great English observer Edmond Halley noted that the cluster is visible without a telescope under a dark sky.

M10 (NGC 6254) is the best known and most frequently observed

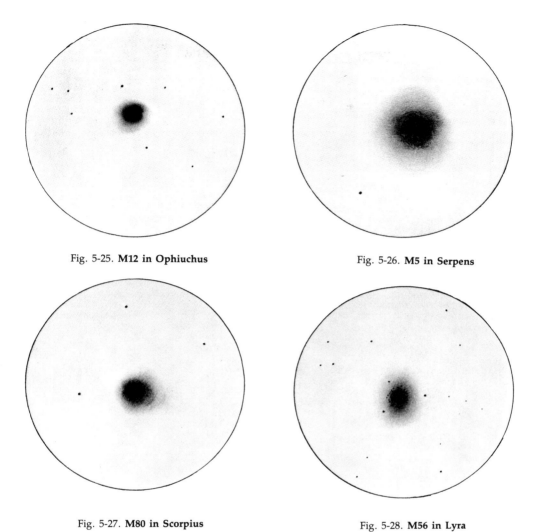

Fig. 5-25. **M12 in Ophiuchus**

Fig. 5-26. **M5 in Serpens**

Fig. 5-27. **M80 in Scorpius**

Fig. 5-28. **M56 in Lyra**

globular cluster in Ophiuchus. It shines at magnitude 6.6 and spans 15.1' across. M10 is a loose, class VII object that can be partially resolved with small telescopes. M10's neighbor is M12 (NGC 6218), an extremely similar globular star cluster also shining at magnitude 6.6. M12 is slightly smaller than M10 (14.5' across) and has a Shapley-Sawyer class of VII. With so many similarities you might think that M10 and M12 are physically related, but they actually lie at vastly different distances and are moving through space in different directions.

Located in a very rich field of stars, M19 (NGC 6273) in Ophiuchus is one of the most striking sights in the entire sky. M19 has a magnitude of 7.2, and the cluster measures 13.5' across. M19 is a hightly unusual globular cluster: it is so elongated that Shapley suspected that it might have a double nucleus, although he did not see any direct evidence of this. You can see M19's oval shape with a 6-inch telescope on a dark night.

Located only 9 degrees away from M13 in Hercules is the impressive globular M92 (NGC 6341). Slightly smaller than M13 and half a magnitude fainter, M92 is nearly as impressive as the great M13, but is frequently passed over by observers because of its famous neighbor. The truth is that were M92 in any other part of the sky, it would be thought of as one of the finest sights in the northern sky.

M28 (NGC 6626) lies less than one degree from the bright star Lambda Sagittarii. M28 shines at magnitude 6.9 and is rather strongly condensed toward its center. M28 occupies 11.2' of sky, and would be far more impressive were it not located behind thick star clouds toward the Milky Way's center.

Also in Sagittarius, M22 (NGC 6656) is a fantastic cluster. This slightly oval object is one of the closest globular clusters and can be resolved quite easily with a small telescope. To best observe M22, use moderate to high magnification on a night of good seeing. Because it is lost in a constellation so rich in other types of objects, M22 is not as popular at star parties as it deserves to be, but should definitely be on your observing list when the summer constellations appear over the horizon.

Shapley classified this globular as a rather loose type VII, reflecting its sparse concentration of stars toward the center. It measures 24.0', an enormous apparent diameter exceeded only by NGC 6397 (25.7'), M4 (26.3'), 47 Tucanae (30.9') and Omega Centauri (36.3'). At magnitude 5.1, it is visible to the naked eye on a dark night. Small telescopes show M22 as a fuzzy, slightly elongated ball of nebulous light peppered with a few resolved stars, the cluster's brightest members. High powers during moments of good seeing show a cleanly resolved disk of hundreds of tiny pinpoints of light.

M54 (NGC 6715) is a highly concentrated, class III cluster covering only 9.1'. It is bright, however, glowing at magnitude 7.7. M54 lies below the Teapot asterism of Sagittarius, and is fairly easy to find by star hopping. A few looks at this object while it's near the meridian should convince you that M54 is one of the summer's nicest clusters, set in a rich Milky Way field.

NGC 6752 in the southern constellation Pavo is one of the best globulars in the sky, although at declination-60 degrees northern observers will need to save it for their next trip to the southern hemisphere. Comparable to M13 in overall appearance, this cluster has "arms" of stars and curved lanes that are most easily visible through an eyepiece than they are on film.

NGC 6752 shines at magnitude 5.4 and is the third largest globular cluster in the sky, exceeded only by its southern neighbors Omega Centauri and 47 Tucanae. The first known observation of NGC 6752 was made in 1828 by J. Dunlop, when he catalogued it as #295 in a list of southern nebulous objects. NGC 6752 is bright because it's so close to us: it lies only 13,000 light-years away. At Shapley-Sawyer class VI, NGC 6752 is an intermediate globular in terms of concentration.

A very loose, class XI globular, Sagittarius' M55 (NGC 6809) is resolvable in small telescopes and provides a very satisfying view. M55 measures 19.0' across and glows at magnitude 7.0, making it an excellent sight in binoculars as well as telescopes.

M71 (NGC 6838) in Sagitta is one of the strangest globular clusters in the sky. Since it has an unusual, almost triangular shape and because it is remarkably unconcentrated, for many years astronomers have argued about whether M71 is a rich open cluster or an unusually loose globular cluster. While looking for Comet de Cheseaux of 1746, Miraldi came across this cluster. It measures 7.2' across and glows at magnitude 8.3. The large number of red giant stars in M71 indicate that it is a globular, and indeed during recent years astronomers have come to agree that indeed it is a loose globular cluster. Its shape also is curious; it looks like a globular, but it has a large row of stars that is unique among globulars. M71 is the highlight of Sagitta, easy to find and interesting to study.

The most concentrated of all of Messier's globulars, M75 (NGC 6864) in Sagittarius is the only Messier cluster with a Shapley-Sawyer class of I. It spans 6.0' and shines at magnitude 8.6. One of the most distant of the Sagittarius clusters, M75 lies 60,000 light-years away. Small telescopes show this cluster as a round, bright ball of light without resolution.

M15 (NGC 7078) in Pegasus is the cluster of choice for the northern hemisphere autumn sky. Just 4 degrees west and a little north of the bright star Epsilon Pegasi, this cluster is easy to find. Even thought it is a fairly concentrated (class IV), M15 is resolvable even with a 6-inch telescope. M15 has a magnitude of 6.4 and measures 12.3' across; like M13, it shows some faint streamers of stars extending far out from the nucleus.

One of finest clusters in the northern fall sky, M2 (NGC 7089) in Aquarius is easily visible as an out-of-focus starlike object through binoculars. A good observer can begin to resolve this cluster with a 6-inch scope on nights of exceptional seeing. M2 is a highly concentrated type II cluster, shines with the light of a magnitude 6.5 star, and lies at the relatively great distance of 37,000 light-years.

You can find M2 by moving west of Alpha Aquarii until you reach a position just north of Beta Aquarii; M2 forms a triangle with these two stars. When you see it, you will get a thrill that discoverers Miraldi and Messier, who both found M2 in 1746, shared with telescopes smaller than yours.

Messier found M2 while searching for comets. In 1975, however, two observers found a comet while searching for M2. Californian Doug Berger came across a fuzzy object that was not resolvable, and a few days later Dennis Milon of Massachusetts also found a fuzzy patch in the region of M2. They had shared in the discovery of Comet Kobayashi-Berger-Milon, one of that year's brightest comets.

"Seen with difficulty in an ordinary telescope of 3 1/2 feet." This is part of Charles Messier's discovery description of M30 (NGC 7099) in Capricornus, penned in 1764. You can find M30 easily just west of 41 Capricorni, usually in the same low power field. M30's magnitude is 7.5, and it is 27,000 light-years distant. Its classification of type V indicates that it is about average in concentration, although some photographs indicate that it has a greater concentration than Shapley and Sawyer gave it.

ADVANCED OBSERVING TECHNIQUES

The following selection presents, in order of increasing right ascension, some of the more esoteric globular clusters. Of the 150 or so known globulars, a list of the finest difficult globular clusters must be somewhat arbitrary. However, after you have seen some of these clusters, I suggest you consult the catalogue section of this chapter for more challenging globes of stars visible in your small telescope.

I have not included merely faint globular clusters in this section. Some clusters in this section are relatively bright. But the bright objects presented here tend to be ignored by beginning observers, and therefore merit some special attention as you become a more experienced observer of globular clusters.

In deciding which clusters you should observe, consider a combination of the two factors of magnitude and angular diameter. A large, faint cluster of large diameter is more difficult to spot than a small, faint cluster because the surface brightness, or magnitude per unit area, is lower for the larger cluster (its light is more spread out).

Also remember that the diameters included are measurements of the total size including outlying cluster members. You will see the disk size of these clusters as somewhat smaller than the figures indicate. They should be used relatively, rather then absolutely.

A magnificent low surface brightness globular is NGC 288, located in the constellation Sculptor near the bright galaxy NGC 253. Measuring 13.8' across and glowing at magnitude 8.1, NGC 288 is visible only as a faint haze in large binoculars. Small telescopes show it as a very loose (class X) cluster recognizable as a large, low surface brightness patch of nebulosity. A good 6-inch telescope on a dark night reveals a few faint specks of light scattered across the cluster's surface. On nights of poor seeing or scattered moonlight, however, NGC 288 is difficult to find because of its low surface brightness.

One of the most unusual objects in the constellation Fornax is NGC 1049. This globular spans a mere 0.4' and dimly glows at magnitude 12.9, making it a very difficult target for small scopes. NGC 1049 is faint and small because it doesn't belong to our Galaxy, but is a globular cluster orbiting a galaxy called the Fornax System, or the Fornax Dwarf Galaxy. The Fornax dwarf is a small collection of stars and dust about 500,000 light-years away; only three times as distant as our own satellite galaxies, the Magellanic Clouds. Because the Fornax galaxy contains so few stars, it is impossible to see with small telescopes. Therefore, NGC 1049 presents a challenge to small telescope users who may be able to see a galaxy's globular cluster, but not the galaxy itself!

Telescopically, NGC 1049 will appear as a faint "star." Under excellent seeing conditions when the sky is very dark, use high power on the object you suspect is NGC 1049. You may see that the little globular has a tiny, fuzzy disk, unlike the point-like stars. If you do find this object with a small telescope, you may congratulate yourself on having achieved a very challenging goal.

If you observe from a spot where you can see the southern sky, try looking for NGC 1261 in Horologium. This globular has a magnitude of 8.4 and a diameter of 6.9', making it readily visible in binoculars as a small, fuzzy spot of nebulosity. NGC 1261 is extremely condensed (class II), and appears as a bright core surrounded by a large hazy envelope of nebulosity.

Another southern globular, NGC 1851 in Columba, is visible at the time of year when globular clusters are hard to find--winter in the northern hemisphere and summer in the southern. NGC 1851 is fairly bright at magntude 7.3, and like NGC 1261 is a concentrated, Class II cluster. NGC 1851 is far larger, however, measuring 11' across, so it is any easy mark for small telescopes placed far enough south so the cluster is more than a few degrees above the horizon.

Harlow Shapley's nickname for globular cluster NGC 2419 was "the intergalactic tramp," since it lies far enough away to escape from the gravitational pull of the Galaxy. Or so Shapley thought. We now know that although NGC 2419 lies at the relatively great distance of 300,000 light-years, the gravitational attraction of the Galaxy will keep it from wandering off through intergalactic space. Lying some 7° north of the bright star Castor, NGC 2419 glows at magnitude 10.4 and measures 4.1' across. It is a class II globular, and is generally considered as one of the most compact and concentrated bright globulars. Through the telescope, NGC 2419 appears as a fuzzy knot of misty gray light; small telescopes fail to show individual stars in this cluster because of its great distance.

M68 (NGC 4590) is an interesting cluster in Hydra. With a magnitude of 8.2 and diameter of 12; M68 is one of the finest globulars in the spring sky. Of all the globular clusters belonging to the Messier catalogue, M68 is one of the loosest (class X), with barely a hint of concentration in its center. Only M55 in Sagittarius is looser (class XI), and M107 in Ophiuchus and M56 in Lyra rate the same as M68.

Coma Berenices holds two unusual globulars separated on the sky by less than 1°. M53 (NGC 5024) is easy to find, as it is located 1° northeast of the bright star Alpha Comae Berenices. With a magnitude of 7.7 and diameter of 12.6', M53 appears as a large, hazy disk of light in small telescopes. M53 is designated a class V cluster, although visually it appears to have a greater than average concentration of stars. With a 6-inch scope under a dark, moonless sky, M53 shows some individual members and is a truly remarkable sight.

If you have a 4-inch or 6-inch scope, take it outside and observe M53 carefully using a low-power eyepiece. Do you see any other nebulous objects in the field of view or just outside the field? If you see a faint, hazy patch of unresolved light, you've spotted the globular cluster NGC 5053. This ball of stars has a magnitude of 9.8 and is some 10.5' across, but is extremely loose (class XI). Therefore, it has an extremely low surface brightness and is difficult to spot if haze or scattered light interferes with seeing and transparency. On a dark night, find this cluster after observing M53 and use medium to high powers on it. You may see a subtle speckled or mottled appearance, indicating near resolution of the cluster's brightest individual members.

Hydra contains a relatively distant cluster in NGC 5694. This object shines at magnitude 10.2 and measures only 3.6' across, giving it a relatively high surface brightness. NGC 5694 is a class VII globular, so although it is small the group's outer stars are resolved with relative ease using a 6-inch scope. Oddly, although William Herschel discovered this globular in May 1784, its real identity was not understood until Clyde Tombaugh came across it in June 1932. During his search for trans-Neptunian planets, Tombaugh made a photographic plate with the 13-inch astrographic camera at Lowell Observatory, and noticed that NGC 5694 "looked like a ninth-magnitude star, except that the border of the image looked slightly ragged." So Tombaugh "called Dr. [Carl O.] Lampland's attention to it and said, 'I think we have a new globular star cluster.'" Just twenty-eight months after his discovery of Pluto, verifying the nature of NGC 5694, a distant globular cluster, was the second major event in Tombaugh's career.

NGC 6144 is a small globular cluster in Scorpius that is easy to find but a challenging object to study. This little cluster lies less than 1° northwest of the brilliant orange star Antares, and very close to the brighter globular M4. NGC 6144 is highly concentrated (class XI), has a magnitude of 9.1, and measures 9.3' across (although it appears much smaller visually). This globular appears as a small nebulosity 2' or 3' across showing no resolution, and is difficult to see at all with Antares in the same telescopic field. Once you've located this object, switch to slightly higher powers and move the bright star outside the field of view.

M107 (NGC 6171) in Ophiuchus is a very compressed (class X) globular cluster with a magnitude of 8.1. This cluster spans 10.0' and is readily visible in binoculars as a fuzzy "star" with a slightly mottled appearance. Small telescopes show this object as a fairly large circular patch of gray light with a hint of resolution at high powers. With a 6-inch scope on a night of good seeing, the outer edge of M107 is resolved into pinpoint specks of light.

Despite its diameter of only 7.1 minutes of arc, the globular M69 (NGC 6639) in Sagittarius is bright at magnitude 7.7. M69 has an average concentration (class V) and is visible in small telescopes as a round nebulosity without detail. If you use a 4-inch or larger telescope, try to resolve M69 on nights when the seeing is especially good. A low-power view of M69 should reveal NGC 6652, just 1° away. This globular cluster shines at magnitude 9 and measures a mere 3.5' across. Although it doesn't show individual stars in small scopes, this cluster and M69 lie in a rich star field that offers a pretty view during summer nights under the stars.

Moving 2° west of the M69-NGC 6652 pair will bring you to the globular cluster M70 (NGC 6681). M70 has the same concentration class as M69, covers almost the same amount of sky, and is very slightly fainter at magnitude 8.1. As a test of observing acuity, can you detect subtle differences between M69 and M70 using different magnifications with your telescope?

Lyra's offering in the globular cluster category is M56 (NGC 6779). This group of stars glows softly at magnitude 8.3 and measures 7.1' across. It is a class X object, but is quite difficult to resolve into component stars in small scopes. However, an exceptionally transparent night with good seeing may allow you to resolve stars at the edge of the cluster, which lies 30,000 light-years away.

M72 (NGC 6981) in Aquarius is one of the best challenging globular clusters in the fall sky. To find M72, aim your telescope 4° south and a little west of the bright star Epsilon Aquarii. Discovered in 1780 by Pierre Mechain and rediscovered by Charles Messier, M72 is a loose globular (class IX) with a magnitude of 9.4 and diameter of 5.9'.

A relatively challenging globular cluster, NGC 7006 in the diminutive constellation Delphinus is one of the more distant globulars observable in small telescopes. Lying some 115,000 light-years away, NGC 7006 shines with the light of a magnitude 10.6 star and covers only 2.8' of sky. It is also one of the most concentrated globulars known (class I), and is consequently impossible to resolve in a small

telescope.   However, observing such a distant globular at all brings
the reward of knowing that you've peeked halfway across the Galaxy
with the aid of your small telescope.

The following is a catalog of 85 globular clusters visible in small
telescopes. They are listed in right ascension order and grouped by
constellations for easy observing. You may be able to detect a small
number of other globulars with small telescopes, but this list
represents the brightest and best such objects.

Explanation of data: The coordinates provided are for epoch 1950.0.
Mag.=visual magnitude of the cluster, unless followed by a "p," which
denotes a photographic magnitude. Size=the cluster's diameter in minutes
of arc. The final column--resolvability class--lists the globular's
degree of concentration, based on a 1 through 12 scale, where 1 means
extremely condensed and 12 means very loose.

CATALOG NUMBER	R.A.(1950) Dec. h m ° '	Mag.	Size '	Class
AQUARIUS				
NGC 6981	20 50.7 -12 44	9.8	2.0	9
	M72. Visible in a 2.4-inch scope as a round hazy smudge.			
NGC 7089	21 30.9 -01 03	6.3	8.2	2
	M2. Small scopes show a bright core and unresolved mottled halo.			
NGC 7492	23 05.7 -15 54	10.8p	3.3	12
AQUILA				
NGC 6760	19 08.6 +00 57	10.7	1.9	11
ARA				
NGC 6352	17 21.6 -48 26	7.9p	2.5	11
NGC 6397	17 36.8 -53 39	4.7p	19.0	9
	Large and bright; easy in a 2.4-inch.			
BOOTES				
NGC 5466	14 03.2 +28 46	8.5	5.0	12
	Large and very dim; low power a must.			
CANES VENATICI				
NGC 5272	13 39.9 +28 38	6.4	9.8	6
	M3. With a 2.4-inch, shows a dense central core surrounded by a bright halo. High power shows many dim stars and a "clumpy" effect in the halo. 6-inch scopes resolve the halo and some of the core.			
CAPRICORNUS				
NGC 7099	21 37.5 -23 25	8.4	5.7	5
	M30. Bright nucleus and unresolved halo in 2-inch.			

CATALOG NUMBER	R.A.(1950)Dec. h m ° '	Mag.	Size '	Class

| NGC 5139 | 13 23.8   -47 03 | 3.7 | 23.0 | 8 |

Omega [ω] Centauri. Naked eye object. A 2.4-inch shows a bright central core and extensive halo of mottled texture, unresolved due to its southerly declination. 6-inchers resolve it to the core.

| NGC 1851 | 05 12.4   -40 05 | 8.1 | 5.3 | 2 |

| NGC 4147 | 12 07.6   +18 49 | 9.4 | 1.7 | 9 |

Very small--almost stellar in 2.4-inch. Takes power well: 6-inch shows a hazy unresolved halo.

| NGC 6541 | 18 04.4   -43 44 | 5.8p | 6.3 | 3 |

Large and bright, but far south.

| NGC 6934 | 20 31.7   +07 14 | 9.2 | 1.5 | 8 |
| NGC 7006 | 20 59.1   +16 00 | 10.3 | 1.1 | 1 |

Hardly distinguishable from a star at low power.

| NGC 6205 | 16 39.9   +36 33 | 5.7 | 10.0 | 5 |

M13, the Hercules Cluster. Extremely large, round, and bright--the halo appears 2 core diameters across with a 2.4-inch, and streamers of faint stars project outward. At medium powers the halo breaks up into a multitude of tiny stars, the huge core partially resolved. The best globular in the northern sky!

| NGC 6229 | 16 45.6   +47 37 | 8.7 | 1.2 | 7 |
| NGC 6341 | 17 15.6   +43 12 | 6.1 | 8.3 | 4 |

M92. Often overlooked because of M13, this cluster reveals a cometary appearance with bright core and fuzzy halo in a 2.4-inch. Some stars visible at medium powers.

| NGC 4590 | 12 36.8   -26 29 | 8.2 | 2.9 | 10 |

M68. Bright and round in a 2.4-inch.

CATALOG NUMBER	R.A.(1950) Dec. h m ° '	Mag.	Size '	Class

HYDRA (Continued)

| NGC 5694 | 14 36.7 -26 19 | 10.9p | 2.2 | 7 |

LEPUS

| NGC 1904 | 05 22.2 -24 34 | 8.4 | 3.2 | 10 |

M79. With 2.4-inch at medium power, shows a stellar core and irregularly shaped halo. Many dim field stars.

LIBRA

| NGC 5897 | 15 14.5 -20 50 | 10.9 | 7.3 | 11 |

Large, bright fuzzy patch, unresolved with 2.4-inch.

LUPUS

NGC 5824	15 00.9 -32 53	10.1	1.0	1
NGC 5927	15 24.4 -50 29	8.8p	3.0	8
NGC 5986	15 42.8 -37 37	8.7	3.7	7

LYNX

| NGC 2419 | 07 34.8 +39 00 | 11.5 | 1.7 | 7 |

Very small and dim; easily overlooked!

LYRA

| NGC 6779 | 19 14.6 +30 05 | 8.2 | 1.8 | 10 |

M56. 2.4-inch scope shows a cometary appearance; lies in a rich starfield.

NORMA

| NGC 5946 | 15 31.8 -50 30 | 10.6p | 1.3 | 9 |

OPHIUCHUS

| NGC 6171 | 16 29.7 -12 57 | 9.2 | 2.2 | 10 |

M107. 2.4-inch shows a small core and large halo --unresolved at medium power.

| NGC 6218 | 16 44.6 -01 52 | 6.6 | 9.3 | 9 |

M12. Small scopes reveal a large halo broken up into faint stars.

| NGC 6235 | 16 50.4 -22 05 | 10.4 | 1.9 | 10 |
| NGC 6254 | 16 54.5 -04 02 | 6.7 | 8.2 | 12 |

M10. A double of M12, its halo is peppered with tiny stars and its core unresolved. Appears larger than M14.

CATALOG NUMBER	R.A.(1950)Dec. h m ° '		Mag.	Size '	Class

| NGC 6266 | 16 58.1 | -30 03 | 6.6 | 4.3 | 4 |

M62. Very bright in a 2.4-inch; faint stars suspected in the halo.

| NGC 6273 | 16 59.5 | -26 11 | 6.6 | 4.3 | 8 |

M19. Much like M62; small and bright, but unresolved in a 2.4-inch.

NGC 6284	17 01.5	-24 41	9.7	1.5	9
NGC 6287	17 02.1	-22 38	9.9	1.7	7
NGC 6293	17 07.1	-26 30	8.4	1.9	4

Just southeast of M19.

NGC 6304	17 11.4	-29 24	9.8	1.6	6
NGC 6316	17 13.4	-28 05	9.9p	1.1	3
NGC 6325	17 15.0	-23 42	11.9p	0.7	4
NGC 6333	17 16.2	-18 28	7.3p	2.4	8

M9. Small scopes show a small bright unresolved core. Globular NGC 6356 in same low power field.

NGC 6342	17 18.2	-19 32	10.0	0.5	4
NGC 6355	17 20.1	-26 19	9.6p	1.0	-
NGC 6356	17 20.7	-17 46	8.7	1.7	2

2.4-inch scope shows an unresolved fuzzball.

| NGC 6366 | 17 25.1 | -05 02 | 12.1p | 4.0 | 11 |
| NGC 6402 | 17 35.0 | -03 13 | 7.7 | 3.0 | 8 |

Small, round and bright.

| NGC 6426 | 17 42.4 | +03 12 | 12.2p | 1.3 | 9 |
| NGC 6517 | 17 59.1 | -08 57 | 12.1 | 0.4 | 4 |

| NGC 7078 | 21 27.6 | +11 57 | 6.0 | 7.4 | 4 |

M15. Bright but unresolved in a 2.4-inch; several bright stars in field.

| NGC 2298 | 06 47.2 | -35 57 | 10.5 | 1.8 | 6 |

Nearly "attached" to a dim star. Be careful!

| NGC 6838 | 19 51.5 | +18 39 | 8.3 | 6.1 | - |

M71. Small scopes show a halo with many dim stars and an irregular shape. Open cluster H20 in the same field.

CATALOG NUMBER	R.A.(1950) Dec. h m ° '	Mag.	Size '	Class
	SAGITTARIUS			
NGC 6440	17 45.9 -20 21	10.4	0.7	5
NGC 6522	18 00.4 -30 02	11.0p	0.7	6
NGC 6528	18 01.6 -30 04	11.8p	0.5	5
NGC 6544	18 04.3 -25 01	11.0	1.0	9

Small but fairly bright; near M8, the Lagoon Nebula. Globular NGC 6553 lies nearby.

NGC 6553	18 06.3 -25 56	10.0p	1.7	11
NGC 6569	18 10.4 -31 50	10.2p	1.4	8
NGC 6624	18 20.5 -30 23	8.6p	2.0	6
NGC 6626	18 21.5 -24 54	7.3	4.7	4

M28. Fairly large and bright; small scopes show a halo beginning to resolve into stars.

NGC 6638	18 27.9 -25 32	9.8	1.4	6
NGC 6637	18 28.1 -32 23	8.9	2.8	5

M69. At low power, small and bright. At high power, appears fuzzy and unresolved. Globular NGC 6652 in same low power field.

NGC 6652	18 32.5 -33 02	8.7p	1.7	6
NGC 6656	18 33.3 -23 58	5.9	17.3	7

M22. Small scopes show an extremely large nucleus and mottled outer halo showing streamers of stars protruding outward. At high powers it appears irregular and shows hundreds of tiny stars. One of the finest globulars.

NGC 6681	18 40.0 -32 21	9.6	2.5	5

M70. Unresolvable in small scopes.

NGC 6715	18 52.0 -30 32	7.1p	2.1	3

M54. Small and bright at low power; high power shows a fuzzy halo.

NGC 6723	18 56.2 -36 42	6.0p	5.8	7
NGC 6809	19 36.9 -31 03	4.4p	10.0	11

M55. 2.4-inch scope shows a large halo with many dim stars--worth spending time on.

NGC 6864	20 03.2 -22 04	8.0	1.9	1

M75. 2.4-inch shows a small unresolved halo.

	SCORPIUS			
NGC 6093	16 14.1 -22 52	7.7	3.3	2

M80. Unresolvable but very bright.

CATALOG NUMBER	R.A.(1950) Dec. h m ° '	Mag.	Size '	Class

| NGC 6121 | 16 20.6 -26 24 | 6.4 | 14.0 | 9 |

M4. Small telescopes reveal a large loose core and extensive halo; at high power the halo breaks up into many bright and faint stars. A bar of bright unresolved stars cuts across the nucleus. A grand globular!

| NGC 6139 | 16 24.3 -38 44 | 9.8p | 1.3 | 2 |
| NGC 6144 | 16 24.2 -25 56 | 10.3p | 3.3 | 11 |

Lies close to bright star Antares. Be careful to avoid the star's powerful glare.

| NGC 6388 | 17 32.6 -44 43 | 7.1p | 3.4 | 3 |
| NGC 6441 | 17 46.8 -37 02 | 8.4p | 2.3 | 3 |

Only 5' away from the bright reddish star G Scorpii.

| NGC 6453 | 17 48.0 -34 37 | 11.2p | 0.7 | 4 |

Lies on the northwestern edge of open cluster M7. A smudge of haze in a 2.4-inch; 6-inch shows little more.

| NGC 6496 | 17 55.5 -44 15 | 9.7p | 2.2 | 12 |

_____SCULPTOR_____

| NGC 288 | 10 50.2 -26 52 | 7.2p | 10.0 | 10 |

A large hazy patch of loosely grouped stars.

_____SCUTUM_____

| NGC 6712 | 18 50.3 -08 47 | 8.9 | 2.1 | 9 |

_____SERPENS_____

| NGC 5904 | 15 16.0 +02 16 | 6.2 | 12.7 | 5 |

M5. In a 2.4-inch, a large collection of pinpoint stars surrounding an intensely bright core. At high powers irregular streamers of resolved stars twist out from the nucleus. A tremendous sight!

| NGC 6535 | 18 01.3 -00 18 | 11.9p | 1.3 | 5 |

_____VELA_____

| NGC 3201 | 10 15.5 -46 09 | 7.4p | 7.7 | 10 |

Visible in binoculars--2.4-inch shows an unresolved mottled halo.

_____VIRGO_____

| NGC 5634 | 14 27.0 -05 45 | 10.4 | 1.3 | 4 |

Fig. 6-1. **The Dumbbell Nebula**

Planetary
Nebulae

F. Michael Witkoski

In 1957 my fourth grade teacher mentioned something called the "Ring Nebula." I don't recall her showing a picture of it, nor do I remember what she said it was. At the time my knowledge of astronomy was limited to the very basics about the sun and its family. Beyond the solar system lay the great abyss, illuminated by scattered beacons--the stars--and populated by multitudes of objects about which I knew practically nothing. In later years I learned that the Ring Nebula lies in the small constellation Lyra and is the most famous of a class of deep-sky objects known as planetary nebulae. But to this fourth grader the term "planetary nebula" was virtually meaningless.

Certainly I had much to learn. Sure, some individuals knew about the sky, knew about the planets, the stars, the galaxies. But we've learned a great deal during the past 25 years. Today, more are probably familiar with the basics than during that first year of the space age. We've still barely scratched the surface: mysteries abound, and solving one often only creates others. However, the situation isn't hopeless, as we are curious beings. And like the stars above, our thirst for answers seems limitless.

As we traverse our Milky Way galaxy via our telescopes and imaginations, we'll encounter an object like the Ring Nebula about every few hundred light years--not far on a deep-sky scale. From afar a planetary nebula resembles an out-of-focus disk, but zooming in, we discover a very tenuous mass of mostly hydrogen gas, gently receding from an extremely hot central star.

Like people, celestial objects are diverse, and the individuality of planetary nebulae has kept astronomers busy sorting out their idiosyncrasies over the past century. In this chapter, with the aid of our small telescopes, we'll befriend these sometimes mysterious, sometimes beckoning, yet always fascinating citizens of the sky.

F. Michael Witkoski
Camp Hill, Pennsylvania

About the Author: F. Michael Witkoski is an avid amateur astronomer, writer, lecturer, and observer who is active in the National Deep Sky Observer's Society, the Astronomical Society of Harrisburg, and the Astronomical League. He has written articles for Astronomy and Deep Sky magazines and is an experienced and talented observer of planetary nebulae and other deep-sky objects.

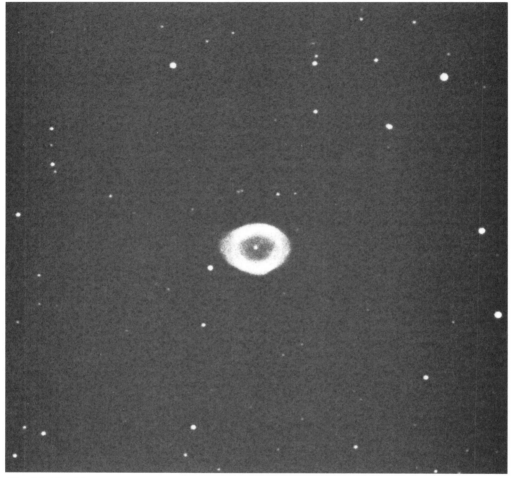

Fig. 6-2. **The Ring Nebula**

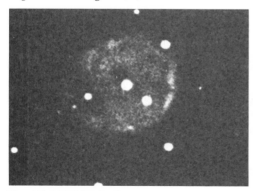

Fig. 6-3. **NGC 246 in Cetus**

Fig. 6-4. **NGC 6369 in Ophiuchus**

HISTORICAL BACKGROUND

Although the telescope was invented in 1608 and quickly revolutionized astronomy by revealing vistas hitherto unimagined by mankind, the planetary nebulae remained undiscovered for more than a century and a half thereafter.   Not until the summer of 1764, when Charles Messier stumbled upon an object in the constellation Vulpecula (we now know this nebula as M27, the Dumbbell Nebula), did their story begin.

By contrast, some members of other classes of deep-sky objects, being well within naked-eye magnitude range, had been known about centuries earlier.   The Persian Al Sufi in the 10th century A.D. mentions M31, the Great Galaxy in Andromeda.   Hipparchus (2nd century B.C.) and Ptolemy (2nd century A.D.) both knew of the Double Cluster in Perseus.   M42, the Great Orion Nebula, and M8, the Lagoon Nebula, were both known about by ancient and perhaps prehistoric astronomers. However, the brightest planetary nebula, the Helical Nebula in Aquarius (NGC 7293), although very near to the naked-eye limit in terms of total luminosity, is spread over half the diameter of the full moon (and is consequently impossible to detect unaided).

In 1779 Antoine Darquier discovered the Ring Nebula in Lyra (M57), a relatively close neighbor to the Dumbbell, and with the proliferation of telescopes and the improvement of observing techniques, many others soon turned up.   From then on, the discovery of planetary nebulae became almost commonplace.

Messier included four entries now known to be planetaries in his famous catalogue of stationary nebulous objects, which was compiled to aid comet hunters (see Appendix 2). They are the Dumbbell Nebula (M27), the Ring Nebula (M57), the Owl Nebula (M97), and the Little Dumbbell Nebula (M76).   Of the four, the Dumbbell is the single planetary that Messier himself discovered.   During the latter part of the 18th century, several individuals were active observers (including Messier), and they succeeded in locating many objects. The most productive was William Herschel. He was born in Germany in 1738, and as a young man became a proficient musician.   By middle age, after having moved to England, he became a world-famous astronomer and today is recognized as the greatest sky observer who ever lived.   Herschel's most famous accomplishment was the discovery of the planet Uranus.   Barely visible to the keen naked eye, this body, a small blue-green disk in the telescope, was the first object of its kind found in historic times.

During his long career Herschel painstakingly surveyed the heavens, cataloguing 703 double stars and 2510 extended deep-sky objects.   In his time no one knew about the fundamental nature of galaxies, star clusters, and nebulae: the task of the day was discovery, and Herschel was a prolific discoverer. He separated his deep-sky finds into eight catagories according to their telescopic appearance, thereby paving the way for the New General Catalogue (NGC) of 1888. The revised edition of this catalog is still a standard reference for astronomers, amateur and professional alike.

The objects in Herschel's Class IV curiously resembled the newly discovered Uranus. They did not move among the stars, so they were not planets; yet their blue-green tone and hazy appearance combined to suggest the name "planetary nebulae," even though they have no connection whatsoever with planets. In the years to follow, many of the Class IV objects were identified as distant galaxies. But what are known as hot, dying stars surrounded by gently expanding gaseous envelopes are still termed planetary nebulae.

Herschel's list of planetary nebulae contains 79 entries. In addition, he knew of the four Messier planetaries but excluded them, not wanting to intrude upon another man's work. Although 59 of the 79 have been reassigned, 13 objects he observed and included elsewhere are now known to be planetaries. Hence he observed an actual total of 37 true planetary nebulae, including Messier's four.

The many discoveries of Messier, Herschel, and their contemporaries spawned numerous interpretations, many of which were diametrically opposed. A key point of contention was the composition and structure of various nebulae--patches of light--inhabiting the night sky. Did they contain stars too distant to be resolved? Were they composed of some mysterious substance? Were they of different varieties? No one at the time seemed to know.

Eventually, astronomers determined that some nebulae--the so-called "white nebulae"--were composed of countless stars. These are the great galaxies. Others, the "blue nebulae" or "green nebulae" (now known to be planetaries), were ultimately shown to be gaseous masses. However, the telescope alone was unable to make this distinction. It needed the help of a newer instrument.

In the 1850's chemists Robert Bunsen and Gustav Kirchoff developed the spectroscope, an instrument which descended from simple prisms. Isaac Newton had employed a prism to separate sunlight into a rainbow like pattern, a spectrum. Using a similar prism, in 1802 William Wollaston noticed several dark lines crossing the sun's spectrum. His first thought was that he had discovered natural boundaries between colors, but this idea soon proved erroneous. By 1826 Joseph Fraunhofer mapped 324 of the lines, although not until the time of Bunsen and Kirchoff did the importance of this surface.

Working in Heidelberg, Germany, Bunsen and Kirchoff studied the spectral characteristics of various laboratory substances. Through their assiduous labors they determined that 1) a glowing solid or dense gas emits a continuum of colors from red to violet, known as a continuous spectrum; 2) a hot diffuse gas emits a series of bright lines of specific color, each corresponding to a particular wavelength, known as an emission spectrum; and 3) the same diffuse gas, when placed in front of a hotter glowing solid (or dense gas), emits an absorption spectrum, a continuum crossed by dark lines which directly correspond to those of the brightline spectrum. Furthermore, they found that all substances display unique spectral lines and that all samples of a particular substance, when subjected to identical conditions, display the characteristic spectrum of the substance.

The findings of Bunsen and Kirchoff explained the dark lines crossing the sun's spectrum. They correspond to chemical elements in its atmosphere (a hot diffuse gas) which absorb wavelengths of light from the continuum spectrum radiating from its surface (a dense glowing gas). Extending spectral observations to all types of celestial objects, astronomers embarked on a new era in their field: one comparable in significance to the invention of the telescope.

In 1864, one hundred years after the discovery of the first planetary nebula, British amateur astronomer William Huggins aimed a spectroscope at NGC 6543, a planetary nebula in Draco. He observed what seemed to be a bright line spectrum, and after briefly checking his instrument for possible overlooked adjustments, he realized that this nebulae was gaseous and not composed of the masses of innumerable stars some astronomers envisioned. At the snap of a finger, one of the great debates of 19th-century astronomy had ended.

Ironically, this discovery led to another mystery. The spectra of planetary nebulae displayed not only identifiable lines, but also several others, the most prominent of which were a pair in the green region which absolutely defied interpretation. Astronomers suspected a new chemical element and even named it "nebulium." In later decades it became quite difficult to fit nebulium into the chemical scheme of things, and not until 1926 did the answer finally arrive. That year Ira S. Bowen determined that the unknown green lines were due to doubly ionized oxygen radiating in a manner possible only in the near-vacuum ambience found to characterize planetary nebulae.

Huggins taught us that a planetary nebula is a mass of gas. Subsequent spectroscopic studies showed that the gas is slowly expanding away from a central star, which is usually far dimmer to the eye than the surrounding nebulosity. In fact, several central stars are all but invisible through even respectably large telescopes. At first these stars were thought to be intrinsically faint, but by the early decades of the 20th century, Edwin Hubble found that this apparent underluminosity is due only to the human eye's restricted range of sensitivity. At high-energy, ultraviolet wavelengths (which are invisible to the eye), the central stars shine ferociously. They are, indeed, among the hottest stars known.

The first central star observed was that belonging to NGC 2392 (the Eskimo Nebula), a bright, yet fairly compact nebula in Gemini. The discovery was made in 1787 by William Herschel. The central stars belonging to Messier's four planetaries are all difficult to view, and only a relatively small percentage of observers ever see them. Had more central stars been found early, the understanding of planetary nebulae might have traced an alternate path.

While controversies stirred, new planetaries continued to be discovered. John Herschel, following in his father's footsteps, visually located several in the southern sky. Visually discovering a nebula with a telescope is limited to objects whose disks are easily distinguishable from pointlike stars, but the development of instrumentation extended to objects much smaller. Two methods, used mainly in the 20th century, have been quite successful: 1) the use of filters which isolate characteristic nebular radiation, and 2) the use of objective prisms, whereby stars show darkline spectra while planetaries show brightline spectra.

In 1964, two hundred years after the discovery of the first planetary nebula, the Czechoslovakian astronomers L. Perek and L. Kohoutek listed 1,036 specimens in their Catalogue of Galactic Planetary Nebulae. As many as 50,000 to 60,000 could inhabit our galaxy, but the overwhelming majority are hidden by sheer distance and by masses of interstellar matter obscuring them.

Beyond the Milky Way several planetaries have been located. In M31, the Andromeda galaxy, at least 315 planetaries are known, and in the Large and Small Magellanic Clouds as well as in galaxies M32, NGC 205, NGC 185, and NGC 147 (four satellite galaxies to M31), discoveries and studies of planetary nebulae have been made. The Space Telescope, scheduled for launch in the mid-1980's, should extend our horizons further still.

Despite our abilities to uncover planetary nebulae in and beyond our galaxy, we have not yet been able to accurately determine the distance to any except those associated with objects of known distance. Nor have we been able to fully describe the events in the life of a star which lead to the planetary nebula stage.

Nevertheless, we have successfully unravelled many of the mechanisms by which planetaries shine, although the road has been full of obstacles. Before the nebulium controversy's denouement in 1926, many astronomers dogmatically espoused the idea that planetaries rotate. The earth, the moon, the other planets, the sun, the stars, all rotate, so why not the planetaries? This belief caused serious discrepancies between observation and hypothesis until its proponents finally conceded that planetaries simply do not rotate.

As long ago as 1911 astronomer Max Wolf recognized that planetary nebulae are fairly complex, in contradiction to the uniformity suggested by some of their early photos and many of their visual appearances. As you might expect, the nearer a nebula is to the illuminating star, the more its atoms are excited by radiation. Spectroscopic observations of various regions of a nebula yield varying results, all of which can be interpreted as responses to the star's radiation intensity. In the late 1930's Bengt Stromgren, a Danish astronomer, proposed that certain gaseous nebulae (some planetaries included) could be stratified into layers which extend outward from a central illuminating source, a star. The further away from the star, the less excited are the atoms in the layers. The boundaries between areas of differing excitation are generally very sharp and are at reasonably similar distances from the star in all directions. They are fittingly called "Stromgren spheres."

As instrumentation improved with the arrival of the space age, more sophisticated techniques developed for studying the heavens. Our planetary nebulae showed faces never dreamt of by Messier, the Herschels, or Huggins. In 1961 the National Radio Astronomical Observatory (NRAO) instrumentation helped to detect the first radio frequency radiation from a planetary nebula. This was followed by a program of observations conducted at the Very Large Array (VLA), a collection of 27 radio telescopes in New Mexico situated on an extensive network of railroad track.

The VLA program surveyed four planetaries at radio frequencies and found comparable visual and radio images indicating, as expected, that planetaries do not exhibit the exotic characteristics of supernova remnants, pulsars, quasars, or other high-energy emitters.

Does this mean that the study of planetary nebulae will cease in favor of more recently discovered classes of deep-sky objects? Not at all, for the planetary nebula stage represents a chapter in the life history of a significant percentage of all stars, without a thorough knowledge of which our picture of the universe as a whole would be sadly incomplete.

Fig. 6-5. **The Helical Nebula**

Fig. 6-6. **NGC 2022 in Orion**

Fig. 6-7. **NGC 6905 in Delphinus**

THE NATURE OF PLANETARY NEBULAE

Without being too facetious, astronomers characterize planetary nebulae as glowing, expanding near-vacuums surrounding intensely hot, dying stars. As puzzling as it may seem, such a tenuous state of matter can be quite complex and consequently worthy of our attention.

Obviously, stars associated with planetary nebulae suffer a catastrophe of sorts, but the exact mechanism by which it occurs is not yet known. The expansion velocities of many nebulae are easily measured by spectroscopy and average 30 kilometers per second. These are very modest compared with, for instance, the several thousand kilometers per second velocities of a supernova explosion, one of the most violent events known.

A reasonable estimate of the typical planetary nebula's diameter is a light year or so. This is based on our most accurate distance approximations and measurement of apparent angular size (coupled with the nebula's speed of expansion), and tells us that most large planetary nebulae are no more than a few tens of thousands of years old. With respect to the age of the galaxy--some 15 billion years--this is indeed a short interval.

In fact, of the various types of deep-sky objects, planetary nebulae are the most temporary. (Supernova remnants are also short-lived.) After 20,000 to 50,000 years of expansion, the gaseous material becomes indetectably thin: in effect only the expired, diminutive central star remains. Assuming that a star destined to become a planetary nebula lives for ten billion years, the planetary nebula stage represents only 0.0005 percent of its lifetime! (As an analogy, the planetary stage would consume 3 hours of a person's 72 year life span.) In contrast, most galaxies and globular clusters are at least 12 to 15 billion years old and show signs of remaining alive and well for at least as long again.

Many of the planetary nebulae in our sky must have arisen in recent centuries. If a nearby star underwent this change, as a respectable number of stars--perhaps 25 percent--is expected to do, it would almost instantly become a feature attraction in the celestial drama. Galaxies and globular clusters don't just "pop" into existence, but on a cosmic time scale planetary nebulae do.

It's difficult to calculate the mass of a nebula, but astronomers have determined that stars which evolve into planetaries are like our sun. Necessarily, then, the nebular mass must be less than the sun's. The prominent Soviet astrophysicist Iosef Shklovskii uses the figure of 0.2 solar mass as a standard in all of his analyses. Imagine the sun's outer 20 percent expanding at a rate of 30 kilometers per second. In a matter of minutes the increase in diameter would equal that of the earth, and in a little more than two months the expansion would equal the earth-sun distance. At this pace it is not difficult to understand how a planetary nebula becomes tenuous within a few thousand years and completely dissipates after a few tens of thousands of years.

The major constituent of a planetary nebula is hydrogen, followed by helium, which is about one-seventh as abundant. Other elements contribute portions barely exceeding trace levels. Ironically, the prominent blue-green appearance of most planetaries results from one of these virtual trace elements--oxygen. Also measurable in planetaries is nitrogen, neon, argon, sulfur, and chlorine.

The near-vacuum of a planetary nebula governs its radiative and spectral properties. Such a condition allows atoms to occupy certain otherwise restricted energy levels for several minutes, which is quite long on an atomic time scale. This results from the scarcity of free electrons which under earth-like conditions would collide with the atoms and remove them from these long-lived energy levels, dubbed "metastable." Because metastable levels do not persist under terrestrial conditions, their spectral lines are referred to as "forbidden." The greenish lines first observed by Huggins are now known to be the result from the return of doubly-ionized oxygen atoms from metastable levels to ground levels. The domination of a planetary's radiation by the green lines of oxygen is not a result of an abundance of oxygen, but rather the high probability of the metastable state to exist there. Ordinary transitions, "permitted" lines, of common elements such as hydrogen are much more likely to occur in the atmospheres of normal stars than in expanding planetary nebulae. In a planetary nebula, where the majority of the nebular material is so far away from the star, the radiation from it is not sufficient to excite an atom to an energy level from which it could radiate a permitted line. Forbidden lines, by contrast, require excitation to much less energetic levels. The physical conditions inside a planetary nebula are very suitable for them.

Let's look beyond the individual planetaries and consider their bulk and distribution. Of the more than one thousand known in our galaxy, most belong to what is known as the disk population, which consists of a (basically) formless concentration of stars around the galactic center. The disk does not include the spiral arms or other areas of highly luminous short-lived stars or diffuse nebulosity; rather, it contains stars similar to our sun.

In addition to the healthy sunlike stars, the disk is populated by numerous white dwarf stars--small dense stars whose thermonuclear reactions have ceased, causing their outer layers to collapse gravitationally. After the planetary stage, the star is almost certain to become a white dwarf, according to most hypotheses.

The on-going generation of planetary nebulae in the galaxy contributes to the enrichment of the interstellar medium with chemical elements heavier than hydrogen and helium. Assuming a lifetime of 50,000 years for the typical specimen in the current population of planetaries, the rate of formation (which of course is accompanied by the gentle expulsion of material) is about one per year. This slow but steady contribution approximately equals that from supernovae, which are less common (occuring perhaps once per century), but which result in the sudden, nearly total destruction of constituent matter from stars much more massive than the planetary nebula stars. It is from the heavier elements such as carbon, nitrogen, and oxygen that lifebearing planets such as the earth form. No other source except the stars can account for the origin of these building blocks. From the standpoint of galactic as well as biological evolution, planetary nebulae are indeed very important.

Fig. 6-8. **The Saturn Nebula**

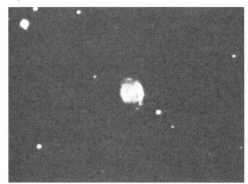

Fig. 6-9. **NGC 40 in Cepheus**

Fig. 6-10. **NGC 6891 in Delphinus**

BEGINNING TO OBSERVE

A planetary nebula, like any other type of celestial object, has special viewing requirements. Foremost, its age profoundly affects its telescopic appearance. A youthful specimen is practically indistinguishable from the pinpoint image of the star it once was, while an aged example is so far spread out it nearly blends in with the darkest background skies. By contrast, a planetary in its prime--such as the Ring Nebula--often shows an easily observed, well-defined disk, detectable through even the smallest of telescopes.

    Either very young or old planetaries are at best difficult to view through small instruments, so we'll confine this beginners' section to middle-aged samples. The apparent sizes of planetary nebulae are measured in seconds of arc (rather than minutes of arc) since they are such tiny objects.

    Because of its low surface brightness (when the light from a bright nebula is spread over a large area so that small individual parts are dim) with respect to the stars and planets, a planetary nebula shows best--as do all deep-sky objects--under dark, moonless skies. A star of a given magnitude, which is a point source, will penetrate moonglow or light pollution better than a planetary nebula of the same magnitude, whose light is spread around. For this reason, the darker the sky, the better the view. This does not mean you should completely avoid planetary nebulae under marginal conditions--it means only that you will notice and appreciate the benefits of observing under really good skies.

    On the other hand, a planetary nebula can absorb a slight amount of atmospheric turbulence, under which the image of Jupiter, Saturn, or the moon may seem to be "boiling." Close double stars fuse together under unsteady conditions through which a planetary nebula will survive. Generally, a planetary lacks delicate detail which can be "smeared" by atmospheric instability.

    The most conspicuous planetary nebulae are shown on elementary star charts and many fortunately have easy reference points from which to star-hop to them. A detailed atlas such as the Atlas of the Heavens or Sky Atlas 2000.0 shows dozens, although some are very challenging, if not impossible to view with small telescopes. Even advanced observers know the frustration of trying to separate a small planetary from a seemingly infinite background of stars.

    Your best starting point is probably the Dumbbell Nebula (M27) and the Ring Nebula (M57), both of which are best situated for viewing during the summer but are still prominent during autumn. Since the two are fairly close neighbors as we see them, you'll be able to make direct and easy comparisons of the two.

    The Dumbbell lies in the inconspicuous constellation Vulpecula, while the Ring lies in the small but brilliant group of stars dubbed Lyra. To locate the Dumbbell, you must first find the small constellation Sagitta, the Arrow. This is not the formidable task it seems to be, because this part of the sky is well marked by the bright stars Vega, Deneb, and Altair, the Summer Triangle. The three dominate their respective constellations--Lyra, Cygnus, and Aquila. If you locate Altair, you need only look five degrees north for Sagitta. Gamma, the easternmost of the five stars which comprise the Arrow, is our next reference point. After locating it, sweep 3-1/2 degrees north and the Dumbbell will show up in your eyepiece. A glance at your chart

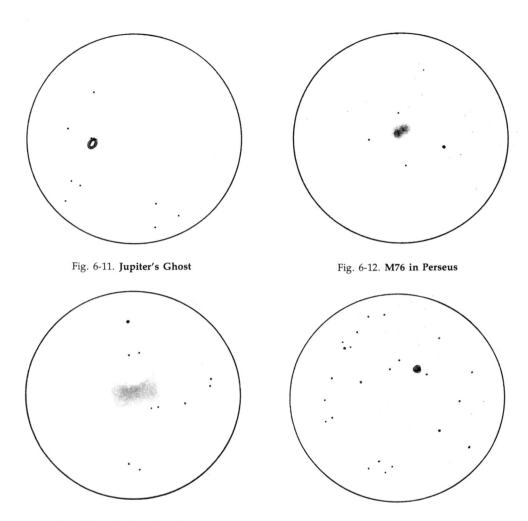

Fig. 6-11. **Jupiter's Ghost**

Fig. 6-12. **M76 in Perseus**

Fig. 6-13. **The Dumbbell Nebula**

Fig. 6-14. **The Blinking Planetary**

will also reveal that the Dumbbell lies about one third of the way on a straight line from Altair to Deneb, so you can scan the sky with your unaided eye to approximate the position of your target.

You should use relatively low magnification (read: wide field of view) when searching for objects, not only to minimize your chances of skimming by the target, but also because you'll be working at high contrast, letting you see faint objects easily. The Dumbbell is best viewed with medium powers--usually about 15x per inch of telescope aperture--and is also a grand sight in binoculars.

Moving on to Lyra, we can find two bright stars, Beta and Gamma, at the southern end of the main figure. The Ring Nebula lies practically on a straight line and a bit more than halfway from Gamma to Beta. As with the Dumbbell, using low powers for finding the object is important, since in this part of the sky the telescopic field is rich with stars. Because the straight line from Beta to Gamma is not exactly east-west or north-south, you'll have to take care not to aim in the wrong direction.

Before trying to examine details of the Ring or the Dumbbell, you should master finding them. You can do this by alternating between the two several times. Remember that in any endeavor, practice makes perfect.

Assuming you can easily locate both of these planetaries, what can you expect to see through your telescope? Certainly you'll notice that neither is pointlike, but beyond this there are important differences and similarities. The noticeable like traits are their symmetry and mutual lack of a central star (although the Dumbbell's central star is perhaps bright enough to be seen with a 6-inch telescope under superb transparency). Among the differences is the relative size of the two: the more diminutive Ring measuring 80x60 seconds of arc versus the Dumbbell's 240x480 seconds of arc. Because of its relative compactness compared to the Dumbbell, the Ring can withstand more magnification--up to several hundred times depending on seeing conditions and telescopic aperture. The visual magnitudes of the Ring and Dumbbell are 9.0 and 8.0, respectively. Despite its brighter magnitude, which places it in a tie for the second brightest of all planetaries, the Dumbbell is dimmer per unit area than its counterpart in Lyra. As the names imply, the Ring is donut or smoke-ring shaped, while the Dumbbell resembles a wide, hazy bow-tie. The two offer a fine study in contrast.

Also prominent among summer planetaries is NGC 6826, the Blinking Planetary, in Cygnus. About 25 arcseconds in diameter, this specimen is quite small compared to the Ring and Dumbbell, but its surface brightness is much higher and its central star is easily seen. It also has a curious trait: it seems to blink on and off as you rapidly shift your eye from the edge of the telescope's field of view to the nebula. This is employing averted vision--using the edge (rods) of your eye to view the faint light it is sensitive to, rather than looking directly at the nebula. When looking at the edge of the field you see the nebula (faint and picked up by averted vision), and when looking directly at the nebula you see only the central star--thus the nebula itself seems to blink. Delta Cygni, a westerly star in the Northern Cross (the major configuration in Cygnus), lies a convenient 5-1/2 degrees south of 6826 and serves as an excellent reference point. Also, the fine double star 16 Cygni lies less than a degree west.

After summer's short nights and hazy skies begin to pass, the autumn void--as it is disparagingly referred to--arrives. This area is roughly and unofficially defined as the part of the sky bounded by the summer Milky Way to the west, by Cassiopeia to the north, and by the

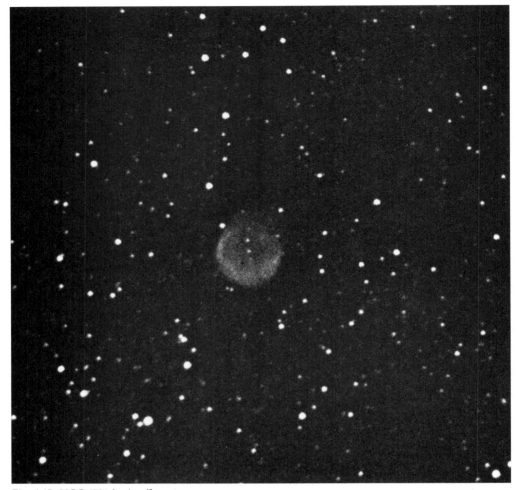

Fig. 6-15. **NGC 6781 in Aquila**

Fig. 6-16. **NGC 1535 in Eridanus**

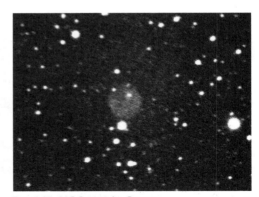

Fig. 6-17. **NGC 7048 in Cygnus**

Orion stream of bright stars to the east. Not only is the void short of bright stars and conspicuous constellations but also, according to some observers, deep-sky objects. Despite a few luminaries such as galaxies M31, M32, and M33, or open clusters M45 and the Hyades, this part of the sky is thought of as being the thinnest of all. And to add insult to injury, it presents itself during the lengthening, yet still mild and often crystal clear evenings of September and October.

A closer look, however, should dispel such claims. Despite the apparent emptiness, the autumn sky is rich if you are willing to seek out its offerings. Among the fine targets in this sector of the sky are two planetary nebulae in Aquarius, NGC 7009 (the Saturn Nebula) and NGC 7293 (the Helical Nebula). Here you'll see a study in contrast more pronounced than that of the Ring and Dumbbell: the Saturn a midget beside the sprawling Helical Nebula.

The Saturn Nebula is among the easiest to locate of all planetary nebulae, lying less than two degrees west of the naked-eye star Nu Aquarii. At magnitude 8.0 it is brighter, on a total basis, than the famous Ring Nebula, and since it covers a smaller area of sky, its surface brightness is also greater.

The name Saturn Nebula stems from the impression gleaned by the Earl of Rosse around 1850. A good photo shows its resemblance to Saturn, as the nebula has two symmetrical lobes-- ansae--at the ends of its main disk. Unfortunately, small telescopes are simply incapable of showing these: the Earl had a 72-inch telescope, the largest in the world at the time! However, the nebula itself is not difficult to identify through a small telescope, its unmistakable nature revealed by the appearance of an out-of-focus blue-green star.

Twenty-two degrees southeast of the Saturn Nebula is the Helical Nebula, the largest planetary nebula in the sky and, at an approximate distance of 1000 light years, probably the closest. Its dimensions are 900x720 arcseconds, about equal to half the diameter of the sun or the moon. The magnitude of this tremendous object is 6.5, ranking it first among the planetaries in total brightness. Paradoxically, it is one of the more difficult planetary nebulae to observe--even William Herschel missed it. The culprit, of course, is low luminosity per unit surface area-- low surface brightness.

A wide-field, low-power eyepiece is almost essential for a comfortable view of this object. It simply will not take much magnification. Through a telescope or binoculars it resembles a large, ghostly wreath. Photographs reveal a figure more complex than just a single ring or wreath. The appearance of a twisted structure suggests the name Helical Nebula.

Visually, you should be satisfied just to find and positively identify the Helical Nebula, as any haze or skyglow will render this sensitive giant impossible to see. No color in 7293 is visible with small scopes, in stark contrast to the Saturn Nebula. The human eye's sensitivity to color critically depends on brightness, which is why we don't easily see color under dark conditions, and the Helix is just not bright enough. Averted vision on 7293 helps tremendously. The 13th magnitude central star is difficult at best with small scopes, but under good conditions a 6-inch instrument may reveal it. To truly appreciate the subtlety of this object, you need only defocus a magnitude 6.5 star until it reaches half the moon's diameter. Then you'll know why observers can be forgiven for not easily detecting the Helix. To make things worse, bright reference points near 7293 are few and far between. From our reference point, this nebula is a cosmic loner.

Fig. 6-18. **NGC 3132 in Vela**

Fig. 6-19. **NGC 1514 in Taurus**

Fig. 6-20. **NGC 6818 in Sagittarius**

While the Saturn and Helix, both residing south of the celestial equator, stay in our skies for only a few months, more northerly specimens remain there for much longer periods. Four of these autumn planetaries which your small scope should reveal are M76 in Perseus, NGC 7662 in Andromeda, NGC 6543 in Draco, and NGC 40 in Cepheus.

Among Messier's planetary nebulae M76 is the second dimmest at magnitude 11.0. If you check the catalog of planetary nebulae at the end of this chapter, you'll notice that nearly two dozen other planetaries are brighter. Was Messier a careless, sporadic observer or a lazy recorder of objects? Not necessarily. Another look at our listing reveals that M76 is among the larger planetaries, as are the other three he knew of. Others brighter than M76 were probably visible to Messier, but such near-stellar visages did not attract his attention. Remember that he was a comet hunter and made it his business to record "imposters" so that he and others like him did not have to sound false alarms. To Messier, M76 seemed cometary.

To locate M76, called the Little Dumbbell Nebula, you need only find 4th magnitude Phi Persei and move the telescope about a degree northwest. This object, which has two distinct components, is far from a normal planetary. So distinct are the two parts that they have separate NGC designations: 650 and 651. The easternmost, 651, is included in Herschel's Class I (very bright nebulae), although it isn't at all bright. This inclusion is the extent of the overlapping between Messier's and Herschel's listings of what are now known to be planetary nebulae.

A telescopic trip to the neighboring constellation Andromeda should include a stop at NGC 7662, a small but bright member of its class. At magnitude 8.5 it is among the easiest of the planetary nebulae to detect, but don't expect to see any real detail, let alone the central star. Instead, look for what appears to be a blue-green out-of-focus star. Through small instruments 7662 resembles the Saturn Nebula, although observatory photographs show the two to be quite different. To locate NGC 7662, look one degree south-southwest of the naked-eye star 13 Andromedae.

Another planetary within reach of your small telescope is Draco's NGC 6543, an object that remains visible year-round from most of the northern hemisphere. At magnitude 8.6 and with a relatively small size, this specimen is one of the brightest per unit surface area and most color conspicuous of the planetary nebulae.

The final autumn planetary in our tour is NGC 40 in the circumpolar constellation Cepheus. It is larger and dimmer than 7662 but offers a fairly conspicuous central star. As with the Helical Nebula, NGC 40 has no fast and easy reference points, but it is well worth seeking out.

Winter's finest planetary, one easily observed through a small telescope, is NGC 2392 in Gemini, also known as the Eskimo Nebula. It shines at magnitude 8.0, and although a bit compact at 40 arcseconds, it is large enough that even low magnification will distinguish it as an extended object. You'll see this nebula's central star as easily as any other--in fact, it was the first such star discovered. Fairly high powers or minimal skyglow supress the nebular intensity, allowing still a better view of the star. Unlike most other planetaries, many of which are dimmer and/or more spread out, 2392 can withstand a slight amount of moonlight or submarginal skies.

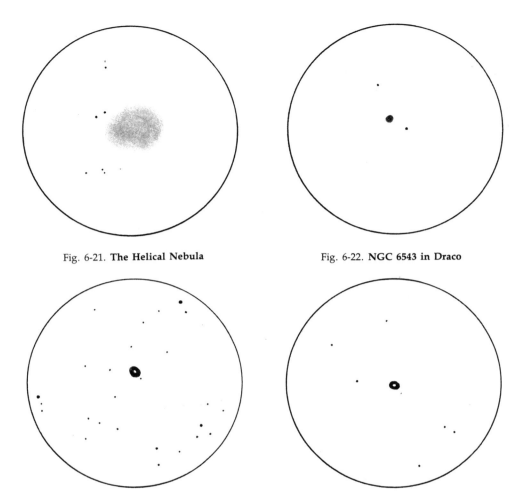

Fig. 6-21. **The Helical Nebula**

Fig. 6-22. **NGC 6543 in Draco**

Fig. 6-23. **The Ring Nebula**

Fig. 6-24. **NGC 6818 in Sagittarius**

Other planetary nebulae visible in winter skies are NGC 1514 in Taurus, NGC 1535 in Eridanus, NGC 2022 in Orion, NGC 2438 and NGC 2440 in Puppis, and IC 2149 in Auriga.

The best known planetary nebula in northern springtime skies is M97, the Owl Nebula in Ursa Major. Discovered in 1781 by Pierre Mechain and soon recorded by Messier, its large size of 150 arcseconds instantly identified it as a nonstellar object. The name Owl Nebula is derived from the Earl of Rosse, who first observed two dark patches reminiscent of eyes, which show well on any photograph. Through your small telescope the eyes are extremely difficult to view--the surface of the object will most likely appear uniform. The Owl lies about three degrees southeast of Beta Ursae Majoris and shares a wide field view with the edge-on galaxy M108.

For observers whose horizons extend beyond -40 degrees a special treat awaits--NGC 3132, also known as the Eight-Burst Nebula. This planetary takes a back seat only to the Ring and Dumbbell in its stunning appearance. It is almost equal in size and shape to the Ring Nebula and shines at magnitude 8.2 (compared to the Ring's 9.0). It also has what was for years considered a very conspicuous central illuminating star, but a 1977 study revealed that a close, dim star near the apparent central star actually powers the nebula. The Eight-Burst Nebula lies on the border of constellations Vela and Antlia, both of which are relative strangers to observers in the north.

NGC 3242, sometimes called the Ghost of Jupiter, is another southerly planetary nebula within the grasp of small telescope owners. An easy guidepost is Mu Hydrae, which lies a mere two degrees to the north. Although not quite comparable to its southerly neighbor 3132, this planetary compares favorably with the likes of the Saturn Nebula, NGC 7662, and NGC 6543. Obvious in any photograph of 3242 is the nebula's unique structure which is, unfortunately, out of reach of small aperture telescopes.

Your 2- to 6-inch telescope might not be capable of duplicating feats conducted at Palomar Mountain, but at any time of the year it can take you out into the Galaxy and show you a glimpse of these ghostly stellar remnants.

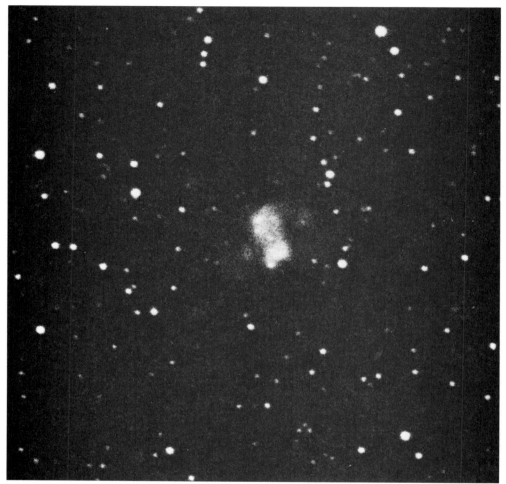

Fig. 6-25. **The Little Dumbbell Nebula**

Fig. 6-26. **NGC 6751 in Aquila**

Fig. 6-27. **IC 1470 in Cepheus**

ADVANCED OBSERVING TECHNIQUES

After having successfully toured the planetary nebulae as a beginner, you can progress further by following one or both of two basic paths: 1) tracking down difficult objects, 2) more challenging work with the brighter objects. Regardless of the option you choose, it is important to consider the limitations of your telescope when you set goals. Your ability to recognize dim objects or subtle features associated with objects will, however, improve with experience.

    Let us first consider difficult objects, which we will confine to magnitude 12.5 or brighter in keeping with the limits for which this book is intended. The planetaries listed near the end of this chapter but not detailed in the previous section are well distributed throughout the sky and form the basis of this section.

    Cygnus and Aquila are particularly rich in hard-to-find planetary nebulae. Aquila's residents are extremely compact, NGC 6781 by far being the largest at 106 arcseconds. With the exception of NGC 7027, whose membership in the family of planetary nebulae is somewhat doubtful anyway, difficult objects in Cygnus are all larger than ones in Aquila. Here are some tips to remember: 1) you should have and be able to use a detailed star atlas, such as Tirion's Sky Atlas 2000.0) for guidance through this overpopulated region of the sky, 2) you should avoid nebulae smaller than five arcseconds diameter on all but the steadiest of nights, and 3) you should learn to competently detect color, no matter how subtle it may seem, as an aid in locating nebulae that may appear nearly stellar. You'll do best by thoroughly studying the easily colorful planetaries such as the Saturn Nebula and NGC 7662 and only slowly tracking the more stubborn examples.

    If you want to stay away from the densely cluttered Milky Way, you may wish to try observing some moderately difficult specimens first. Two fine examples are NGC 6210 in Hercules and NGC 6818 in Sagittarius. Progressively more trying examples away from the Milky Way mainstream lie in Ophiuchus, Sagitta, and Delphinus.

    NGC 6210 and NGC 6818 are nearly identical as viewed through small telescopes. Their magnitudes are 9.7 and 10.0 respectively, their sizes are 20x16 and 22x15 seconds of arc respectively, and neither possesses a conspicuous central star. Since both are compact and fairly bright, they display the typical planetary blue-green, although not nearly as much as similarly sized objects a magnitude brighter. Both are accessible by way of bright reference stars, which lead to dimmer, albeit closer, markers. Zeta Herculis lies about 8 degrees north of NGC 6210, while Delta Herculis lies 7 degrees east and less than a degree north. NGC 6818 resides about 10 degrees west of the midpoint between Alpha and Beta Capricorni. Although neither 6210 or 6818 has a close reference point, both are much simpler to locate than their relatives hiding among the literally thousands of stars cramming the Milky Way region. The likes of 6210 and 6818 are logical follow-ups to the Ring and Dumbbell, and for ambitious observers, springboards to tasks more trying.

    Near the fringes of the Milky Way's thickest area lies a good example of a challenging planetary, NGC 6629--a magnitude 10.5 specimen in Sagittarius. It is overshadowed by bright neighbors, most notably the giant globular cluster M22, and nearby globular M28, which lies a short 2 degrees south. NGC 6629 is small--15 arcseconds in diameter--so you'll do best on a steady night, using medium to high powers. Avoid turbulence that may "swell" nearby stars of similar brightness (thus hopelessly confusing them with the planetary). Such malady eases as you start to

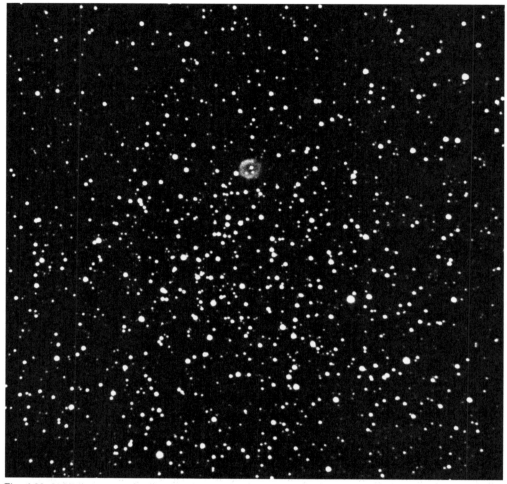

Fig. 6-28. **NGC 2438 in cluster M46**

Fig. 6-29. **The Blinking Planetary**

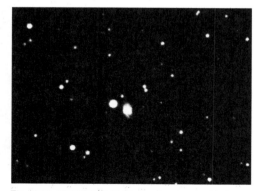

Fig. 6-30. **NGC 7026 in Cygnus**

learn the telescopic star fields of the various objects--a task no more difficult than star-hopping to predetermined targets. After several observations--preferably on different nights--you will become quite familiar with the star arrangements in the eyepiece. (A word of caution: if you switch telescopes of different types, you will switch orientations of fields of view.)

In contrast to the diminutive NGC 6629 is the large, challenging autumn planetary NGC 246 in Cetus. It lies six degrees north and less than a degree east of Beta Ceti, the brightest star in its area of the sky. Its immediate telescopic neighborhood is identified by four very dim stars, but a good night will reveal the sprawling nebula itself, which can barely compete with the most minimal skyglow. If 6629 suffers from being too small, 246 has the opposite problem. A mastery of such extreme objects is important for a well-balanced observing program and is a goal worthy of achieving.

In winter we'll find the moderately difficult planetary NGC 2438 in Puppis. It lies in the same line of sight as the fine open cluster M46 (and so appears to be suspended in the group), but distance measurements bear out that the nebula is not associated with the star cluster. A planetary nebula which is associated with a star cluster is K-648, a member of the globular cluster M15 in Pegasus. It was photographically discovered in 1927, shows no disk, and at a dim 13th magnitude is nearly impossible to separate from the multitudes of stars surrounding it.

Returning to Puppis we can find NGC 2440, a planetary easily located 3-1/2 degrees south of NGC 2438. At magnitudes 11.0 and 11.5, respectively, this pair of medium-size objects, although not impossible to find, may challenge your small telescope under certain conditions. But it will also sharpen your eye for more difficult targets, such as NGC 2022.

NGC 2022 is a faint (12th magnitude) nebula which extends out to 25 arcseconds in diameter. Although small, it will outsize any stellar image through any telescope, thus revealing itself as a nebula. Such a dim planetary fails to show any color, but its disk immediately betrays its identity, despite low surface brightness. Beyond this point, however, the trade-off between magnitude and size will catch up to you. We've reached the limit of our instruments.

Let's now consider features of some brighter objects available to small scopes. A challenging task associated with a bright planetary nebula is the sighting of its dim central star, the sun that powers the nebulosity to shine. The Ring Nebula possesses the most sought-after such star. Reports on this famous 14th magnitude bluish-white star have conflicted for decades. Some observers with professional-size instruments have failed miserably after many attempts to find it, while others, using instruments as small as 8-inch aperture, have spotted it (or so say the reports). Explanations for this disparity are twofold. Firstly, an object as dim as magnitude 15 will be extremely sensitive to atmospheric conditions--the slightest amount of turbulence will strike a fatal blow. Such a problem, of course, will only be magnified by the use of a larger telescope. When surrounded by a ring of much brighter nebulosity, a faint central star could easily blend in with it. Even when there is space between the star and the inner fringe of the nebula, as is the case wih the Ring Nebula, the glare can be overpowering. By contrast, the central star in the Helical Nebula is in no way vulnerable to washout from the bright nebular glow. Secondly, the Ring Nebula's central star is suspected of variability, although its proximity to the nebula hinders reliable magnitude estimates. (The point must also be made that seeing conditions play an important role in this--I have seen,

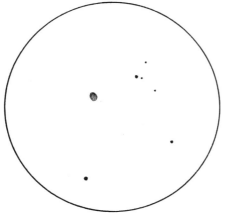

Fig. 6-31. **The Saturn Nebula**

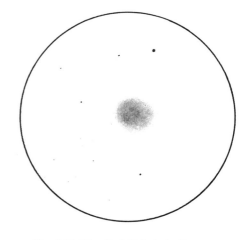

Fig. 6-32. **The Owl Nebula in Ursa Major**

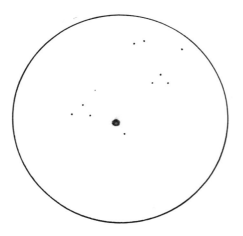

Fig. 6-33. **NGC 6210 in Hercules**

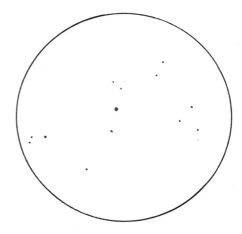

Fig. 6-34. **NGC 2022 in Orion**

rather easily, the central star in M57 using a 16-inch reflector near McDonald Observatory in Texas and have failed to see it using a 20-inch reflector in humid southern Ohio.--Editor.) Perhaps an ideal night coupled with a keen eye and a good quality small telescope will yield a fortunate observer a glimpse of this tantalizing point of light.

Among possible projects involving the Messier planetaries is the comparison between visual and photographic appearances of the nebulae. Granted that no view through a scope of 6-inch aperture or smaller will begin to equal the light-gathering qualities of good photographs, still there are definite possibilities, although excellent seeing conditions are necessary.

For the Ring Nebula you might chart the aperture sizes and magnifications for which the smoke-ring appearance definitely manifests itself. For the Dumbbell and M76 you may attempt to compare the maximum distance from the center for which nebulosity can be detected or the minimum telescope aperture required to ascertain two components. For the Owl Nebula, the only features detectable are the eyes--which unfortunately are almost too subtle for our purposes, but you can attempt to estimate the angular extent and verify the shape of the disk for various magnifications and telescope sizes.

For the Helix, which is far larger (and dimmer) than the Messier planetaries, a very ambitious observer might attempt to compare the twisted structure seen photographically with any subtle gradations of light which may show up with 6-inch scopes. For this project skillful use of averted vision may be the only key to success.

Unfortunately, features such as the face in the Eskimo Nebula or the rings in the Saturn Nebula are far beyond the capabilities of 2-inch to 6-inch telescopes (and most amateur telescopes, for that matter). Nevertheless, there are plenty of observational projects ready for the owner of a small telescope. You shouldn't scoff at its shortcomings, but rather capitalize on its potential. Given enough confidence, you'll be surprised at how your modest telescope will bring the planetary nebulae closer to you.

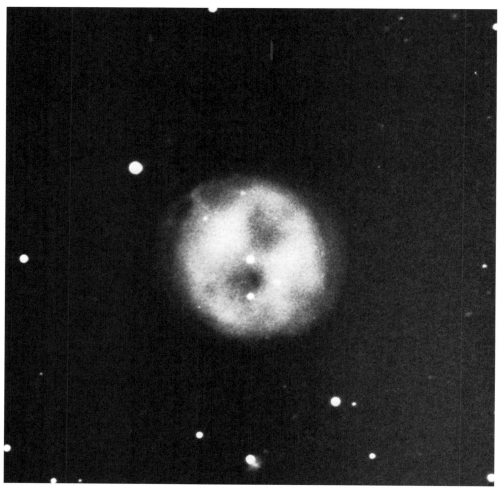

Fig. 6-35. **The Owl Nebula**

Fig. 6-36. **The Eskimo Nebula**

Fig. 6-37. **NGC 1501 in Camelopardalis**

A CATALOG OF PLANETARY NEBULAE

The following is a catalog of 63 planetary nebulae specifically selected for their fine appearance in small telescopes. This list is not inclusive, but in practical terms is nearly so. All planetaries north of -45 degrees declination and brighter than magnitude 12.6 are listed: you'll find that these will become your favorites to observe, although a few small and dimmer planetaries are observable with small scopes.

   Explanation of data: Coordinates are provided for epoch 1950.0. Mag.=visual magnitude of nebula. (Note: these magnitudes were largely derived from visual observations around 1930, and they are not absolutely accurate.) M*=magnitude of nebula's central star. (These are estimates as well because of the difficulty of obtaining good photometric measurements.) The size of each nebula is listed in arcseconds. Also included are observing notes and popular names where applicable.

CATALOG NUMBER	R.A.(1950)Dec. h m ° '	Mag.	M*	Size "
ANDROMEDA				
NGC 7662	23 23.4 +42 12	8.5	14	30
Bluish-green planetary with moderately visible central star. Visible in a 2.4-inch scope--shows well in a 6-inch.				
ANTLIA				
NGC 3132	10 04.9 -40 11	8.2	10	84x52
The Eight-Burst Nebula. Much like the Ring Nebula but with a bright conspicuous central star.				
AQUARIUS				
NGC 7009	21 01.4 -11 34	8.0	12	44x26
The Saturn Nebula. The "rings" which give this nebula its name are not visible in small telescopes. It appears as a small oval bluish disk, like an out of focus star.				

CATALOG NUMBER	R.A.(1950)Dec. h m ° '	Mag.	M*	Size "

_____AQUARIUS_(Continued)

| NGC 7293 | 22 27.0   -21 06 | 6.5 | 13 | 900x720 |

The Helical Nebula. The largest planetary in the sky, it is visible with a 6-inch on dark nights. Named for its resemblance to a twisted DNA double-helix.

_____AQUILA

NGC 6741	19 00.1 -00 31	12.0	17	8x7
NGC 6751	19 03.2 -06 05	12.0	13	20
NGC 6781	19 16.0 +06 26	12.5	15	106

Large dim nebula resembling a ghostly hollow shell of pale green gas.

NGC 6790	19 20.4 +01 24	11.5	18	2
NGC 6803	19 28.9 +09 58	11.0	14	4
IC 4846	19 13.7 -09 09	12.0	--	2

_____AURIGA

| IC 2149 | 05 52.6   +46 07 | 10.0 | 14 | 10 |

_____CAMELOPARDALIS

| NGC 1501 | 04 02.6   +60 47 | 12.0 | 13.5 | 55x48 |
| IC 3568 | 12 32.4   +82 51 | 11.6 | -- | 18 |

_____CANIS MAJOR

| IC 2165 | 06 19.6   -12 57 | 12.5 | -- | 8 |

_____CASSIOPEIA

| IC 289 | 03 06.2   +61 08 | 12.0 | 15 | 45x30 |

_____CEPHEUS

| NGC 40 | 00 10.2   +72 15 | 10.5 | 11.5 | 60x40 |
| IC 1470 | 23 03.2   +59 59 | 8.9 | 12 | 70x45 |

Bright roundish patch with conspicuous central star.

_____CETUS

| NGC 246 | 00 44.6   -12 09 | 8.5 | 12 | 240 |

Large low surface brightness incomplete ring. 6-inch high power view shows central star and three others involved in the nebulosity.

_____CORONA AUSTRALIS

| IC 1297 | 19 14.0   -39 42 | 11.5 | -- | 2 |

CATALOG NUMBER	R.A.(1950) Dec. h m ° '	Mag.	M*	Size "

_____CORVUS_____

| NGC 4361 | 12 21.9   -18 29 | 10.5 | 13 | 80 |

6-inch shows a dim roundish patch surrounding a dim star.

_____CYGNUS_____

| NGC 6826 | 19 43.4   +50 24 | 8.8 | 11 | 25 |

The Blinking Planetary. Note blinking effect by
quickly alternating between direct and averted
vision.

NGC 7008	20 59.1 +54 21	12.0	13	85
NGC 7026	21 04.6 +47 39	12.0	15	25
NGC 7027	21 05.1 +42 02	9.0	--	18x11

Small but bright oval nebulosity. Central star
invisible in small telescopes.

| NGC 7048 | 21 12.6   +46 04 | 11.0 | 18 | 60x50 |

_____DELPHINUS_____

| NGC 6891 | 20 12.8   +12 35 | 10.0 | 11 | 15x7 |
| NGC 6905 | 20 20.2   +19 57 | 12.0 | 14 | 44x38 |

_____DRACO_____

| NGC 6543 | 17 58.8   +66 38 | 8.6 | 10 | 22x16 |

Small bright bluish-green disk with
bright central star.

_____ERIDANUS_____

| NGC 1535 | 04 12.1   -12 52 | 9.0 | 11.5 | 20x17 |

4-inch scope at high power shows a tiny disk
and faint central star.

_____GEMINI_____

J900	06 23.0 +17 49	12.0	--	10
NGC 2371/2	07 22.4 +29 35	12.5	--	50x30
NGC 2392	07 26.2 +21 01	8.0	10	40

The Eskimo Nebula. 6-inch shows some faint outer
nebulosity arcing around a bright circle, giving
the nebula its name. 4-inch at high power shows
the bluish-white central star.

CATALOG NUMBER	R.A.(1950) Dec. h m ° '	Mag.	M*	Size "
_____HERCULES				
NGC 6058	16 02.8 +40 49	12.0	--	25x20
NGC 6210	16 42.5 +23 53	9.7	12.5	20x16

4-inch at high power shows a tiny blue-green disk. Central star is dim; a tough test for a 6-inch.

IC 4593	16 09.4 +12 12	11.0	--	13x10
_____HYDRA				
NGC 3242	10 22.4 -18 23	8.9	11	40

The "Ghost of Jupiter." Named so because its large pale creamy disk is similar to the telescopic appearance of Jupiter. Six-inch shows an elongated bright patch of nebulosity in the center.

_____LEPUS				
IC 418	05 25.4 -12 44	----	--	14x11
_____LIBRA				
Merrill 2-1	15 19.5 -23 27	12.9	--	6
_____LUPUS				
NGC 5873	15 09.4 -37 54	12.0	--	3
_____LYRA				
NGC 6720	18 51.7 +32 58	9.0	14	80x60

The Ring Nebula (M57). Probably the finest planetary in the sky. Even large binoculars reveal the bright smoke-ring of high surface brightness gas. 6-inch at high power shows an oval shape, and some observers claim the elusive central star.

_____OPHIUCHUS				
IC 4634	16 58.5 -21 44	12.0	17	20x10
NGC 6309	17 11.2 -12 51	11.5	14	20x10
NGC 6369	17 26.3 -23 44	11.0	16	28
NGC 6572	18 09.7 +06 50	9.0	12	15x12
_____ORION				
NGC 2022	05 39.3 +09 03	12.0	14	25
_____PERSEUS				
NGC 650/1	01 38.8 +51 19	11.0	16	140x70

The Little Dumbbell Nebula (M76). Smaller and fainter version of M27. 3-inch shows it as a dim double nebula.

CATALOG NUMBER	R.A.(1950) h m	Dec. ° '	Mag.	M*	Size "

PERSEUS (Continued)

| IC 2003 | 03 53.2 | +33 44 | 12.0 | 18 | 5 |

PUPPIS

| NGC 2438 | 07 39.6 | -14 36 | 11.0 | 17 | 65 |

Ring nebula appearing much like M57, suspended among the stars of open cluster M46. 6-inch shows elongated shape.

| NGC 2440 | 07 39.9 | -18 05 | 11.5 | 16 | 50x20 |

SAGITTA

NGC 6879	20 08.1	+16 46	11.0	15	5
NGC 6886	20 10.5	+19 50	11.0	16.5	9x6
IC 4997	20 17.9	+16 35	11.0	14	2

SAGITTARIUS

NGC 6537	18 02.2	-19 51	12.0	--	5
NGC 6567	18 10.8	-19 05	11.5	15	11x7
NGC 6629	18 22.7	-23 14	10.5	13.5	15
NGC 6644	18 29.5	-25 11	12.0	--	2
NGC 6818	19 41.1	-14 17	10.0	15	22x15

Tiny bluish nebula 0.5 degree north of Barnard's Galaxy, NGC 6822. Use high power.

| IC 4776 | 18 42.6 | -33 23 | 12.5 | 16 | 8x6 |

SCORPIUS

| NGC 6153 | 16 28.0 | -40 08 | 11.5 | -- | 20 |

TAURUS

| NGC 1514 | 04 06.1 | +30 38 | 11.0 | 10 | 120 |

URSA MAJOR

| NGC 3587 | 11 12.0 | +55 18 | 11.0 | 14 | 150 |

The Owl Nebula (M97). One of the faintest Messier objects. The "eyes"--dark patches--giving M97 its name may be visible with a 6-inch under great skies.

VULPECULA

| NGC 6853 | 19 57.4 | +22 35 | 8.0 | 13.5 | 480x240 |

The Dumbbell Nebula (M27). A bright binocular object, the Dumbbell is a fine wispy bow-tie in a 2.4-inch refractor. A 4-inch shows two bright lobes and hazy outer nebulosity in a rich star field.

Fig. 7-1. **The Orion Nebula**

7 Bright and Dark Nebulae

David H. Levy

As is the case with many budding amateur astronomers, the first deep-sky object I saw through a telescope was the Orion Nebula. With a 3.5-inch reflector and substandard eyepieces, I didn't know that I was seeing a rather poor rendition of the Great Nebula in Orion. I was excited nonetheless, since I knew I was looking out at an object through 1,600 light-years of space. I didn't need a book, nor did I need a teacher, to tell me that something special was happening in Orion.

In the years since that view of the Orion Nebula I've learned about many more nebulae. Hundreds are visible in small telescopes. Distributed throughout the sky, these softly glowing clouds of hydrogen gas and opaque pockets of dust grains will be visible during any observing session you have. My small telescope of long ago displayed a beautiful nebula. Today, I look at the Orion Nebula with a 16-inch reflector and nebula filter and wonder how I could have been impressed by my small telescopes of yesteryear. But impress me it did, just as the view through the larger telescope does now.

Bright nebulae occur in two basic types. Emission nebulae are clouds of hydrogen gas glowing because their atoms have been ionized by hot stars nearby. These nebulae are emitting visible light as a byproduct of the energy they receive from the hot stars. Reflection nebulae, on the other hand, are composed of dust grains that reflect light from nearby stars. Consequently, they tend to be much fainter than emission nebulae, although fine examples of each type are visible in small telescopes.

Observationally, dark nebulae are a challenge. So many photographs of the Horsehead Nebula have been printed in magazines that one gets the impression it is easy to see. Unless they are projected either against bright nebulae or against very dense, starry backgrounds. In the southern sky the Coalsack, near the Southern Cross, is clearly visible with the unaided eye because it happens to be in front of a rich star background. The tiny Horsehead Nebula is projected against rather faint nebulosity, and thus the resulting contrast between dark nebula and background is so low that it is difficult to see visually. However, under a dark sky, with a wide field eyepiece and a nebula filter to increase contrast, it is certainly possible to see this elusive dark nebula with a 6-inch telescope.

A good session of observing nebulae offers an unparalleled way to get acquainted with the life cycles that characterize the stars. Dark nebulae are stellar wombs, pockets of gas that eventually will condense into new stars. Many of the bright nebulae are star nurseries; the hot stars that light them are no more than a few million years old. On the other end of the cycle of stellar evolution are supernova remnants, the remains of exploded stars.

In the southern hemisphere lies perhaps the strangest nebula of all, a huge and colorful mass of material, bright and dark, that surrounds the star Eta Carinae. What a nebula! Eta Carinae itself is a star that may have as much as 150 times the mass of the Sun, and it loses about one solar mass every year. Most people who have seen the surrounding bright nebula call it the most fabulous in the whole sky. I am not sure. Every nebula I have viewed is different, and each offers something special.

David H. Levy
Tucson, Arizona

Fig. 7-2. **The Lagoon Nebula**

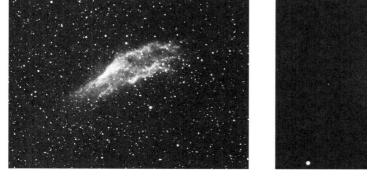

Fig. 7-3. **The California Nebula**

Fig. 7-4. **M78 in Orion**

HISTORICAL BACKGROUND

"My God! There is a hole in the sky!" With this excited comment made some 200 years ago, William Herschel discovered a hitherto unknown type of deep-sky object, the dark nebula. Historically, Herschel is the most influential single observer of bright and dark nebulae, cataloguing hundreds of such objects with his large telescopes in England. However, the true beginnings of the story of nebulae are not rooted in 17th-century observation, but in early philosophy.

Although their nature was not understood until this century, nebulae have attracted the imaginations and eyes of free thinkers well before the time of Herschel and Messier. The German philosopher Immanuel Kant completed his theory of the formation of the solar system from gaseous material "not as the result of observation and computation," but from philosophical ponderings. Later, in 1796, French scientist Pierre Simon Laplace provided a mathematical "nebular hypothesis," stating that the "cloud of fire-mist in the universe" did not take the shape of any of the nebulae visible with telescopes but instead was homogeneous and infinite. Gravitation eventually contracted this matter into a huge ball which by now had parts of greater and lesser densities. For many philosophers this idea of a nebular contraction of the matter in the universe seemed to prove Moses' outline of creation. But not for Laplace, who announced to Napoleon that "I have no need of the hypothesis of a god."

Many hundreds of bright and dark nebulae lie scattered across the sky. Charles Messier's catalogue of fuzzy patches published in 1781 listed 103 objects, some of which turned out to be bright nebulae. Whereas Messier began the concept of an orderly listing, Herschel carried the idea to an extreme, compiling notes on thousands of faint objects. Presented to the Royal Society in 1786, Herschel's first listing offered 1,000 previously undetected objects, and in 1789 he announced 1,000 more. In 1802, another supplement added 500 new objects. Each object was meticulously described, and we can appreciate how Herschel sensed the nature of these nebulae when he described "cloudy stars, surrounded with a nebulous atmosphere; a different sort again contain a nebulosity of the milky kind, like that wonderful inexplicable phenomenon about Theta Orionis."

Herschel also stressed the need for a classification system of some sort, coming close but not quite understanding at first that the different appearances resulted from different types of deep-sky objects. "Nebulae," he wrote, "can be selected so that an insensible gradation shall take place from a coarse cluster like the Pleiades down to a milky nebulosity like that in Orion, every intermediate step being represented." He felt that a simple increase in power and telescope size would eventually resolve every object he saw.

With increased confidence in using his telescopes, Herschel changed his mind in 1791 and wrote that one of his objects showed "nebulosity about the star [that] is not of a starry nature." Once he suspected that many nebulae could not be resolved into stars, however, he erroneously thought they may be relatively close.

At first, Herschel's discovery of a "hole in the sky" in southern Scorpius was left as an unresolved mystery. When Herschel's son John set up a telescope at the Cape of Good Hope, John's aunt Caroline--another of the family's expert astronomers--suggested that he observe "truly a hole in the heavens." The nebulosity that first attracted his interest lay just east of the globular cluster M80, around the bright star Rho Ophiuchi. Visually, this nebular complex is extremely dim, appearing as dark nebulosity simply blocking innumerable faint stars. But John didn't know exactly how to interpret this apparent lack of stars in a region where some spots showed hundreds per square degree.

In fact the Herschels' ideas about these starless regions were nearly the opposite of what we know today. William Herschel saw them as old regions that "have sustained greater ravages of time" than their surroundings. Clearly these areas needed more observation, and John Herschel followed his aunt's advice and catalogued about 50 prominent starless regions. Another early observer of nebulae was Admiral William Henry Smyth, whose Cycle of Celestial Objects was published in 1844. Smyth had retired and built himself an observatory for scanning the sky in search of unusual and interesting objects.

Visual drawings of nebulae were considered extremely important in the early nineteenth century. The amateur astronomer Ebenezer P. Mason was so impressed with the brightness contrasts in various nebulae that he began drawing contour maps based on his visual impressions. Mason sketched out contour lines showing the relative brightnesses of different parts of a given nebula, and his fanatic enthusiasm made him destined to contribute a great deal to the science. However, Mason's life was tragically cut short in 1840 when he died of tuberculosis at age 21.

Late in the nineteenth century the age of the great visual observers came to a close with Edwin Emerson Barnard, a Tennessee astronomer renown for his keen eye and great abilities as an observer. For all their intricate structure and beauty, nebulae can be the most frustrating of objects when they are faint. Visually, they demand a highly trained, patient, and careful eye that can discern the most subtle differences in sky brightness. In a sense Barnard's keen eye told us much of what we know about nebulae, from his discovery of the extraordinarily huge and faint nebulosity in Orion now known as Barnard's Loop, to his meticulous observations of the dark nebulae. One of the most thorough and prolific observers in history, Barnard made his most lasting contributions through his study of dark nebulae. Barnard's catalogue of dark objects, published in 1923 as An Atlas of Selected Regions of the Milky Way, is still used as the fundamental catalogue for dark nebulae observing. A fitting tribute to such an observer, this is a listing of some of the most difficult to detect objects in the sky.

The age of the Herschels, Messier, Smyth, and Barnard defined the swansong of visual astronomy. We now stand at the beginning of a grand epoch of electronic astronomy. But the relatively short period between the two was dominated by the golden age of astronomical photography, when observers did research by exposing photographic plates and measuring them to obtain data. This is still done today, but computers are fast eliminating much of straight photography's usefulness. The high tide of photography as far as nebulae are concerned began in the mid nineteenth century, when astornomers like England's Andrew Ainslie Common and America's Henry Draper and George Bond produced the first excellent photographs of sky objects. Common went on to make a career of making high-quality photographs of nebulae, especially M27 and M45, through his 60-inch reflecting telescope with a homemade mirror.

By the mid 1930s, astronomers' understanding of gaseous nebulae was beginning to develop, although top astronomers like James Jeans still talked of nebulae and galaxies as if they could be compared. "True nebulae," he wrote, "are of two distinct types, which can be distinguished by their shapes. The first type are regular in shape,

Fig. 7-5. **The Trifid Nebula**

Fig. 7-6. **The Horsehead Nebula**

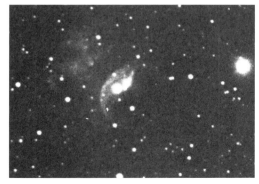

Fig. 7-7. **The Bubble Nebula**

Fig. 7-8. **The Crab Supernova Remnant**

Fig. 7-9. **NGC 7023 in Cepheus**

Fig. 7-10. **NGC 2174/5 in Orion**

or very nearly so. The second type are completely irregular in shape, like drifting masses of smoke such as one sees when a house or a haystack is on fire," Even though by the 1930s our understanding of "galactic" and "extragalactic" nebulae was becoming clearer--galaxies were only first identified in 1923 as islands of stars separate from the Milky Way--the nomenclature did not follow until much later. Today we speak of nebulae and galaxies as they should be spoken of, as distinctly different physical objects that occasionally appear similar when viewed through telescopes.

Early in the twentieth century astronomers began to understand more about the nature of nebulae. Spectroscopes attached to telescopes revealed what astronomers at first thought was a new element, "nebulium." However, in 1927 Ira S. Bowen of the Mount Wilson Observatory in California discovered that nebulium was not an element, but rather doubly-ionized oxygen.

Several decades later astronomy was on the move, as the eminent galactic astronomer Bart J. Bok wrote, and interest quickly moved from the precursors of stars to supernovae and back again. By the 1970s, according to astrophysicist Geoffrey Burbidge, there were only two astronomies: the astronomy of the Crab Nebula, and the astronomy of everything else. During this period, observers discovered the extremely hot source of illumination for the Crab Nebula, a pulsar.

At the same time, other astronomers were considering what they should concentrate on studying. Bart Bok had earlier recognized the importance of very small dark blobs of nebulosity that seemed to show up in and around emission nebulae. He called these patches globules one morning when he stepped outside a door to receive his milk delivery. After researching these globules, it was discovered that they are small clouds of material condensing into protostars. When these protostars accumulate enough mass and heat up, they begin nuclear fusion and become stars. Star birth had been unraveled!

An extremely important provider of information on bright and dark nebulae was NASA's Infrared Astronomical Satellite, or IRAS. This orbiting observatory was launched in 1983 and surveyed the entire sky in the infrared wavelengths, detected many shells of dusty material surrounding young, nearby stars. Following up the IRAS observations, Bradford Smith of the University of Arizona detected a circumstellar shell around the star Beta Pictoris. These shells are thought to be clumps of warm material orbiting other stars, and logically indicate the presence of planetary systems. So the quest for information on nebulae over the past several centuries may well have paid off with the first evidence that indeed planetary systems are commonplace in the Milky Way Galaxy.

For all the centuries of study, however, we still need to discover much more about bright and dark nebulae. Astronomers need to find accurate distances for most of them, and their structure is difficult to map. The unresolved question of how much dark matter exists in the Galaxy and in other galaxies holds keys to the fate of the universe. In the mean time, we can continue to watch bright and dark nebulae, watch them surrounding the births of stars, marking their deaths, and floating gracefully throughout interstellar space.

The Nature of Bright and Dark Nebulae

Not so many years ago, anything in the sky that appeared nebulous and wasn't a comet was called a nebula. Even galaxies were known as "extragalactic nebulae" and the objects we are about to address were known as diffuse nebulae. We now know that the term "diffuse nebula" is really too vague to hold much significance. The term is used today to describe bright nebulae other than planetaries. In any case, bright and dark nebulae play a seminal role in the evolution of stars in our Galaxy and throughout the universe.

Observationally, nebulae are best described as bright (gas or dust clouds emitting or reflecting light), or dark (dust obscuring light from beyond). Bright nebulae are further categorized into two distinct basic types. Emission nebulae are clouds of ionized hydrogen gas called HII regions that glow by fluorescence. Following the same basic principle as fluorescent light bulbs, emission nebulae shine because the atoms composing them are excited by energy from nearby hot stars. Prominent examples of emission nebulae are the Lagoon Nebula (M8), the Omega Nebula (M17), and the Orion Nebula (M42). The second type, reflection nebulae, are clouds of dust grains and molecular hydrogen (HI) reflecting light from nearby stars. The Pleiades nebulosity in Taurus (NGC 1435), M78 in Orion, and the northern half of the Trifid Nebula (M20) are good examples of such objects. Photographically, emission nebulae appear red, while reflection nebulae are blue. Visually, color other than a weak gray-green tint is difficult to spot in any nebula without large backyard telescopes.

Dark nebulae are composed of opaque dust grains and are visible only if they block light from behind bright objects. Prominent examples of dark nebulae lie scattered all along the Milky Way Galaxy. So-called Bok globules are tiny dark nebulae usually seen against bright nebular backgrounds. Most dark nebulae are difficult telescopic objects, and only the brightest several dozen are easily visible with small scopes.

Another, more specialized type of bright nebula is the supernova remnant. Supernovae are catastrophic explosions that result when a massive star runs out of nuclear fuel to burn and collapses inwardly. The material left over after a supernova blast can be observed for several tens of thousands of years afterward. The two best examples of this type of object are the Crab Nebula in Taurus (M1) and the Veil Nebula in Cygnus.

When astronomers view a typical spiral galaxy using a large telescope, they see the galaxy's arms irregularly studded with bright patches that look like hazy clumps of light. These areas are not stars, but giant HII regions. Galaxies also contain enormous HI regions composed of neutral hydrogen. American astronomer Walter Baade recognized that these giant emission nebulae can be used to trace out spiral arms in distant galaxies. It is still a challenge to use the same idea to trace all the spiral arms in our own Galaxy.

Our Galaxy has its share of magnificent HII regions. All this interstellar material composes the "interstellar medium," which is distributed throughout the space between stars. The composition of this material varies is sometimes pure hydrogen gas, frequently cosmic dust, and often complex combinations of gas and dust that characterize nebulae like M8 and M42.

Cosmic dust may consist of carbon, silicate, or iron particles no bigger than cigarette smoke particles, probably coated with an icy mantle of water, methane, or ammonia. Since much of the interstellar medium is unlit and virtually unobservable, its composition is difficult to estimate.

Why do large nebulae exist in the spiral arms of galaxies? As they rotate about a central bulge, galaxies propogate waves that send ripples throughout. These "density waves" seem to collect a galaxy's gas and dust and compress them into areas that spiral out from the galaxy's center.

A typical dark nebula that we see is obviously irregular in shape, so it is reasonable to assume that such a nebula will also be irregular in density. Over incredibly long periods of time, dense pockets of gas and dust attract still more material by gravity, becoming denser and more massive. With ever greater amounts of material, such an area's gravitational attraction increases and eventually, by what astronomers call "gravitational accretion," collects gas and dust amounting to several times the mass of the Sun.

When a pocket of gas and dust reaches this point in mass it is called a Bok globule, so named because astronomer Bart Bok demonstrated their importance to star birth. Bok described his globules as "roundish, dark nebulae of various dimensions, usually quite small, which may well be the precursors of protostars." He catalogued about 200 globules, of which half are quite small, perhaps slightly larger than our solar system. Millions upon millions of Bok globules must exist in the Galaxy, but since they are not projected against bright nebulosity, we cannot see them. If a globule is situated in the midst of dark nebulosity, it would be very difficult to detect. However, if a globule is projected against the background of a bright nebula, it would be more easily detected.

By the time the mass of cosmic dust has become large enough to be considered a Bok globule, it is attracting surrounding mass rapidly. By this time, the surrounding gas is pushing on it and the pressure inside increasing as the globule gets more massive. At some critical point, the weight of so much material causes the globule to start contracting. Probably the pressure of radiation of the surrounding field aids in the collapse. As material falls toward the center, the internal pressure increases until eventually the pressure is strong enough to support the huge mass of the material that surrounds it. The mass achieves what astronomers call "hydrostatic equilibrium" and the Bok globule has transformed itself into a protostar.

A protostar maintains itself through convection, by which hot material flows out of the core into the cooler, surrounding area. to maintain equilibrium, cooler material then moves closer to the core. This process will work for a short time. But as more and more material is heated and transferred away from the protostar, the core contracts again. As the pressure on the core continues to increase, material cannot leave the core as easily as before and convection slows down, letting the heat transfer from the core continue through radiation.

Now the core continues to contract, becoming hotter and hotter toward an eventual temperature of four million degrees Kelvin--a far cry from the 10 degree K temperature of the globule. At the moment the core reaches this high temperature, its hydrogen atoms start to collide and fuse together. Where gravitational contraction stops, and a newly born star flashes into existence.

The beginning of a star's life also changes the status of the nebulosity, as the star's light excites the surrounding nebula's atoms and causes them to fluoresce. Much of the material around newborn stars is blown outward by hot stellar winds.

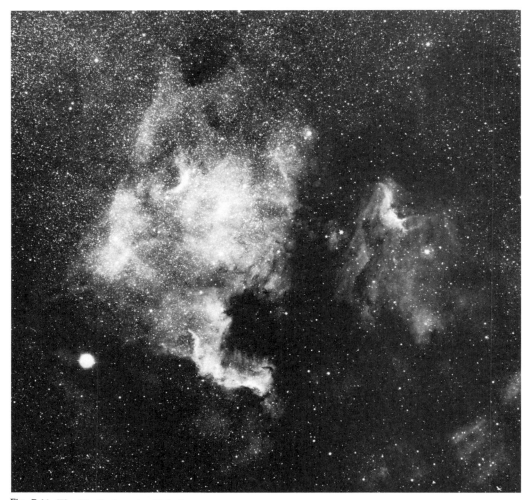

Fig. 7-11. **The North America Nebula**

Fig. 7-12. **The Omega Nebula**

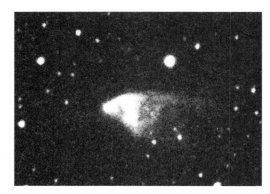

Fig. 7-13. **Hubble's Variable Nebula**

Some of the light that reaches a nebula from a nearby star is reemitted directly, by reflection. This process is simple to identify in a spectroscope; the nebula's spectra is the same as that of the star. However, some of the light that reaches a nebula is actually absorbed by these elements, and then when the gases are excited, the light is reemitted in a form that we can see. The spectrum of such a nebula would show strong emission in the hydrogen-alpha line, and to a lesser extent in the hydrogen-beta and oxygen lines. It is the hydrogen-alpha emission that causes a nebula to appear red. In a complex region like the Orion Nebula, several ionized areas emit light, causing the nebula to be different colors in different places.

The sky's principal emission nebulae, like M42 in Orion and M8 in Sagittarius, are huge masses of material. Around 1930 American astronomer Edwin P. Hubble discovered that nebulae do not shine by themselves but need hot stars as energy sources to provide illumination. The primary ingredient in a nebula is hydrogen, but these clouds also contain helium, carbon, nitrogen and oxygen. Astronomers know this because they examine nebulae with spectroscopes, showing distinct lines traceable to various chemical elements. Spectroscopes also show some heavier elements, like potassium, calcium, sulphur, and iron, present only as ions.

In 1927, Ira S. Bowen made the startling discovery that spectral lines in some nebulae appeared to contain "forbidden lines" of mysterious, hitherto unknown elements. These spectral lines didn't exist anywhere in a laboratory on Earth, and so provided a strange puzzle for some time. Bowen discovered, however, that these lines were attributable to ionized oxygen and nitrogen. When an electron jumps from a lower orbit to a higher one, the resulting emission appears in a spectrum. This cannot happen in the laboratory when the gases involved are too dense, and the electron could not stay in the new orbit long enough before a collision with another electron would knock it away. Thus, these lines cannot be observed in the laboratory and are therefore called forbidden. But in the near-vacuum of a nebula in space, the chances for collisions are greatly reduced, and electrons freely jump from orbit to orbit. Thus, forbidden lines appear, breaking our carefully conceived notions of how matter behaves, at least on Earth.

These forbidden lines are very prominent in the spectra of gaseous nebulae and thus the ionized elements are responsible for a good deal of a nebula's illumination. In fact, a typical emission nebula emits up to 50 times more visible light than can be supplied by the host star. The energy is there, and certainly the star is emitting it, but not in the form of visible light. Emission nebulae are hosted by stars so hot that much of their radiation is in the invisible ultraviolet part of the spectrum. This energy is strong enough to cause an electron to become detached from its atom, leaving the atom positively charged, or ionized. The negatively charged free electron proceeds to wonder around and get recaptured by another proton. Both ion and electron could wonder around the nebula for weeks in search of new partners.

When a free electron does find a proton, it lands in any one of several lower or higher orbits. If it lands in the lowest orbit, it stays there as a newly formed atom of hydrogen. But it may just as well land in a higher orbit. Then, since the conditions in the nebula are so sparse, the electron will almost instantly return to a lower orbit, emitting energy in visible light as it does so. The new atom is stable until another quantum of ultraviolet radiation from the host star comes along to start the process again.

Nebulae tell us as much about stellar death as they do about starbirth. Old stars of certain masses produce gaseous nebulae called planetary nebulae. These thin shells shine by the same process as emission nebulae, absorbing ultraviolet radiation from the host star and reemitting this energy as visible light. In this sense, and this sense only, they are related to emission nebulae. Observationally they are different, especially in size and shape. Typical emission nebulae are amorphous and sometimes filamentary in appearance, whereas planetary nebulae are usually symmetrical and compact.

Supernova remnants form by an entirely different process. These are rare events, with possibly several dozen visible in other galaxies each year. So when a supernova explodes in a nearby galaxy, research interest is intense. For example, the bright supernova explosion in February 1987 in the Large Magellanic Cloud (Supernova 1987A) has provided astronomers with a laboratory to study the supernova process for years to come. In our own Galaxy, bright supernovae appeared in 1054, 1572, and 1604. Undoubtedly there have been others, but the thick obscuring dust of the interstellar medium prevents us from seeing them.

A truly catastrophic event, a supernova at the height of its outburst can outshine the combined light of all the stars in its host galaxy. At maximum light, a supernova of Type I may be 1,000 million times as bright as the Sun. A Type I is the most energetic form of a supernova explosion, in which a highly evolved star with up to 10 times the mass of the Sun exhausts its nuclear fuel. After depleting its supply of hydrogen the star undergoes a helium burning phase, then uses the resulting carbon for fuel. When this is converted into an iron core, the star attempts to keep on burning. At this stage the iron simply gets hotter and hotter, causing the core to contract faster and faster until it eventually blows itself apart. Type II supernovae differ from Type I objects in that their maxima are not as bright, and often last much longer. Moreover, the decline of a type II is erratic and often involves short-lived fluctuations in brightness.

Not much remains of a star after it has blown all its outer layers away. What is left of its core is a tiny, highly compressed object whose protons and electrons have combined to form neutrons. This "neutron star" may not be more than a few kilometers in diameter, and rotates very rapidly--in the case of the Crab Nebula neutron star, thirty times every second. The great energy of this "pulsar" is enough to illuminate the Crab Nebula, the remains of the supernova of 1054.

Lord Rosse first remarked on the shape of the strange nebula in Taurus. To him it resembled a Crab, and with today's higher performance (and smaller) telescopes it still looks like a Crab. Measurements of the expansion of the gas within the Crab confirm that it began as a point source that exploded as a supernova some 900 years ago.

About 6,300 light years away, the Crab nebula consists of an amorphous mass and a system of filaments. The filaments contain considerable amounts of helium; in fact, the proportion of helium to hydrogen is about seven times what one might find on the surface of a star. This condition is known as an "overabundance" of helium. After the explosion, the helium released from the stellar core joined with the hydrogen.

The Crab Nebula has provided some of the most extraordinary discoveries made concerning nebulae. In 1948, radio waves were discovered leaving the center of the nebula, and in 1964 the Crab

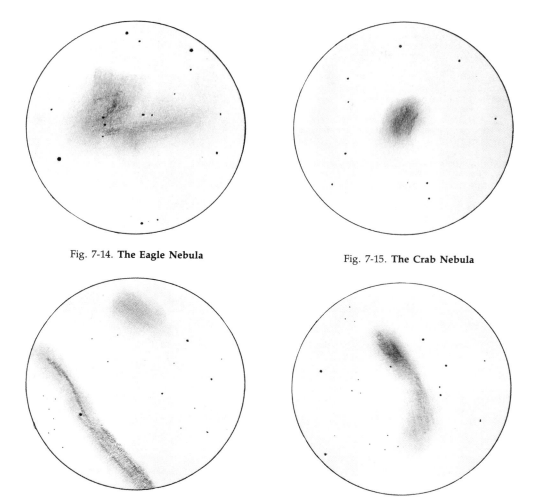

Fig. 7-14. **The Eagle Nebula**

Fig. 7-15. **The Crab Nebula**

Fig. 7-16. **NGC 6960**

Fig. 7-17. **NGC 6992/5**

was revealed as a source of X rays. In July 1967 Anthony Hewish and Jocelyn Bell at Cambridge University discovered pulsars, and in November 1968 a pulsar was discovered at the center of the Crab Nebula.

Older supernovae remnants are more difficult to study since they have had more time to diffuse. In Cygnus, the Veil Nebula consists of streamers of gas several light-years long. Its material, however, is tenuous: the entire mass of the Veil Nebula may be about equal to that of the Sun. Eventually the material from a supernova explosion diffuses into the interstellar medium, providing material for future compression into Bok globules and eventually protostars and newly born stars. A large supernova remnant in the southern constellation Vela exploded perhaps 20,000 years ago, and its remains are spread out over a huge area of sky. Like the Veil, its expansion is being slowed by interaction with the interstellar medium.

These supernovae occurred relatively recently in galactic history. On the average, a Type II supernova may occur every fifty years in our Galaxy, producing a gaseous emission nebula as a remnant. It is not as easy to calculate an average appearance time for Type I supernovae, since we know only of a few that have appeared in our Galaxy. However, even if they occur once in 30 years, they provide a good mechanism for adding hydrogen and helium to the intestellar medium. They may provide the only mechanism for adding the heavier elements, like carbon, to the Galaxy. Because of this fact, we may well owe our very lives to the fact that supernovae salt the Galaxy with elements necessary for life.

We have now completed a cycle of star formation and death, all portrayed by the births and deaths of bright and dark nebulae. Shining by emission or by reflection, shining by hot new stars or by even hotter remnants of stars, or not shining at all, these exquisite objects enrich the sky. In our fascination with nebulae, we look back at our origins and ahead to our eventual demise.

Fig. 7-18. **The Eagle Nebula**

Fig. 7-19. **The Rosette Nebula**

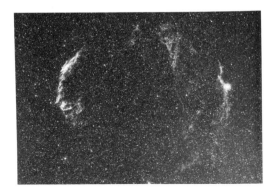

Fig. 7-20. **The Veil Nebula**

BEGINNING TO OBSERVE

This chapter includes two observational discussions of bright and dark nebulae, the following for beginners and a more advanced list later on. Bright and dark nebulae form a complicated group of objects to observe in backyard telescopes, some glowing so faintly that they appear as subtle brightenings of the background skyglow. Dark nebulae are not visible at all, except when they block light from other objects that lie behind them. The distances to many nebulae (and consequently their sizes) are far from certain, and the diameters given represent photometric measurements by professional astronomers. The visual sizes of these objects are typically far smaller. Descriptions of these nebulae should be taken with a grain of salt, since telescopes, individual observing skills, sky conditions, and other factors conspire to give different observers dramatically differing impressions of the same object.

You will find some of these nebulae with relative ease, but others will elude you until your sky conditions are perfect and your visual acuity is operating at full efficiency. Some nebulae will be visible with a good pair of binoculars but not through your large telescope! Most bright and dark nebulae mark places where star formation is taking place, but some of them represent the dying glory of a supernova visible only by its diffusing gaseous remnant.

Plan your night's program judiciously, choosing objects when they are high enough above the horizon to provide a fair view. A dark, moonless night is very helpful for getting fine views of the brightest objects and a necessity for spotting the fainter ones.

NGC 1931 is a small nebula in Auriga, illuminated by both emission and reflection of light from an open star cluster embedded in the nebulosity. Although photographs show the nebula as amorphous and filamentary, the visual appearance in a small telescope is simply an irregular patch of nebulosity whose light is almost overwhelmed by the cluster.

The constellation Taurus holds one of the sky's best examples of a supernova remnant, M1 (NGC 1952). Called the Crab Nebula because of crab-like filaments that extend outward from the nebula's center, M1 is a bright oval easily visible in small scopes. Over 900 years ago Chinese astronomers witnessed a star so bright it was visible during the daytime for several weeks. That star produced the remnant we see today as the Crab Nebula. The youth of this expanding cloud accounts for the Crab's easy visibility. Since the nebulosity has expanded for a mere 900 years, the remnant is small and surface brightness of the nebulosity is relatively high. The crab-like appendages aren't visible in a backyard telescope, but you will see a bright, 6' by 4' patch of evenly-illuminated gray light.

Also in Taurus is the Pleiades star cluster, the most obvious clustering of stars to the naked eye. The bright, dipper-shaped group of suns is easy to inspect with any optical instrument, but there's another feature that is rather difficult to see by comparison. Surrounding several of the brightest stars in the Pleiades is a faint reflection nebula, the brightest part of which is called NGC 1435. To see the nebulosity that surrounds some of the Pleiades stars, use either binoculars or a low power, wide field, telescope on a moonless night. The nebulosity is particularly evident around the stars Merope (NGC1435) and Maia. However, make sure that you don't mistake reflections caused by the bright stars or moisture on a lens or eyepiece as the nebulosity!

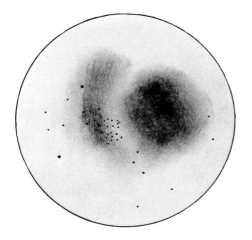

Fig. 7-21. **The Lagoon Nebula**

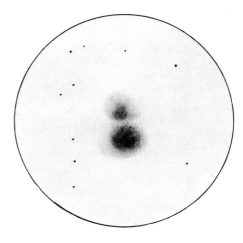

Fig. 7-22. **The Trifid Nebula**

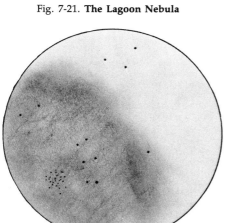

Fig. 7-23. **The Rosette Nebula**

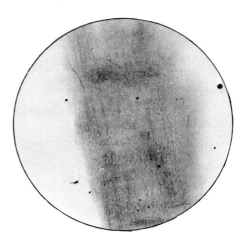

Fig. 7-24. **The California Nebula**

Perhaps the finest nebula visible to northern hemisphere observers--and maybe the most loved deep-sky object of all--is M42 (NGC 1976), the so-called Orion Nebula. The Orion Nebula is the brightest part of an enormous complex of emission and reflection nebulosity. M42 proper spans 66' by 60' and shines with the light of a 3rd-magnitude star. Physically, the nebula measures some 25 light-years across and lies at a distance of 1,600 light-years. M42 is visible to the naked eye as a hazy patch of light in the middle of Orion's sword, south of the easily-recognizable line of three "belt stars."

M42 is the picture-perfect nebula for small scopes. Even when the seeing is slightly poor, M42 appears as a bright, grayish-green nebulosity in binoculars. A 3-inch telescope shows it as a large cloud of shining haze surrounding a tiny cluster of stars. A 6-inch telescope under a moonless sky reveals a low-power field full of subtle green nebulosity varying in brightness and contrast but with an impressive form. When the seeing is good and transparency absolutely crisp (during and early morning in winter or after the passage of a late fall cool front), M42 appears as a fluid painting of subtle nebular shades, gently glowing against the dark sky background.

At the center of M42 lies the Trapezium, a quadruple star so named because of its shape. The star is catalogued as Theta^2 Orionis, and these very suns are responsible for providing the energy to excite the nebula's hydrogen gas into shining. All the stars in this region are young, and many are variable. The variable stars in this field are either slow irregulars or rapid flickerers, which can vary by as much as one fifth of a magnitude over the course of a few minutes.

If you view M42 carefully you'll see a detached blob of bright nebulosity to the north of the main nebula that surrounds a bright star and appears like a backwards comma. This is M43 (NGC 1982), a part of the same nebular complex that appears separate due to obscuring dark nebulosity in the foreground. M43 measures 20' by 25' and glows at magnitude 9, making it an easy target for small scopes if the sky is dark. In fact, if M43 weren't overshadowed by its giant neighbor, the little comma-shaped blob of light would probably be much more popular.

Moving northward in Orion back up to the easternmost belt star, we come to NGC 2024. This oddly shaped nebula is rather bright but occasionally difficult to see since the belt star Zeta Orionis lies so close. The trick to seeing NGC 2024 is to move a few arcminutes east of the bright star and increase the magnification such that Zeta lies outside the field. Now slowly sweep your telescope and look for a ghostly brightening of the field. When you find NGC 2024 you'll be impressed by the broad swath of dark nebulosity that bisects this emission nebula.

Still further north in Orion is one of the brightest examples of a reflection nebula in the sky, M78 (NGC 2068). This object is smaller and much easier to spot than the reflection nebulosity around the Pleiades cluster. M78's surface brightness is considerably higher, allowing you to use greater magnification to inspect details of the nebula. Viewed in a 4-inch scope, M78 appears as a faint comet-like cloud of gray light surrounding two bright stars.

The summer sky holds several spectacular examples of bright nebulae. The best of these is M8 (NGC 6523), also called the Lagoon Nebula because of a wide band of dust that crosses the nebulosity. When Sagittarius is on the meridian, the Lagoon Nebula is visible to the naked eye as a large (90' by 40') patch of fuzz above the spout

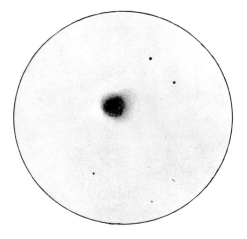

Fig. 7-25. **M78 in Orion**

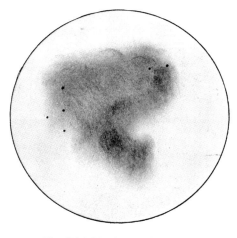

Fig. 7-26. **North America Nebula**

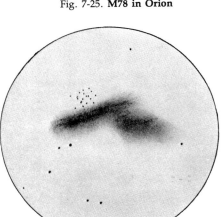

Fig. 7-27. **The Omega Nebula**

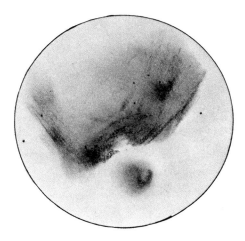

Fig. 7-28. **The Orion Nebula**

of the constellation's "teapot" shape. Small telescopes show M8 as one of the most impressive nebulae in the sky: visible is NGC 6530, a large scattered group of stars, and two bright patches of nebulosity. Gazing the M8 for several minutes reveals a fainter "layer" of nebulosity in which the cluster and bright nebulae are immersed, and the central dark band of dust that separates the two main areas of nebulosity.

Only 2° north of the Lagoon Nebula is another bright emission object designated M20 (NGC 6514). This object consists of two distinct parts as well, a bright, southern section of emission nebulosity and a northern part that is mostly reflection nebulosity. Nicknamed the Trifid Nebula by the English astronomer John Herschel, the southern section contains three prominent lanes of dark nebulosity that meet at the nebula's center. Also at the center is a bright double star that is visible in small scopes.

A marvelous object for small telescopes because of its exceptionally high surface brightness, M17 (NGC 6618) in Sagittarius is known as the Omega Nebula. One night in March I observed nearly all of the Messier objects, and decided that M17 is my favorite because of its attractive shape. The Omega Nebula's brightest sections, consisting of a straight bar of nebulosity and a curved extension on one side, appear like an omega or a squashed figure "2." To William Herschel this shape appeared distinctly like an omega, but to me it looks more like a swan, so I use an alternate nickname of the "Swan Nebula."

Three degrees north of M17 lies the considerable expanse of a bright open cluster surrounded by the so-called Eagle Nebula, M16 (NGC 6611). Covering 35' by 28', the Eagle Nebula provides a sharp contrast to M17 since its surface brightness is far lower. On nights of poor seeing, in fact, you may see only the bright open cluster that lies in this spot. But on dark, transparent nights you'll see a large, milky haze covering the cluster. With a 6-inch scope, you may see several indistinct dark patches projected onto the face of this gray-green nebulosity. M16 actually does look something like an eagle, but only on long-exposure photographs made with large telescopes.

Cygnus holds one of the sky's grandest examples of any type of nebula. NGC 7000 is an immense nebulosity covering 120' by 100' and lying only 3° east of the bright star Deneb (Alpha Cygni). Deneb is the star that illuminates this giant cloud of emission nebulosity, which is plainly visible to the naked eye under a dark sky, and usually surprises first-time viewers with its size. Although its exact shape is difficult to make out visually, in photographs this object greatly resembles the continent of North America, thus giving rise to the nickname North America Nebula.

Fortunately, NGC 7000's outline of North America is defined by extremely opaque dark nebulae, making the bright nebulosity relatively easy to see. Binoculars show the ghostly haze peppered with faint stars, and small telescopes at low power show the nebula's basic shape. NGC 7000 is a fine example of an object best observed by small telescopes, since larger scopes are incapable of staying at low enough powers to show much of the object. A faint open cluster, NGC 6997, lies in the northwestern quarter of the North America Nebula.

ADVANCED OBSERVING TECHNIQUES

Faint nebulae offer one of the most difficult challenges for small telescope observers. Since the surface brightnesses of many nebulae are extremely low, you must observe these nebulae on a clear, dark, moonless night when the seeing and transparency are at their best. Once you've mastered finding and spotting details in objects described in the previous chapter, use your telescope to locate some of the following nebulae. Don't be discouraged if some of these objects remain elusive during many observing sessions, however: they are some of the most difficult objects for small telescopes in the sky.

Less than one degree north and east of the 3rd-magnitude star Gamma Cassiopeiae lie two large, faint patches of nebulosity called IC 59 and IC 63. These nebulosities measure 10' by 5' (IC 59) and 10' by 3' across and have extremely low surface brightnesses, shining in part by reflected light supplied by Gamma Cassiopeiae. The best method for locating these elusive patches of light is to position your telescope northeast of Gamma and, with good dark adaptation, sweep slowly using a low-power eyepiece while avoiding Gamma. If you let the bright star inside the eyepiece field, your dark adaptation will be sufficiently hurt by the glaring light that you may not see the nebulosity!

Some 4° south of Gamma Cassiopeiae lies a much larger emission nebula designated NGC 281. This object is relatively easy to photograph, but fairly difficult to spot visually due to a low surface brightness. Spanning 35' by 30', NGC 281 requires using your absolute lowest power in order to fit the nebulosity inside the telescope's field of view and include in the field some dark sky; this will help to show the faint milky light from NGC 281 by contrasting it against the slightly darker sky background.

NGC 1491 is a small emission nebula located 2° northwest of the 4th-magnitude star Lambda Persei. Surrounding an 11th-magnitude star, NGC 1491 is a round patch of hazy light some 3' in diameter that is relatively easy to make out on dark, transparent nights. However, challenge yourself on nights when the sky is extremely dark by attempting to spot a larger, much fainter envelope of light that surrounds the bright patch.

Fifteen degrees south of NGC 1491 lies one of the most famous--and elusive--emission nebulae in the sky. NGC 1499, popularly known as the California Nebula because of its distinctive shape, is a real challenge for small telescope users. The center of this magnificent nebula is placed 1° northeast of the 4th-magnitude star Xi Persei, the star responsible for exciting the California Nebula's gas into fluorescence.

The California Nebula measures a whopping 145' by 40' and its subtle light can be photographed with a telephoto lens under a dark sky. To see this nebula, however, you'll need a pair of large binoculars or a small RFT (a 6-inch f/5 scope may be ideal) and an extremely dark, moonless night. As with NGC 281, use a low-power eyepiece. (A nebular filter normally helps observing very low surface brightness objects like the California Nebula; use one if you have it.) Sweep slowly north of the star Xi, and carefully compare any nebulous light you suspect with a patch of sky a degree or two away. Use averted vision, which may help to spot the brightest parts of the nebulosity. So subtle may be the California Nebula's light that you may perceive it as a ghostly brightening of the sky background, barely perceptible to the untrained eye.

The constellation Auriga holds an easier yet still challenging target. IC 405, occasionally called the Flaming Star Nebula, is an emission nebula measuring 30' by 19' that surrounds (and is lit by) the erratic variable star AE Aurigae. AE Aurigae is an Orion-type nebular variable star, but its slight fluctuations in brightness are difficult and unpredictable to follow. The nebula has a low surface brightness but is visible in a low-power field as a wispy haze peppered with faint stars. A 20'-diameter reflection nebula lies just southeast of the brighter emission region, and is faintly visible on very dark nights.

One of Orion's most elusive objects is the Horsehead Nebula, a dark dust cloud catalogued as object number 33 in E.E. Barnard's catalogue of dark nebulae. One of the most photographed objects in the sky, this 6' by 4' cloud is silhouetted against the faint strip of emission nebulosity IC 434. To locate the Horsehead's position, start by moving your telescope south of the bright star Zeta Orionis (the easternmost of Orion's "belt stars") by about 30'. This will place you in the immediate vicinity of the Horsehead, and you should see a faint north-south nebulosity. (If you don't see this nebulosity after diligent searching, give up: you won't see the Horsehead.) Once you see the faint nebulosity, you may scan up and down a slight amount until you spot a small dark "blob" projected over the eastern edge of the nebulosity. This is the Horsehead Nebula.

If you absolutely cannot find the Horsehead Nebula, don't worry. Relatively few observers ever see this exceptionally difficult object with a small telescope. Although the nebula has been spotted under perfect conditions by observers with 4-inch or 6-inch telescopes, you may have to place the Horsehead on your list of objects to observe when you get a larger instrument.

Another difficult object in Orion is an enormous ancient supernova remnant called Barnard's Loop. E.E. Barnard discovered this object using a 5-inch refractor, but the faint outlines of this gently glowing emission gas require a very crisp, clear night to be seen. The eastern section of Barnard's Loop, the brightest of three main parts, covers 600' by 30', or 10 by 0.5 degrees. This loop begins in central Orion and winds southward through the star cluster NGC 2112, ending finally at a declination equal to that of the central belt star. A great deal of patience, a wide field, a nebular filter, and much slow, careful sweeping will be required to spot the highest surface brightness parts of this enormous objects.

Nearby in the rather dim constellation Monoceros is an object that is, like the Horsehead Nebula, much celebrated but difficult to visually observe. Located 3° east of the 4th-magnitude star Epsilon Monocerotis, the Rosette Nebula is a large wreath-shaped ring of nebulosity surrounding the bright star cluster NGC 2244. Known by the NGC numbers 2237-9 and 2246, the nebulosity shines by emission and covers an area 80' by 60' across. To spot this nebulosity, follow the same rules--averted vision, slow sweeping, nebular filter, and wide field of view--you've used with the other challenging objects in this section.

Four degrees northeast of the Rosette is a much smaller, oddly-shaped nebula that varies in brightness and size with time. NGC 2261, or Hubble's Variable Nebula (so called because Edwin Hubble discovered its variability in 1916), is one of the strangest nebulae you'll get the chance to observe with a small telescope. The star that powers this nebula is called R Moncerotis, an irregular variable whose light fluctuations cause the nebula to vary in brightness and shape. NGC 2261 normally appears as a faint triangular patch of gray

light 2' by 1' in extent. Observe this object over several weeks
and ultimately over several years, and you may see that it appears
distinctly different at different times.

The constellation Ophiuchus holds one of the sky's best examples
of a dark nebula. Barnard 72, called the "S" Nebula because of its
winding shape, lies 1.5 degrees north and slightly east of Theta
Ophiuchi. Stretching over about 30', B72 is outlined by a rich field
of stars visible in small scopes on a dark night. Because this dark
nebula is relatively large, be sure to use a wide-field eyepiece when
searching for it. Also near Theta Ophiuchi is Barnard 78, the so-called
Pipe Nebula. This object is a marked contrast to B72, requiring a
telescope of at least 6-inches in aperture and a very dark night.
If you can't find this object, don't be discouraged.

Barnard 92, on the other hand, is an easy dark nebula. This
oval patch of darkness lies on the northeastern side of the star cloud
M24 in Sagittarius, and can be observed in large binoculars. B92
measures 12' by 6' and stands out well because of the remarkable
contrast between the dark nebulosity and star cloud. Barnard 93,
another dark nebula, lies 30' east of B92 and covers 12' by 2'.

Several patches of dark nebulosity lie about 3° northwest of
Altair, in the constellation Aquila. Designated B133, B142, and B143,
these objects are striking in contrast to the surrounding star fields
and can be observed with a 4-inch RFT on a dark night. B133 is just
south of Lambda Aquilae, and B142 and B143, which together form a
"E" shape, are about 1.5 degrees west of Lambda Aquilae.

Barnard 86, a dark nebula just 4' in diameter, lies just east
of the bright star cluster NGC 6520 in Sagittarius. It is visible
because it is projected against the dense Sagittarius Milky Way, and
hence is a beautifully delicate sight in large instruments. Barnard
90 is nearby, lying south of NGC 6520.

The following is a list of 223 bright and dark nebulae specifically
selected for their fine appearance in small telescopes. You will need
very dark, very clear skies to see most of these objects; the slightest
light pollution, haze, or moonlight will render many of these objects
invisible. Most of these nebulae require a low power eyepiece for
detection.

Explanation of data: The coordinates provided are for epoch 1950.0.
Type: E=emission nebula, R=reflection nebula, D=dark nebula, S=supernova
remnant, ER=complex region of nebulosity. Mag.=visual magnitude of
bright nebula, unless followed by a "p," which denotes a photographic
magnitude. Size=nebula's angular size in arcminutes. Opacity=Lynds
Opacity Level Number for dark nebulae; 1=least opaque, 6=most opaque.

CATALOG NUMBER	R.A.(1950)Dec. h m ° '	Type	Mag.	Size '	Opacity
_____AQUILA					
B127	18 59 -05 30	D	---	4.5	5

Irregular; very opaque in southeast portion--B129
and B130 connected on the western side.

| B135 | 19 05   -04 00 | D | --- | 13.0 | 6 |

Dusky spot--9th mag. stars on north and southeast
edges.

B136	19 06 -04 05	D	---	8.0	6
B139	19 15 -01 30	D	---	8.0	5
B142	19 37 +10 25	D	---	40.0	5
B143	19 39 +10 55	D	---	30.0	6
B340	19 46 +11 15	D	---	7.0	5
_____AURIGA					
B221	04 40 +31 40	D	---	45.0	3
L1490	04 49 +35 35	D	---	18.0	4
	04 50 +38 00	D	---	15.0	4
B26	04 52 +30 33	D	---	5.0	6
L1475	05 00 +45 00	D	---	41.0	3
B29	05 03 +31 30	D	---	10.0	6
L1510	05 13 +34 45	D	---	33.0	3
IC 405	05 13 +34 16	E	---	25.0	-

Very faint nebula surrounding variable star AE
Aurigae. 2.4-inch shows a tiny wisp of gas in a
horseshoe shape. 4-inch shows little more.

| IC 410 | 05 19   +33 28 | E | --- | 20.0 | - |

Involved with open cluster NGC 1893; faintly visible
in 6-inch.

| IC 417 | 05 20   +34 12 | E | --- | 20.0 | - |
| NGC 1931 | 05 28   +34 13 | E | 12? | 3.0 | - |

Bright small nebula encapsulating three faint stars.

CATALOG NUMBER	R.A.(1950) h m	Dec. ° '	Type	Mag.	Size '	Opacity

AURIGA (Continued)

	05 30	+30 00	D	---	100.0	5
NGC 1985	05 35	+31 58	E	---	1.0	-
B34	05 40	+32 35	D	---	20.0	5
L1555	05 58	+31 50	D	---	20.0	4

CAMELOPARDALIS

| B8 | 04 14 | +55 05 | D | --- | 150.0x30.0 | 5 |
| B12 | 04 26 | +54 10 | D | --- | 24.0 | 5 |

Isolated dark spot southeast of B11; round.

CANIS MAJOR

NGC 2327	07 02	-11 14	R	---	20.0	-
IC 2177	07 03	-10 29	E	---	85.0x25.0	-
NGC 2359	07 15	-13 07	E	---	7.0	-

A dozen stars involved in milky nebulosity.

CASSIOPEIA

	00 05	+60 00	D	---	---	6
	00 07	+58 35	D	---	45.0	3
L1299	00 36	+55 00	D	---	50.0	5
L1290	00 39	+60 50	D	---	60.0	5
NGC 281	00 51	+56 19	E	---	25.0	-

Faint horseshoe shaped nebulosity around the multiple star Burnham 1; faint in 2-inch scope.

L1305	01 00	+67 30	D	---	---	4
L1332	01 42	+61 40	D	---	30.0	4
L1336	01 50	+66 30	D	---	---	4
L1370	02 28	+60 15	D	---	25.0	4
IC 1805	02 28	+61 15	E	---	150.0	-

Enormous patch of faint nebulosity involved with open cluster Mel 15. Very faint but visible in a 6-inch.

| IC 1848 | 02 48 | +60 13 | E | --- | 60.0x30.0 | - |

Very faint patchy nebula in 2-inch; group of 8th mag. stars near center.

| NGC 7635 | 23 19 | +60 54 | E | --- | 4.0 | - |

The Bubble Nebula. Near open cluster M52; faintly visible as nebulous arc in 6-inch.

| L1238 | 23 30 | +59 30 | D | --- | --- | 6 |

CEPHEUS

| B150 | 20 50 | +60 05 | D | --- | 25.0 | 5 |

A great curved dark marking; contains 8th mag. star on northeastern edge.

CATALOG NUMBER	R.A.(1950)Dec. h m ° '	Type	Mag.	Size '	Opacity
_____CEPHEUS (Continued)_____					
NGC 7023	21 01 +67 58	R	---	18.0	-

Faint and challenging for a 4-inch.

| B160 | 21 36   +56 00 | D | --- | 31.0 | 4 |
| IC 1396 | 21 38   +57 14 | E | 13.5? | 150.0 | - |

Large roundish nebula; covers entire low power field
in 2-inch scope. Four dark nebulae involved, and a
bright open cluster; reddish star Mu [ ] Cephei--
Herschel's "Garnet Star"--lies on northern tip.

| B161 | 21 39   +57 35 | D | --- | 13.0 | 6 |

Small black spot shaped like a comet.

NGC 7129	21 42 +65 52	R	---	7.0	-
NGC 7133	21 43 +65 56	R	---	3.0	-
B169	21 57 +58 30	D	---	60.0	3

Elliptical black ring which encloses an island of
bright stars.

B173	22 06 +59 25	D	---	4.0	6
L1204	22 25 +63 00	D	---	---	3
_____CORONA AUSTRALIS_____					
NGC 6726/7	18 58 -36 58	R	---	2.0	-

A complex region of bright and dark nebulae involved
with the nebular variable stars R and TY Coronae
Australis. Visible as a fuzzy spot in a 2-inch.

NGC 6729	18 58 -37 02	R	---	1.0	-
IC 4812	19 02 -37 08	R	---	---	-
_____CYGNUS_____					
M1-92	19 35 +29 29	R	---	0.2	-

The Footprint Nebula. Stellar in a 2-inch; nebulous
in a 6-inch. Involved with tiny dark nebula.

	19 50 +29 30	D	---	---	4
B144	19 56 +35 10	D	---	360.0	1
B145	20 01 +37 35	D	---	45.0	4

Sharply defined and triangular. Contains 10th mag.
star in center; 7th mag. star just north.

| NGC 6888 | 20 11   +38 16 | S | 14.5? | 15.0x8.0 | - |

Supernova remnant; visible in 2-inch as a large
faint loop amidst a diamond shaped group of 7th and
8th mag. stars.

CATALOG NUMBER	R.A.(1950)Dec. h m ° '	Type	Mag.	Size '	Opacity

CYGNUS (Continued)

| IC 1318 | 20 15 | +41 39 | E | --- | 24.0x17.0 | - |
| IC 1318 | 20 22 | +40 35 | E | --- | 70.0x20.0 | - |

These two patches bear the same NGC number and lie near the star Gamma [γ] Cygni. Large and faint in a 2-inch at low power; lies on western edge of dark nebula Lynds 888. On eastern edge is nebula NGC 6914. Larger portion contains open cluster NGC 6910. Many bright field stars involved.

| NGC 6914 | 20 23 | +42 10 | R | --- | 6.0 | - |

Faintly visible in 2-inch; routine in 6-inch.

L864	20 40	+32 00	D	---	100.0	3
	20 40	+47 30	D	---	30.0	5
NGC 6960	20 44	+30 32	S	12.5?	70.0x6.0	-

Western half of the Veil Nebula, a huge supernova remnant. Bisected by bright star 52 Cygni. Appears as long misty streamer of light in 2.4-inch; 6-inch shows it well at high power.

| NGC 6979 | 20 46 | +31 30 | S | 14.0? | 40.0x20.0 | - |

Middle patch of the Veil Nebula. Tough for a 6-inch.

| IC 5067 | 20 47 | +44 11 | E | --- | 85.0x75.0 | - |

The Pelican Nebula. Visible as a large faint milky patch in 7x35 binoculars--better seen in 4-inch RFT.

| IC 5076 | 20 54 | +47 13 | R | --- | 9.0x6.0 | - |
| NGC 6992/5 | 20 54 | +31 30 | S | 12.0? | 78.0x8.0 | - |

Eastern half of the Veil Nebula. Brighter than NGC 6960; visible as a twisted curving streamer in a 4-inch RFT. Binoculars show a thin milky strip.

| B352 | 20 56 | +45 40 | D | --- | 22.0 | 5 |
| NGC 7000 | 20 57 | +44 08 | E | 13.0? | 120.0x100.0 | - |

The North America Nebula. An enormous greenish patch of light in binoculars on dark nights. 4-inch and 6-inch RFTs easily show its continental outline, various dark nebulae surrounding its borders.

| B356 | 20 58 | +46 30 | D | --- | 24.0 | 5 |
| B358 | 21 04 | +43 05 | D | --- | 20.0 | 6 |

This long dark area contains the reddish orange star Xi [ξ] Cygni and connects with a dark region between the North America and Pelican Nebulae.

| NGC 7027 | 21 05 | +42 02 | E | --- | 0.4x0.3 | - |

CATALOG NUMBER	R.A.(1950)Dec. h m ° '	Type	Mag.	Size '	Opacity

_____CYGNUS (Continued)_____

B364	21 32	+54 20	D	---	75.0	5
B159	21 36	+43 00	D	---	25.0	5
L1035	21 43	+47 30	D	---	80.0x40.0	5
B164	21 45	+50 50	D	---	20.0	5

A V-shaped vacancy running north-south.

| B168 | 21 51 | +47 00 | D | --- | 10.0 | 3 |
| IC 5146 | 21 51 | +47 02 | E | 13.5? | 12.0 | - |

The Cocoon Nebula. 2-inch shows a large milky spot involved with several dark lanes and many faint stars.

_____ERIDANUS_____

| IC 2118 | 05 05 | -07 17 | R | --- | 140.0x40.0 | - |

The Witch Head Nebula. Large faint nebula illuminated by Rigel (Beta [β] Orionis). Fainter than the California Nebula in Perseus, it requires excellent transparency.

_____HERCULES_____

| L659 | 18 39 | +14 00 | D | --- | --- | 4 |

_____LUPUS_____

| B228 | 15 41 | -34 20 | D | --- | --- | 4 |

_____MONOCEROS_____

| NGC 2149 | 06 02 | -09 45 | R | --- | 3.0 | - |
| NGC 2170 | 06 05 | -06 23 | R | --- | 1.0 | - |

Faint reflection nebula visible in a 4.5-inch scope.

NGC 2182	06 07	-06 19	R	---	3.0	-
NGC 2183	06 08	-06 12	R	---	1.0	-
NGC 2185	06 09	-06 12	R	---	2.0	-
NGC 2237/9	06 30	+04 40	E	13.5?	60.0	-

The Rosette Nebula. This object requires a wide field of view: visible in a 2-inch as a large hazy patch.

NGC 2245	06 30	+10 12	R	---	5.0x3.0	-
B37	06 30	+10 30	D	---	150.0	4
NGC 2247	06 30	+10 22	R	---	4.0x3.0	-
NGC 2261	06 36	+08 46	R	var.	5.0x3.0	-

Hubble's Variable Nebula. Surrounding the 11th mag. star R Monocerotis, this bright nebula fluctuates in brightness with the star. Easy in a 2-inch, requires high power to see triangular fan-like shape.

| NGC 2316 | 06 57 | -07 40 | ER | --- | 4.0x3.0 | - |
| IC 466 | 07 04 | -04 15 | E | --- | 1.0 | - |

CATALOG NUMBER	R.A.(1950)Dec. h m ° '	Type	Mag.	Size '	Opacity
OPHIUCHUS					
B42	16 22 -23 20	D	---	210.0	6

The Great Nebula of Ophiuchus. This vast dark cloud is centered on the star Rho [σ] Ophiuchi.

| IC 4603/4 | 16 22   -23 20 | R | --- | 145.0x70.0 | - |
| B44 | 16 37   -24 00 | D | --- | 600.0x30.0 | 5 |

Great dark lane running eastward from Rho Ophiuchi to south of B63, a stretch of 10° of sky.

B45	16 43 -21 30	D	---	120.0x20.0	5
B51	17 02 -22 10	D	---	20.0	6
B244	17 08 -28 20	D	---	30.0x20.0	5

Irregular; sharp on western side.

B59	17 08 -27 25	D	---	60.0	5
B60	17 09 -22 25	D	---	13.0	3
B63	17 13 -21 25	D	---	100.0x20.0	3
B64	17 14 -18 25	D	---	30.0	6

A cometary nebula showing a very black head and widening tail. Just southwest of globular M9.

B65	17 17 -26 40	D	---	12.0	6
B66	17 17 -26 50	D	---	8.0	6
B254	17 17 -30 05	D	---	60.0x20.0	5
B67	17 18 -26 50	D	---	---	6
B67A	17 20 -21 50	D	---	13.0	6
B68	17 20 -23 45	D	---	4.0	6

20' southwest of B72.

| B72 | 17 21   -23 35 | D | --- | 30.0 | 6 |

The "S" Nebula; a small S-shaped dark patch about 2' thick. The southeast branch passes close to a 9th mag. star. Theta [θ] Ophiuchi lies 1.5° south-southwest.

| NGC 6360 | 17 22   -29 57 | R | --- | 5.0 | - |
| B78 | 17 29   -25 35 | D | --- | 180.0 | 4 |

The Pipe Nebula. Visible to the naked eye, it runs south of Theta Ophiuchi.

| B270 | 17 30   -19 35 | D | --- | 11.0 | 5 |
| B272 | 17 34   -23 25 | D | --- | 45.0 | 3 |

Irregular dark markings; 8th mag. star near middle.

| B79 | 17 34   -19 35 | D | --- | 30.0 | 6 |
| B 276 | 17 37   -19 50 | D | --- | 45.0 | 6 |

| ORION | | | | | |
| NGC 1788 | 05 05   -03 24 | ER | 12.0? | 8.0x5.0 | - |

CATALOG NUMBER	R.A.(1950)Dec. h m ° '	Type	Mag.	Size '	Opacity

_____ORION (Continued)_____

| B30 | 05 27 | +12 45 | D | --- | 67.0 | 4 |
| NGC 1973/5/7 | 05 33 | -04 46 | E | 13.0? | 40.0x25.0 | - |

A patch of nebulosity involved with a star cluster near the Orion Nebula (M42). Visible in a 2-inch as a large faint patch of nebulosity.

| NGC 1976 | 05 33 | -05 25 | E | 5.0 | 85.0x60.0 | - |

M42, the Great Nebula in Orion. Visible as a misty patch in Orion's belt to the naked eye; binoculars show a large bright patch involved with a small star cluster. Even a 2-inch at high power shows a wealth of detail in the greenish gas--a 6-inch reveals over a degree of nebulosity. The finest gaseous nebula in the sky.

| NGC 1980 | 05 33 | -05 56 | E | --- | 14.0 | - |

2-inch shows a faint misty patch surrounding Iota [ι] Orionis; 6-inch easily reveals it.

| NGC 1982 | 05 33 | -05 18 | E | 9.1 | 20.0 | - |

M43, a detached portion of the Orion Nebula. Easily visible in a 2-inch surrounding a 9th mag. star.

| NGC 1999 | 05 34 | -06 45 | ER | --- | 15.0 | - |
| B33 | 05 38 | -02 30 | D | --- | 4.0 | 4 |

The Horsehead Nebula. Notoriously difficult, it can be glimpsed in a 6-inch under excellent conditions. Projected in front of nebula IC 434, 30' south of Zeta [ζ] Orionis.

| IC 432 | 05 39 | -01 31 | R | --- | 8.0x4.0 | - |
| IC 434 | 05 39 | -02 26 | E | 13.5? | 60.0x10.0 | - |

Very difficult because of nearby Zeta Orionis. Requires excellent transparency and Zeta out of field to show in a 6-inch.

| NGC 2023 | 05 39 | -02 15 | ER | --- | 10.0 | - |

Round and faint in 2-inch; 4-inch shows a round easy nebula with absorption on east side.

| NGC 2024 | 05 39 | -01 52 | E | 12.0? | 30.0 | - |

Adjacent to Zeta Orionis: 2-inch barely shows it with Zeta out of telescopic field. 4-inch shows it well, complete with dust lane splitting the gas into two parts.

| IC 435 | 05 41 | -02 20 | R | --- | 3.0 | - |

CATALOG NUMBER	R.A.(1950) Dec. h m ° '	Type	Mag.	Size '	Opacity

CATALOG NUMBER	R.A.(1950) Dec.		Type	Mag.	Size	Opacity
B35	05 43	+09 00	D	---	20.0x10.0	5
NGC 2068	05 44	+00 02	R	8.0	8.0x6.0	-

M78. 2-inch shows a cometary appearance, tail
protruding southward. Two 10th mag. stars involved.

CATALOG NUMBER	R.A.(1950) Dec.		Type	Mag.	Size	Opacity
NGC 2071	05 45	+00 17	R	---	4.0	-
B36	05 47	+07 25	D	---	120.0x10.0	4
L1629	06 07	+02 30	D	---	60.0	3
NGC 2174/5	06 07	+20 31	E	---	29.0x20.0	-

Involved with a bright star cluster. 2-inch shows a
large round nebulosity surrounding an 8th mag. star.
4.5-inch improves view and shows the cluster well.

CATALOG NUMBER	R.A.(1950) Dec.		Type	Mag.	Size	Opacity
	06 10	+12 30	D	---	60.0	5

CATALOG NUMBER	R.A.(1950) Dec.		Type	Mag.	Size	Opacity
NGC 1333	03 26	+31 12	ER	---	9.0x5.0	-

2-inch shows a bright nebular complex right in the
midst of dark nebula Barnard 1.

CATALOG NUMBER	R.A.(1950) Dec.		Type	Mag.	Size	Opacity
B1	03 30	+31 00	D	---	60.0	4
B5	03 45	+32 45	D	---	60.0	5

6th mag. star Eta [η] Persei near northeast side.

CATALOG NUMBER	R.A.(1950) Dec.		Type	Mag.	Size	Opacity
NGC 1491	04 00	+51 10	E	---	3.0	-

Very faint; visible in a 4.5-inch scope.

CATALOG NUMBER	R.A.(1950) Dec.		Type	Mag.	Size	Opacity
NGC 1499	04 00	+36 17	E	14.5?	145.0x40.0	-

The California Nebula. Very faint and extremely
difficult to view, it can nevertheless be observed
with binoculars or wide-field 2-inch scope under
ideal conditions. The southern half is quite a bit
brighter than the northern half, especially where
a 6th mag. star lies inside the nebula's border.

CATALOG NUMBER	R.A.(1950) Dec.		Type	Mag.	Size	Opacity
L1459	04 05	+39 30	D	---	---	3
NGC 1579	04 27	+35 10	R	---	12.0x8.0	-

A complex nebula with a 10th mag. star near the
nucleus. 2-inch shows a condensed nucleus, and two
streamers of nebulosity; one pointing toward an 8th
mag. star, the other toward a 9th mag. star. 6-inch
shows dark structure in the object.

CATALOG NUMBER	R.A.(1950) Dec.		Type	Mag.	Size	Opacity
B15	04 28	+46 30	D	---	10.0x15.0	5

Elliptical; a very fine dark nebula!

CATALOG NUMBER	R.A.(1950) Dec.		Type	Mag.	Size	Opacity
B20	04 33	+50 55	D	---	8.0	2

CATALOG NUMBER	R.A.(1950)Dec. h m ° '	Type	Mag.	Size '	Opacity
_____PERSEUS (Continued)_____					
NGC 1624	04 37 +50 21	E	---	3.0x5.0	-

Nebulous patch with condensed northern end in 2-inch; 4.5-inch scope revealed a Y-shaped cluster of stars.

_____PUPPIS_____					
NGC 2467	07 51 -26 16	E	---	4.0	-
_____SAGITTA_____					
	19 00 +20 00	D	---	60.0	5
_____SAGITTARIUS_____					
B84	17 43 -20 15	D	---	20.0	6

Irregular looped figure; 8th mag. star near western end, 9th mag. star near eastern end.

B289	17 53 -29 00	D	---	35.0x7.0	4
B84A	17 55 -17 40	D	---	16.0	5
B291	17 56 -33 55	D	---	5.0	5
NGC 6514	17 59 -23 02	ER	9.0	29.0x27.0	-

M20, the Trifid Nebula. 2-inch shows large faint hazy nebulosity, with bright star in center. 6-inch shows a enormous nebulosity with three conspicuous intersecting dark lanes--north of the main nebula is a fainter patch of reflection nebulosity. The star in the nebula's center is a double.

B85	17 59 -23 00	D	---	---	5

Encroaches on the southern end of M20.

B86	18 00 -27 50	D	---	5.0	5
B87	18 01 -32 30	D	---	---	4

The Parrot's Head Nebula. Contains 9th mag. star in center; several others.

B296	18 01 -24 30	D	---	6.0x1.0	5

On southern edge of M8.

NGC 6523	18 02 -24 20	E	5.0	60.0x35.0	-

M8, the Lagoon Nebula. Visible to the naked eye, this giant patch of bright nebulosity is an easy 2-inch scope target. It shows a large circular patch of gas surrounding a bright star cluster and a second long section of nebulosity separated by a broad dark lane. 6-inch shows a great amount of detail. One of the finest nebulae in the sky!

B88	18 02 -24 10	D	---	2.7x0.5	5

CATALOG NUMBER	R.A.(1950) h m	Dec. ° '	Type	Mag.	Size '	Opacity

CATALOG NUMBER	R.A. h m	Dec. ° '	Type	Mag.	Size	Opacity
IC 4678	18 05	-23 53	E	---	4.0x1.0	-
IC 4684	18 06	-23 27	E	---	10.0x5.0	-
IC 4685	18 06	-24 01	E	---	10.0	-
B90	18 07	-28 15	D	---	3.0	5
NGC 6559	18 07	-24 08	E	---	8.0x5.0	-
B91	18 07	-23 40	D	---	5.0	5
B304	18 10	-18 45	D	---	90.0x10.0	3
B92	18 13	-18 15	D	---	15.0x9.0	6

Black spot with 12th mag. star near middle.

| NGC 6589 | 18 13 | -19 49 | R | --- | 3.0x2.0 | - |
| NGC 6590 | 18 14 | -19 54 | R | --- | 15.0 | - |

NGC 6589 and 6590 are two faint reflection nebulae barely visible in a 2-inch.

| B93 | 18 14 | -18 05 | D | --- | 15.0 | 4 |

Cometary; 2' diameter head with 15' long tail south.

IC 1283/4	18 15	-19 41	R	---	15.0	-
B307	18 16	-18 00	D	---	6.0	3
NGC 6618	18 18	-16 12	E	6.0	46.0x37.0	-

M17, the Omega Nebula. One of the brightest emission nebulae in the sky; binoculars show a small hazy bar of nebulosity. 2-inch reveals a large bright bar and extended misty nebulosity, involved in a bright open cluster. A marvelous object!

| B98 | 18 30 | -26 05 | D | --- | 3.0 | 6 |

Very small but sharply defined; 9th mag. star about 10' southwest.

_____SCORPIUS_____

| IC 4592 | 16 09 | -19 20 | R | --- | 175.0x45.0 | - |

Faint reflection nebula around Nu [ν] Scorpii. Shows well in 6-inch scopes on dark nights.

| B40 | 16 12 | -18 50 | D | --- | 15.0 | 3 |
| IC 4601 | 16 16 | -20 06 | R | --- | 22.0x12.0 | - |

Visible in 2-inch on excellent nights; involved with the large dark nebula B41.

B233	16 41	-35 20	D	---	55.0x20.0	3
B237	16 46	-29 55	D	---	---	4
IC 4628	16 53	-40 18	E	13.5?	34.0x16.0	-

2-inch shows a circular nebula around a single star. Lies just northwest of the open cluster H12.

| B240 | 16 56 | -35 15 | D | --- | 20.0 | 5 |

CATALOG NUMBER	R.A.(1950)Dec., h m ° '	Type	Mag.	Size '	Opacity
_____SCORPIUS (Continued)_____					
B48	16 58 -40 35	D	---	40.0x15.0	5
B50	17 00 -34 20	D	---	15.0	3
B55	17 04 -31 55	D	---	16.0	5

Irregular; 9th mag. star near center.

| B58 | 17 08   -40 20 | D | --- | 30.0 | 5 |
| NGC 6302 | 17 11   -37 03 | E | --- | 2.0x1.0 | - |

The Bug Nebula. Difficult to find--2-inch at high power shows a round bright patch with two starlike points in its center.

| B252 | 17 12   -32 05 | D | --- | 20.0 | 5 |

Triangular; 8th mag. star near northeastern end.

| NGC 6334 | 17 17   -36 01 | E | --- | 20.0 | - |

Lies partly within a triangle of bright stars; 2-inch shows a round, uneven, very faint nebula with a number of faint stars involved.

B257	17 19 -35 35	D	---	15.0	3
B258	17 20 -34 40	D	---	40.0	4
NGC 6357	17 21 -34 07	E	---	57.0x44.0	-

2-inch shows a very faint patch of light superimposed upon a row of four 7th mag. stars.

| B271 | 17 30   -34 15 | D | --- | 120.0x10.0 | 3 |
| B275 | 17 36   -32 20 | D | --- | 13.0 | 4 |

Round; 20' west of open cluster M6.

| _____SCUTUM_____ | | | | | |
| IC 1287 | 18 28   -10 50 | R | --- | 44.0x34.0 | - |

A bright nebula within the dark nebulae B97 and B314. 2-inch shows faint nebulosity southwest of a double.

B312	18 29 -15 40	D	---	105.0x30.0	4
B100	18 30 -09 10	D	---	16.0	5
B101	18 30 -08 50	D	---	13.0x4.0	5

Separated from B100 by a scattering of small stars.

| B103 | 18 37   -06 45 | D | --- | 4.0 | 6 |
| B111 | 18 47   -05 00 | D | --- | 120.0 | 3 |

A wide crescent of dark structure east of 4th mag. star 6 Aquilae and north of open cluster M11.

| B112 | 18 48   -06 45 | D | --- | 18.0 | 5 |
| B125 | 18 56   -04 25 | D | --- | 9.0 | 5 |

CATALOG NUMBER	R.A.(1950) h m	Dec. ° '	Type	Mag.	Size '	Opacity

_____SERPENS_____

| B284 | 17 47 | -14 20 | D | --- | 35.0x5.0 | 6 |

Curved; 8th mag. star 5' northwest of center.

| NGC 6611 | 18 16 | -13 48 | E | 6.5 | 35.0x28.0 | - |

M16, the Eagle Nebula. This large patch of milky nebulosity is intermixed with a bright open star cluster, both of which show in good binoculars. 2-inch shows many cluster stars and a general hazy light; a 6-inch shows bright nebulosity and tiny dark lanes.

_____TAURUS_____

| NGC 1435 | 03 43 | +23 36 | R | 13.5? | 30.0 | - |

The Merope Nebula. This difficult reflection gas is associated with the star Merope in the Pleiades Cluster (M45). 6-inch at high power shows a broad fan-shaped streamer of nebulosity running south from the star.

B209	04 10	+28 12	D	---	30.0	5
B7	04 14	+28 25	D	---	30.0	5
B18	04 28	+24 15	D	---	60.0	5
B19	04 30	+26 10	D	---	60.0	4
B22	04 35	+26 00	D	---	120.0	4
IC 2087	04 37	+25 38	E	---	2.0	-
B23	04 37	+29 50	D	---	5.0	5
L1552	05 15	+26 00	D	---	---	4
NGC 1952	05 32	+21 59	S	9.0	8.0x6.0	-

M1, the Crab Nebula--supernova remnant. Easily visible in 2-inch as fuzzy oval patch; 6-inch shows an elongated grainy nebulosity.

_____VULPECULA_____

L769	19 22	+23 00	D	---	60.0x30.0	6
	19 26	+20 00	D	---	---	3
NGC 6813	19 38	+27 11	E	---	3.0	-
NGC 6823	19 41	+23 11	E	---	40.0x30.0	-
	20 12	+26 20	D	---	30.0	5
	20 20	+24 45	D	---	120.0x60.0	5

Fig. 8-1. **M31 in Andromeda**

Galaxies

Alan Goldstein

Have you ever looked up in the sky and wondered how far you can see? With your naked eye, under dark skies, the most distant celestial object visible is the Andromeda Galaxy (M31), which lies 2.25 million light years away. The light you see left the individual stars in that galaxy about 2,250,000 years ago--before our species, Homo sapiens, had evolved!

Under good transparency, you can observe members of the Coma Galaxy Cluster with a 6-inch telescope--they lie some 100 million light years away. Their light has traveled through space since the time when dinosaurs roamed earth. Under good seeing conditions, you also can observe a quasar named 3C 273 in the constellation Virgo; it is an enigmatic relative of the galaxies and lives over three billion light-years away. The light you see from it left when our solar system was in its infancy.

When you observe a galaxy, you are looking at the combined glow of several hundred billion stars. All of the objects in earlier sections of this book are members of the Milky Way galaxy. But here we turn our attention away from the local neighborhood and probe deep space.

How many galaxies can a small telescope show? At a good site a 4-inch reflector reveals several hundred examples varying from pinwheel-shaped spirals to tiny round ellipticals. Because of the great distances to galaxies, it is exceedingly difficult to observe detail in them. Generally you must be satisfied simply with finding the galaxies and appreciating what they represent.

I wish to thank my friends in the Louisville Astronomical Society and the National Deep Sky Observer's Society, who have kept me observing over the years. I also wish to thank Halton C. Arp, who kindled my interest in galaxies, and Joel Gwinn and John Kielkopf of the University of Louisville, who have allowed me to use their equipment to observe the great galaxies.

Alan Goldstein
Louisville, Kentucky

About the Author: Alan Goldstein is a graduate student in geology and an avid amateur astronomer. In 1976 he founded the National Deep Sky Observer's Society, the sole U.S. national organization of deep-sky observers, which holds annual conventions and publishes the newsletter Betelgeuse. He is also a contributing editor of Deep Sky magazine and has written articles for Astronomy.

Fig. 8-2. **The Whirlpool Galaxy**

Fig. 8-3. **M63 in Canes Venatici**

Fig. 8-4. **Edge-on Spiral NGC 4565**

HISTORICAL BACKGROUND

With the exception of the Magellanic Clouds in the southern hemisphere and the Andromeda galaxy in the northern, no galaxies are visible to the naked eye.   Because of their apparent faintness, galaxies were not studied before the invention of the telescope.

Hypotheses on the nature of huge "island universes" in the sky date back only to 140 years after Galileo turned his crude telescope to the heavens.   In 1750, the philosopher Thomas Wright formulated the idea that the Milky Way--the luminous band of light in the sky--was isolated in space and that other hazy patches littering the heavens were other Milky Ways at greater distances. The German philosopher Immanuel Kant expanded on this theory five years later. Kant freely disregarded speculations that the patches were openings in the firmament or single enormous bodies, flattened by rotation. He correctly considered them to be systems of stars so far away that they appeared unresolved in telescopes. In a book entitled Kosmos, published in 1850, Alexander von Humbolt introduced the term "island universes"; hence Kant's suggestion eventually became known as the "Theory of Island Universes."

Only a small number of galaxies were observed in the 1700s. Out of the 109 objects on Charles Messier's catalog of luminous patches in the sky, 40 are galaxies. In the late 1700s, Sir William Herschel turned his speculum mirror telescopes to the skies and, before he died in 1822, he added some 2500 objects to the list of known deep-sky objects. The luminous patches he couldn't resolve into stars he simply called nebulae, from the Latin word for clouds. Many of Herschel's   nebulae are actually galaxies. William's son John catalogued several thousand additional objects, including many from the southern hemisphere. Today astronomers have photographed hundreds of thousands of galaxies on sky-survey plates, and estimate that several billion exist.

In the middle 1800s a clue to the nature of galaxies arose. William Parsons, the Third Earl of Rosse, revealed spiral structure in some of the nebulae with his 72-inch telescope, the largest in the world at the time. Among the most spectacular examples were M51, M100, M99, and M101.   However, because stellar resolution of even the nearest galaxies was difficult with instruments of the era, the galaxies remained mysterious objects, unwilling to give up their secrets.

Sir William Huggins was the first to examine the spectrum of the nebulae. In 1864 he discovered that the Orion Nebula was a cloud of hot gas (earlier observers had thought nebulae showed a continuous spectrum similar to stars.) The major problem of the day was determining distances. Supernovae--exploding stars--flare up from time to time in galaxies and became important in proving that galaxies are large bodies at great distances from us. In 1885 a supernova exploded near the nucleus of M31. Not knowing of different types of novae, astronomers measured the distance on the assumption that the nova belonged to the Milky Way. This caused distances to be grossly underestimated; M31 was thought to be only 1600 light-years away, when we now know that it lies over 2.2 million light years off. The German astronomer Max Wolf, working at Heidelberg and using a method based on dark nebulae research, obtained the substantially larger figure of 26,000 light years--closer but still off by a factor of 100.

In 1912, Vesto Melvin Slipher, working at Lowell Observatory, found that spectrograms showed many nebulae moving away from us at incredible speeds. The Dutch astronomer Adrian van Maanen undertook a program that lasted several years; he measured the angular motion of spiral "nebulae." His measurements indicated revolutions on the order of 85,000 years, which would be impossible for an object very far away. This was for those who thought galaxies were nearby. As it turned out, his measurements were so small that they were well within the systematic error of the measuring devices. Adrian van Maanen was wrong.

In 1914 the Harvard astronomer Henrietta Swan Leavitt discovered a certain class of variable stars called Cepheids--after Delta   Cephei, the prototype--which showed a definite relationship between brightness fluctuation and period. This proved to be a key breakthrough that would eventually solve the riddle of the galaxies.

Three years later astronomers discovered a supernova in galaxy NGC 6946 in Cepheus, and searches confirmed that three other such explosions occurred earlier in the same year; one in NGC 4527 and two in M100. This added more fuel to the debate on the physical significance of galaxies, a debate carried out formally by two men in Washington. In 1920, Harlow Shapley, an astronomer at Harvard, and Heber D. Curtis, an astronomer from Lick Observatory, met face to face to discuss the Milky Way and the universe. Neither conclusively won or lost because of the paucity of information. Later, after astronomers had made many more observations, Shapley was proven right about the size of the Milky Way and Curtis prevailed on the issue that galaxies are separate bodies.

In 1923, the American astronomer Edwin P. Hubble, working with the Mount Wilson 100-inch reflector, made photographic plates of galaxies M31 and M33 showing them resolved into stars--"dense swarms of images which in no way differ from those of ordinary stars." The question of the nature of galaxies was well on its way toward being solved once and for all. On October 6, 1923, Hubble made a plate of M31 on which he identified faint Cepheid variable stars; using the period-luminosity relationship developed by Henrietta Leavitt, Hubble found that these stars were faint because they lie at great distances. He had cracked the code of the spirals and proved that they are enormous systems of stars lying at great distances.

In the late 1920s, when the external nature of galaxies had been accepted by most of the astronomical community, research turned to finding out what makes a galaxy "work." Hubble continued his interest in the island universes and derived a classification scheme for fitting them into some kind of order. A "tuning fork" diagram illustrated the system.

The 1940s and 1950s was an era for spectroscopy, photography, and photometry in astronomy. Galaxies with enormous redshifts were found (meaning that they were moving away from us at great speeds), and clusters of galaxies grouped together were found, both near and far away. The fairly even distribution of galaxies throughout the sky brought about speculation on the creation of the universe. Studies of galaxies with radio telescopes opened a window to the universe as important as visual and photographic observing. Just what is the nature of galaxies? How do they work? How did they form?

Fig. 8-5. **The Sombrero Galaxy**

Fig. 8-6. **NGC 2903 in Leo**

Fig. 8-7. **M81 in Ursa Major**

Fig. 8-8. **Pinwheel Galaxy M33 in Triangulum**

Fig. 8-9. **NGC 6946 in Cepheus**

Fig. 8-10. **M77 in Cetus**

THE NATURE OF GALAXIES

Before 1923, astronomers thought galaxies were parts of the Milky Way. Some considered them to be distant solar systems in formation; others were simply dumbfounded by their nature. When Edwin Hubble identified Cepheid variables in M31, the argument ended for good. Galaxies, like stars, are not alike. Two galaxies may appear quite alike in some ways, but they are certain to have differences. Stars are classified by their spectral type--determined by their luminosities and temperatures--but galaxies, entire hodgepodges of stars, are classified according to their morphological characteristics.

Out of the 1000 brightest stellar systems, spiral galaxies make up about 75%. Spirals come in two basic shapes--normal or barred--and are flattened disk-shaped systems rich in gas and dust. Many spirals look like glowing pinwheels and are among the most beautiful objects in the universe. Normal spirals show spiral arms extending from the nucleus on out, while in barred spirals a broad central bar cuts across the nucleus, turning into spiral arms some distance out. Most spirals have two arms, but some have only one and others three or four. (The Milky Way is thought to be a four-armed spiral.)

There are four components of a typical spiral galaxy. The first is the nucleus, a dense central region composed of relatively old stars composed only of hydrogen and helium. These old, massive, and relatively cool stars are known as Population II red giants. The second major component of a spiral is the disk component, the flattened disk that contains the spiral arms. A spiral galaxy's disk contains bright, young Population I stars (those rich in elements heavier than hydrogen and helium), regions of ionized hydrogen (HII), hot gas associated with star formation, cool clouds of neutral hydrogen (HI) gas, open star clusters, and stellar associations--virtually all of the deep-sky objects we observe in the Milky Way. The third significant part of a spiral galaxy, the so-called spheroidal component, consists of a halo of globular clusters and old stars centered on the nucleus. The final component of a typical spiral is its corona, a vast cloud of cold molecular hydrogen. Astronomers have only recently recognized the significance of the corona, which may contain most of the mass of a galaxy.

Spiral galaxies are classified according to their hub-to-arm ratio. Broadly speaking, a galaxy with a large central hub and inconspicuous arms is classified as an Sa galaxy. If its arms are as conspicuous as the hub, it is an Sb type; if the arms dominate, it is a type Sc. Here is a brief rundown of the characteristics of different spiral galaxy classifications: S0 = lenticular galaxy. These transition galaxies between spirals and ellipticals will be discussed shortly. Their central regions resemble elliptical galaxies, but their outer halos are flattened into a plane. Thus "lenticular"--lens-shaped. Examples: M102, NGC 404, NGC 2685, NGC 4526, NGC 7332. Sa = spiral galaxies with amorphous nuclei and tightly wound unresolvable spiral arms. Late-type Sa galaxies have prominent dust lanes. Examples: M65, M96, NGC 2775, NGC 3081, NGC 4274. Sb = spiral galaxies which exhibit "middle of the road" characteristics: moderately tightly wound arms, prominent dark lanes, and amorphous nuclei. Examples: the Milky Way, M31, M58, M63, M64, M66, M77, M81, M90, M94, M104, NGC 488, NGC 891, NGC 1964, NGC 2841, NGC 4565, NGC 7217, NGC 7331. (Many of the brightest galaxies, as you might have guessed, are Sb types.) Sc = galaxies with small nuclei and multiple spiral arms which are easily resolved into dusty clumps and knots. Examples: M33, M51, M61, M74, M99, M100, M101, M106, M108, NGC 253, NGC 1232, NGC 2403, NGC 2903, NGC 5907.

Barred spiral galaxies are classified in much the same manner; they are subgrouped into the catagories SB0, SBa, SBb, and SBc. SB0 =

galaxies which resemble lenticulars but have the addition of a bar cutting through their nuclei. Examples: NGC 2859, NGC 2950, NGC 4262, NGC 4643, NGC 5101. SBa = barred spirals with a characteristically smooth unresolved bar and often faint and inconspicuous spiral arms. Examples: NGC 175, NGC 2217, NGC 3185, NGC 4314, NGC 7743. SBb = barred spiral galaxies with a smooth well-defined bar structure unresolvable into stars. Examples: M95, NGC 1097, NGC 1300, NGC 4548, NGC 4593. SBc = barred spirals with open resolvable arms. Examples: NGC 1073, NGC 2525, NGC 3359, NGC 7640, NGC 7741. If a barred spiral's arms start tangent to a ring, it receives the notation (r). If the arms start from the bar, the galaxy is dubbed with the suffix (s).

Some galaxies apparently show characteristics of both normal and barred spirals, and are known as transition barred spirals--dubbed S(B) or S/SB. These are basically barred spiral objects but with ill-defined bars and strong nuclear regions. Examples of this rare type of galaxy are M83, NGC 925, NGC 4088, NGC 4725, and NGC 5364.

Perhaps the oddest variation of a spiral is the "anemic" spiral galaxy, recognized by the Canadian astronomer Sidney van den Bergh in 1975. These are galaxies weak in star forming properties; they are most commonly found in rich galaxy clusters where collisions with intergalactic gas clouds literally knock the star-forming dust out of the galaxies. HII regions and bright supergiant stars are virtually nonexistent in these systems. They can occur as barred or transition barred types. Examples: NGC 3312 in the Hydra cluster of galaxies, NGC 4921 in the Coma Berenices galaxy cluster.

Elliptical galaxies, accounting for another 20% of our nearby 1000 galaxies, are spheroidal homogenous balls of stars without any real internal structure. They contain mainly old yellow and red Population II stars and very little interstellar gas and dust, making them analogous to gigantic globular star clusters or galactic nuclei. (They do contain a low density gas but not in enough quantity to cause star formation.) Elliptical galaxies are classified in degree of roundness from E0 (round) to E7 (highly flattened). Examples of the various catagories are as follows: E0 -- M87, NGC 750/51; E1 -- NGC 4278; E2 -- NGC 2986; E3 -- M86; E4 -- NGC 4889; E5 -- NGC 4697; E6 -- NGC 3377; E7 -- NGC 3115.

Elliptical galaxies exhibit the greatest range of masses for any galactic type: dwarf ellipticals lying near the Milky Way--such as the Sculptor or the Fornax dwarfs--measure only a few thousand light years across and contain several million stars. They are quite close to being expanded globular clusters. But so-called supergiant ellipticals like M87 measure over 120,000 light-years from end to end and may contain over a trillion stars! These are truly the most impressive collections of matter in galaxies; some spirals measure as large in diameter but are essentially thin disks, whereas ellipticals contain a uniform and much larger volume of material in a sphere. Like spirals, ellipticals contain a halo of globular clusters. Some dwarf galaxies contain only a half dozen, while the supergiants hold 2000 or more in their gravitational grip.

Elliptical galaxies are present in all clusters of galaxies, and some such groups of galaxies are almost solely made up of ellipticals and lenticulars. An odd type of elliptical galaxy is the "cD galaxy," predominently found in rich clusters. A cD galaxy is one that acts as a central supergalaxy in a cluster by devouring other galactic nuclei and becoming larger and larger, gaining an enormous halo of gas and dust. Thankfully there are no such galaxies near the Milky Way.

A small number of galaxies--about 5%--show no apparent underlying structure; these are irregular galaxies, loose masses of stars, gas and dust. Most irregular galaxies are relatively small and have low luminosities, and are younger than spirals and ellipticals, containing mostly Population I stars and many HII regions. Our Local Group contains a large number of these dwarf systems, including the Large and Small Magellanic Clouds (although the Large cloud shows a weak spiral structure in long exposure photos). Some irregulars undergo bursts of star formation, and are thus made up of individual cloudlets of stars. Such a galaxy is IC 1613 in Cetus. Some irregulars have a, major and minor axis, while others show a barred structure, such as NGC 6822 in Sagittarius. Although they are inherently dim, irregulars contain large numbers of variable stars--especially Cepheids--which makes determining their distances relatively easy. Studies of anemic and lenticular galaxies are not so easy because none lie nearby.

An even smaller percentage of galaxies do not fit into any of these classifications, and are known as peculiar galaxies. These systems are often distorted or eruptive, and the suggestions put forward to explain this appearance range from tidal interaction with a gas cloud or another galaxy to mass ejection from a central black hole. They are, along with their cousins the quasars, the most enigmatic and bizarre objects in the universe. M51, the Whirlpool Galaxy, and its sidekick NGC 5195 offer the best chance to see two galaxies interacting: other fine examples are NGC 4567 and NGC 4568 in Virgo, NGC 4038 and NGC 4039 in Corvus. These galaxies reveal themselves by the intense radio noise produced by their clashing gas clouds. This happens principally with spirals whose giant gas clouds get in each other's way; colliding elliptical galaxies may be less catastrophic because of their lack of gas between stars. When a small galaxy penetrates a large Sc-spiral, the result is a hole punched through the center of the spiral, leaving a so-called ring galaxy. These are very rare, and all known examples are too faint to observe with small telescopes.

The eruptive galaxies--also called Active Galactic Nuclei (AGN)--are the most violent and disturbed stellar systems. Each displays intense radio, ultraviolet, and X-ray radiation emanating from a small dense point at its nucleus. The bright galaxies M87 in Virgo and NGC 5128 in Centaurus are violently ejecting a great amount of material, hurling hot gas millions of light years into space. What causes this behavior in otherwise normal galaxies? Such galaxies may become unstable after a collision. Many astronomers believe that a centrally located black hole is responsible for the peculiar behavior of these systems. Curiously, astronomers have suggested that all galaxies may undergo periodic disruption and subsequently return to normal--suggesting in essence that galaxies with AGN have a sort of the "cosmic flu."

Several types of objects have AGN. One such class is the Seyfert galaxies, named for American astronomer Carl K. Seyfert, who first identified it in 1943. These systems--accounting for 10% of all large spirals--emit large amounts of radiation (mostly X-rays) from their nuclei. This indicates that they have a powerful region of hot gas only a few light months across in their centers. These objects mimic quasars, but are about 100 times less energetic. It is possible that all spirals go through a Seyfert phase at some point in their lives, including the Milky Way. About 150 Seyfert galaxies are known; bright examples are M77 in Cetus and NGC 4151 in Canes Venatici.

Another type of high-energy galaxy is the BL Lacertae object, named for its prototype in the constellation Lacerta. These are intensely energetic systems which vary in their light output (hence the variable star designation BL) and whose powerhouse is only a few light-months across. Distance measurements place BL Lac objects much farther away than Seyfert galaxies, at about the same distance as the nearest quasars. They are quite like quasars, except that BL Lac objects lack the distinctive quasar emission and absorption lines in their spectra.

The energy from BL Lac objects is highly polarized, indicating an intense magnetic field possibly created by electrons orbiting in the whirlpool of matter around a central black hole. The only observable example for small scopes is the prototype, BL Lacertae, which appears merely as a star.

The most mysterious objects in the universe are the quasars (or QSOs, for quasi-stellar objects), extremely distant and incredibly energetic galaxylike objects. They were discovered in 1963 when astronomers searched for the optical components of intense radio sources. That year, astronomer Maarten Schmidt of Caltech showed that the quasars are extragalactic in nature. About 1500 quasars are known, of which the brightest, 3C 273 (the 273rd object in the third Cambridge University catalog of radio sources) is visible as a "star" in small telescopes. The QSO 3C 273 is some three billion light-years away, yet it shines at 12th magnitude. To be so luminous at such a great distance, the object must have an absolute magnitude of -27--yet its energy source must be only a light year across. This poses a problem in explaining how such a small object can be so energetic. Many astronomers believe that these objects contain supermassive black holes.

Fig. 8-11. **Face-on Spiral M101**

Fig. 8-12. **NGC 253 in Sculptor**

Fig. 8-13. **NGC 2841 in Ursa Major**

Fig. 8-14. **NGC 5128 in Centaurus**

Fig. 8-15. **NGC 404 near Beta Andromedae**

Fig. 8-16. **Barred spiral NGC 1300**

STARTING TO OBSERVE THE GREAT GALAXIES

Galaxies are generally rather difficult objects for beginning stargazers to observe, owing largely to their low surface brightnesses--their light being spread over a large area so individual parts appear dim. Nevertheless several hundred can be observed with a small telescope, and several dozen in normal binoculars. Galaxies are not so evenly distributed across the sky when compared to double stars and variables. Radiation from local objects--primarily from millions of stars in the Milky Way--blocks the light from many faint galaxies. Thus it is easy to find galaxies away from the galactic plane, but difficult to find them progressively nearer to our own galaxy.

You'll have to find dark skies to observe most of the galaxies well; even slight light pollution from cities or merely light from streetlamps will render their delicate glow invisible. Though galaxies are generally the second most difficult deep-sky object (after many faint nebulae), 6-inch telescopes in a black sky site offer glimpses of detail in many of the closest, showing their gas clouds, stellar associations, dust lanes, nuclei, and even a few globular clusters. To observe this type of detail, you'll need to train your eye and use techniques like averted vision (using the rods of your eye) and field sweeping (gently rocking the telescope to sweep around the field). These techniques make the subtle details of a galaxy much easier to see.

To find the best examples of galaxies, we must look past the "zone of avoidance" caused by the winter and summer sections of Milky Way. Most galaxies are concentrated in the evening skies of spring and fall. The finest galaxy in the sky is our sister spiral in the Local Group of galaxies, M31, the Andromeda Galaxy. Located about 1° west of the bright star Nu [ν] Andromedae, M31 is an easy naked-eye object in dark skies and with binoculars shows its oval milky-white core and fainter outer extensions of subtle light. With a small scope, you'll do best to place a low-power, wide-field eyepiece on your instrument--perhaps 8x to 10x per inch of telescopic aperture--and center the fuzzy mass. With a 4-inch telescope you'll see a condensed core, sharply defined at its center, surrounded by a huge oval of low surface brightness nebulosity which may extend out of the field of view by some 1° on either side of the galaxy's nucleus. M31 is inclined only 15° from our line of sight--close to edge-on--causing it to appear oval. This allows us to observe the galaxy's nearest dark lane, which cuts along the disk's edge; a 6-inch scope on good nights should show this feature. A 6-inch also shows a "stellar" or pointlike nucleus and--near the southwestern edge--the star cloud NGC 206, which appears as a bright condensation floating amidst the tenuous gas.

M31 is a most famous galaxy for historical and astrophysical reasons: it is the farthest single object visible to the naked eye, at a distance of 2.2 million light years; it is the galaxy in which Edwin Hubble discovered Cepheid variable stars in 1923, and is one of the larger spirals known, containing 300 billion stars and measuring 180,000 light-years across. It is the "big brother" of the Milky Way in a Local Group also consisting of M33, NGC 6822, the Sculptor and Fornax dwarf systems, IC 1613, and the Magellanic Clouds.

The Andromeda galaxy gravitationally controls several companions, two of which are visible in the same telescopic field with large binoculars or a 3-inch scope. The smallest and brightest is M32, which shines at magnitude 9.5 and measures 3.6' x 3.1' (in comparison to M31's magnitude of 4.5 and angular extent of 160.0' x 35.0'). M32 appears as a bright condensed circular glow 24' south of M31's core. It has a relatively high surface brightness and takes magnification well; on a night of excellent seeing, turn up the power to 170x or 200x and see

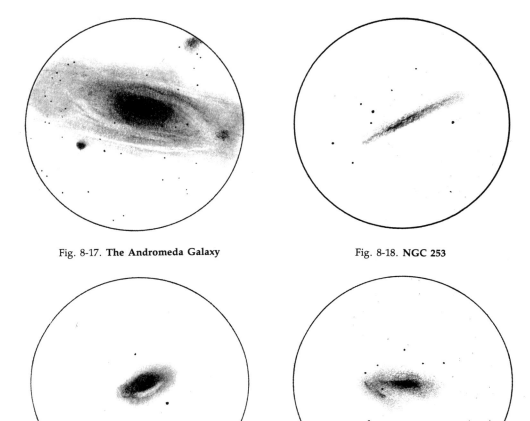

Fig. 8-17. **The Andromeda Galaxy**

Fig. 8-18. **NGC 253**

Fig. 8-19. **The Blackeye Galaxy**

Fig. 8-20. **NGC 925 in Triangulum**

what M32 offers. The other nearby satellite galaxy is NGC 205, a larger but dimmer elliptical found 35' northwest of the nucleus, which has a much lower surface brightness. It appears as a ghostly oval, only slightly condensed toward its center. NGC 205 measures 8.0'x3.0' in extent and glows at magnitude 10.8; a medium power eyepiece on a good night will give you sufficient magnification and a contrasty sky background to enjoy viewing this elliptical. The Andromeda galaxy controls several other companions, some of which are tiny dwarf galaxies invisible to amateur telescopes. But two of its relatively large dwarf galaxies are observable with a 6-inch scope, albeit dim and of low surface brightness. The easiest to find is NGC 185, located about 7° north of M31 across the border into Cassiopeia. NGC 185 is a typical low surface brightness galaxy, showing itself only on the best nights and to clever observers; its magnitude of 11.8 is deceivingly bright because its light is spread over almost 12 square degrees of sky. Use a low power eyepiece to find this object, which is housed between a triangle of faint stars. When you think you've found the correct area, employ averted vision and rock the field of view--very slowly--back and forth, scanning the area. The subtle nebulosity, moved about the field, should show up as a patch slightly brighter than the sky background. NGC 147, about 58' away, is within the limits of the same low power field, but requires full attention. This galaxy shines at only 12th magnitude and its light is spread over a whopping 6.5' x 3.8', making it far more difficult to spot than NGC 185.

Back in neighboring Andromeda lies a fine high surface brightness example of a lenticular galaxy that is quite easy to find. Just 6' from the glaring 2nd magnitude star Beta [β] Andromedae lies NGC 404. This galaxy shines at magnitude 11.9 but measures only 1.8' x 1.5' across; thus it is easily found as a "fuzzy star" in any small telescope, providing the glow from Beta isn't sufficient to blot it out. Once you find this little ball of haze, try moving Beta slightly out of the field and adding more magnification while keeping the galaxy as centered as possible. You'll see a bright condensed uniform glow--although NGC 404 isn't detailed, it's a pleasing sight.

Nearby, in the diminutive constellation Triangulum, lies another Local Group member and the second brightest spiral galaxy in the sky--M33. This Sc-type spiral is oriented directly face-on to our line of sight, and so offers us the best chance to view galactic detail outside the Milky Way. M33 has a total magnitude of 6.5 (making it very bright!) but is spread over an area of 65.0' x 35.0', causing it to be quite elusive for small telescopes on poor nights. Binoculars show M33 as a dim hazy patch of milky light, barely penetrating over the sky's natural glow. Light pollution causes M33 to disappear in binoculars. But a 4-inch telescope at a good site shows an oval nuclear region surrounded by a faint nebulous glow. Telescopes of 5- or 6-inch aperture reveal a sharp pinpoint nucleus, obvious mottled nebulosity around the core, and faint gas extending over an entire field of view. The huge emission nebula known as NGC 604 appears as a bright knot, and on superior nights the galaxy's faint spiral structure is visible.

M74 in the constellation Pisces is a galaxy similar in type to M33 but much farther away. This object measures some 10.9' x 9.0' across and glows at around 10th magnitude. As with M33, the face-on angle causes M74's surface brightness to be low, and it can be an elusive target on poor nights. Found about 1° east-northeast from Eta [ϵ] Piscium, good finder telescopes show M74 as a small grainy patch of nebulosity. A 3-inch or 4-inch scope at medium power shows the galaxy's bright hub, encapsulated in a smooth faint envelope of gas.

Another galaxy prominent during the crisp fall evenings is M77 in the constellation Cetus. This is a small but bright galaxy whose general

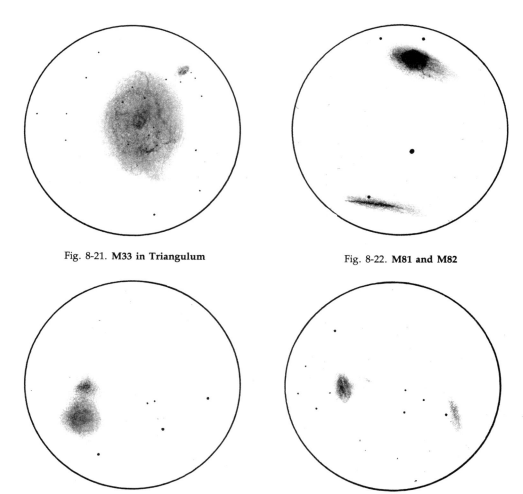

Fig. 8-21. **M33 in Triangulum**

Fig. 8-22. **M81 and M82**

Fig. 8-23. **M51 in Canes Venatici**

Fig. 8-24. **M65 and M66**

appearance in small telescopes resembles a moderately sized globular cluster. M77 lies 1° southeast of the bright star Delta [δ] Ceti, and its high surface brightness gives it away in most finderscopes. A 10th magnitude object occupying 2.5' x 1.7' of sky, M77 is one of the brightest of the Seyfert galaxies. Nothing of its unusual nature is visible in small amateur telescopes. But a good 6-inch telescope reveals a bright core and small outer nebular halo.

Another active galaxy in the fall sky is NGC 1097 in the constellation Fornax. This galaxy is quite bright, shining at magnitude 10.6, and large, measuring 9.0' x 5.5'. Its peculiar nature--symmetrical jets of material shooting out from its nucleus--is impossibly faint in the optical range of the spectrum, but the galaxy does show a bright core even to 2-inch scopes. A 6-inch telescope under dark skies reveals a large nuclear region involved with subtle dark patches, and faint extensions suggesting spiral arms. The only difficulty with this galaxy is its southern declination of -30°, making even its highest elevation inadequate for real dark sky viewing to many Northern Hemisphere observers.

Perhaps the fifth finest galaxy--after M31, M33, and the Magellanic Clouds--is NGC 253, a large Sc-type system inclined near edge-on in the constellation Sculptor. Despite a southerly declination of -25°, causing it to appear rather low in the sky for Northerners, its very high surface brightness cuts through with a commanding punch: at magnitude 7, 22.0' x 6.0' in diameter, binoculars show it to be a sharp spike of greenish light. A good 4-inch telescope reveals a long thin oval of bright nebulosity with a roundish bright core; 6-inch instruments show a stellar nucleus surrounded by haze and, on good nights, some dark structure.

The winter sky is dominated by the bright Milky Way in Orion, Auriga, Perseus, and Canis Major, and has few galaxies within the reach of small backyard telescopes. One that is visible is the large Sc-type spiral NGC 2403, found in the northern circumpolar constellation Camelopardalis. This is one of the nearest spiral galaxies outside our Local Group, and is probably best described as a miniature version of M33 in Triangulum. Measuring 16.0' x 10.0', its 10th magnitude light gives it a fairly high surface brightness, affording good views with medium magnifications. In a 3-inch scope, the galaxy is an unobtrusive oval of milky light. But a 6-inch at high power begins to display some of NGC 2403's true nature, given away by small patches of mottling near the nucleus, corresponding to dark lanes and patches in the galaxy's hub.

The spring sky is really the place to look for sheer quantities of galaxies. The "Realm of the Nebulae," centered on the constellations Virgo and Coma Berenices, represents the nearest big cluster of galaxies to our own; here lie dozens and dozens of distant, relatively "run of the mill" galaxies which can be picked off at the rate of four per field of view. The giant elliptical M87 and its companions M84 and M86 crowd for attention among numerous fainter NGC galaxies. The finest galaxy in Virgo lies away from the heart of the cluster--it is M104, also known as the Sombrero Galaxy. This galaxy received its nickname for the broad obvious dark patch which cuts across its edge-on tilt and is apparent in a 2-inch telescope at high power. A 4- or 6-inch scope shows a bright (magnitude 8.2) lens-shaped disk, whacked in half by the band of dust. The galaxy measures 7.0' x 1.5', takes magnification well, and is a pleasant sight in virtually any telescope during good observing conditions.

NGC 5128--also known as Centaurus A in radio source catalogs--is another galaxy showing an obvious dark bisecting band of dust across its

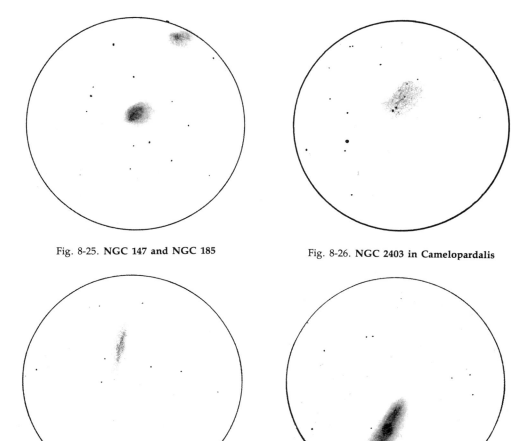

Fig. 8-25. **NGC 147 and NGC 185**

Fig. 8-26. **NGC 2403 in Camelopardalis**

Fig. 8-27. **NGC 2841**

Fig. 8-28. **NGC 2683 in Lynx**

face. This galaxy lies at the southerly declination of -42°, and so is invisible to many U.S. observers, save for those located in Texas, Florida, Arizona, or southern California. This giant elliptical galaxy may hold up to two trillion solar masses, and is ejecting matter from its nucleus in a violent sort of way. The view through a 2- or 3-inch telescope suggests two half-moons separated by a black line; a good 6-inch telescope shows mottled gas about the face of the galaxy and dark lane.

Moving northward to the constellation Ursa Major, we find three bright galaxies among numerous fainter examples. The most prominent pair of galaxies in the sky, M81 and M82, lie 10° northwest of Alpha Ursae Majoris and 2° east from 24 Ursae Majoris. They are separated by 38', thus comfortably fitting in one field of view in binoculars or a low-power telescope. M81 is an 8th magnitude Sa/Sb galaxy measuring 18.0' x 10.0'. Its bright oval core is striking in a 3-inch scope beside M82's sliver of green light, which measures 8.0' x 3.0' in extent. A good 6-inch scope shows a large faint halo of nebulosity surrounding M81, and dark mottled structure across the surface of M82, which also reveals a stellar nucleus at high power. These two galaxies are physically attached by an "umbilical cord" of hydrogen gas.

The Sc-type galaxy M101 is not quite as obvious in small instruments; it measures a whopping 22.0' x 20.0' across and glows at 9th magnitude, making it a low surface brightness object barely visible in finders on many nights. Three- and 4-inch telescopes show a large, uniform circular glow without a hint of detail, whereas a 6-inch at high power shows a mottled, irregular structure in the elusive nebulosity, which surrounds a small knot of a core. Seeing conditions and the sky's transparency greatly affect all galaxies, but particularly low surface brightness objects like M101.

In nearby Canes Venatici lies the brightest pair of interacting galaxies in the sky, M51 and NGC 5195. M51 is known as the Whirlpool Galaxy due to its pristine spiral shape; it is a large bright Sc-type spiral seen face-on, offering good views to large binoculars and small telescopes. M51 is located about 3.5° southwest of the bright star Eta [ε] Ursae Majoris, measures 10.0' x 5.5', and shines brightly at magnitude 8.7. Its companion, little NGC 5195, is a lenticular system passing the big galaxy and colliding with it: small telescopes show the scene as a merger of two circular patches of misty light. A good 6-inch telescope reveals detail in M51 like dusty regions near the core, a star superimposed on the face of the galaxy, an irregular shape to 5195, and on excellent nights spiral structure in M51 and a hint of the tenuous bridge of material extending to 5195.

The constellation Coma Berenices--back toward that mythical Realm of the Galaxies--contains the entire heaven's finest example of an edge-on spiral galaxy, NGC 4565. This beautiful streak of bright light is visible in large binoculars, and is a showpiece on 4- or 6-inch telescopes. Lying 1.7° east of the star 17 Comae Berenices, near the sprawling Coma Star Cluster, NGC 4565 measures 15.0'x1.1' and glows at magnitude 10.5, giving it a high surface brightness. Thus it can withstand magnification well, and its slender form is obvious in a 2-inch or 3-inch scope. Six-inch telescopes show a central bulge near the nucleus and, on nights of good seeing, a slim but impressive dark lane running alongside the entire length of the object.

Many other galaxies which are bright and easy to observe inhabit the spring and fall skies. After you've practiced hunting them down for awhile, consult the catalog section at the end of this chapter. It lists over 700 galaxies, some of which are always visible to small scopes under good skies. Keep at it, and pretty soon you'll be finding spirals and ellipticals and dust lanes with the best of experienced stargazers.

Fig. 8-29. **The Blackeye Galaxy**

Fig. 8-30. **M83 in Hydra**

Fig. 8-31. **M99 in Coma Berenices**

ADVANCED OBSERVING TECHNIQUES

After you've observed many of the brighter galaxies, you can expand your skills by tackling more difficult and challenging aspects of galaxy observing. Keep some sort of record of your observations, or at least mark the ones you observe in this chapter's catalog section. Include information on the telescope's aperture and magnification, the date, time, and a measure of the sky's seeing condition and transparency. Having gained a fundamental knowledge of what a certain type of galaxy looks like through your telescope, you'll be able to estimate the worth of a night for observing "faint fuzzies." Begin to observe with a critical eye: What does a galaxy's nucleus look like? Is an overall spiral shape visible? How does the surface brightness of the nebulosity change with different parts of the galaxy? Is dark structure of any sort visible? By looking at these objects and describing them in full detail, you'll build a valuable record of how your eye and your telescope work together.

The next logical step is to begin to sketch the galaxies. This may put you off at first, but it's really quite easy to do and helps you assemble a beautiful and descriptive picture of your observations. Deep-sky sketches are much easier to make than deep-sky photographs, and they are important because they capture the object as the eye sees it. It is a favorite pastime of deep-sky observers to compare their sketches with other observers' drawings. Differences with similar aperture scopes can indicate not only the observer's ability, but the quality of sky transparency and seeing. For basic sketching techniques, see Appendix 2.

The Revised New General Catalogue of Nonstellar Astronomical Objects by Jack W. Sulentic and William Tifft (known as the RNGC), the basic deep sky reference list, contains over eight thousand objects, 84% of which are galaxies. There are several hundred and probably a couple of thousand galaxies visible to experienced observers with small telescopes. With a 6-inch telescope, a trained eye, and dark skies, detail is visible in many of the brighter galaxies. A mere sample of some interesting examples follow: check the catalog for several hundred more.

The fall sky is loaded with fine galaxies for small scopes: one of the more challenging is IC 1613 in the constellation Cetus. This is a low-surface-brightness dwarf irregular galaxy which is a member of our Local Group, lying 1.8 million light-years off. The problem with this galaxy is its low luminosity: it dimly glows at 12th magnitude, and its light is spread over the large area of 11.0' x 9.0'. In the beginner's section we looked at NGC 147, a difficult dwarf elliptical with the same magnitude but only half as large; IC 1613 is much more difficult because of lower surface brightness. You must have very dark skies to successfully observe IC 1613, and then it appears as a hazy, grainy patch of weak light seemingly filling a low power eyepiece.

Not quite as difficult to observe is NGC 891 in Andromeda, a fine edge-on spiral that appears as a fainter version of NGC 4565 in Coma Berenices. This 12th magnitude type Sb spiral rests near the midpoint of an imaginary line drawn fromrenices. This 12th magnitude type Sb spiral rests near the midpoint of an imaginary line drawn from Gamma [γ] Andromedae and the bright open cluster M34 in Perseus. With dimensions of 12.0' x 1.1', this galaxy has a low surface brightness but is easily visible under good conditions with a 4-inch telescope as a thin streak of grey light. A 6-inch at high power reveals the most interesting feature of NGC 891, a narrow dust band running alongside the   edge.

NGC 520 is a faint galaxy in nearby Pisces which is classed as one of the "active" galaxies, or AGN. A photo of this galaxy shows a twisted, unorganized shape: this is not cleanly visible with amateur telescopes, but a 6-inch instrument on a dark night does show an irregular blob of light and occasionally dark mottled structure. Astronomers suspect this system to habor a black hole, which is expelling matter at high velocities. This system is also apparently associated, or at least aligned, with four quasars, leading astronomers to believe that some quasars may be closer to us than we think.

Another fine galaxy in the fall sky is the Sc-type spiral NGC 925 in the diminutive constellation Triangulum. Not nearly as commanding as its neighbor M33, this galaxy spans nearly 10' across its long axis and shines at magnitude 12. Because its total luminosity is much greater, it is more easily observed than the similarly shaped and sized galaxy IC 1613 in Cetus. A 4-inch telescope shows this object as an oval shaped patch of light with a slightly condensed core. A 6-inch telescope sharpens the view by revealing a large irregular region of greyish nebulosity inhabited by a softly brighter nucleus.

Moving to the winter sky, but looking slightly away from the plane of the Milky Way, we find the low surface brightness object IC 342 in Camelopardalis. This galaxy, a large Sc-type spiral, is a tough customer for small telescopes. It has a magnitude of 12 but also whopping dimensions of 12.0' x 12.0', providing it with a despicably low surface brightness. It is one of the nearest large spirals, and may even be an outlying member of the Local Group. Why, then is it so difficult to see with backyard scopes? It is placed some 10° off the galactic plane, meaning that considerable interference from the star clouds of the galaxy exists. Under dark skies a 6-inch glass shows it as a small round nebulosity surrounded by a large faint envelope of gas.

The constellation Perseus harbors a fine peculiar elliptical galaxy, NGC 1023. This object is an easy mark at 11th magnitude and shows its bright core to any small telescope. It measures 4.0'x1.2' in diameter, so is an excellent object for medium or high power views. A 3-inch scope shows an elongated oval nucleus, encapsulated in a very faint halo of nebulosity. A 6-inch telescope at medium power reveals a larger outer package of hazy light and a sharp nucleus. NGC 1023 is classed as peculiar because it is a strong radio source; it is the "kingpin" member of a small group of galaxies called, appropriately, the NGC 1023 group.

Spring skies mean lots of galaxies, and indeed, dozens and dozens of small and faint spirals and ellipticals vie for telescopic attention around the constellations Virgo and Comas Berenices, as well as the Ursa Major area and many others. The giant elliptical galaxy M87, the heart of the Virgo cluster of galaxies, is a truly supermassive and superluminous galaxy, containing perhaps two trillion solar masses and as many as 4000 globular clusters. This galaxy is a powerhouse of electromagnetic energy, and shows a knotty jet of matter being ejected out of its nucleus, indicating a supermassive black hole. Through small telescopes M87 is rather plain looking, a bright but featureless ball of high surface brightness gas. Its magnitude is 9.2, its dimensions 3.0'x3.0'; high power views of this system are quite pleasing but don't stand a chance of showing any detail, including the exceedingly faint jet of matter.

Also in the constellation Virgo is a fine pair of interacting galaxies, NGC 4567 and NGC 4568, sometimes called the Siamese Twins. Both of these physically connected systems have a total magnitude of about 12 and measure roughly 2' across in small telescopes (NGC 4568 is slightly larger). They would not be impressive targets were they isolated in the sky, but together--two nebulous fuzzballs appearing to be connected--they offer a marvelous sight. They comprise perhaps the finest example of an interacting pair of galaxies in the sky.

One of the most unusual galaxies in the spring sky has two NGC numbers, NGC 4038 and NGC 4039, because of what appear to be separate bright portions of the same object.   This galaxy lies 1° northeast of the 31 Crateris, and about 4° northwest of the brighter star Epsilon Corvi.   NGC 4038-9 is a distorted galaxy called the Ring-tail Galaxy because of its strange shape.   The object appears in a 6-inch scope as a pale disk of gray light with two distinct bands of slightly brighter light looping around the galaxy's edges.   This is a highly peculiar object, and may warrant close study on a dark night to see if you can observe details in the galaxy's structure.

Many other challenging galaxies are scattered across the sky, a great number of which are bright enough to observe with 4-inch and 6-inch telescopes.   Before you plan a night of galaxy hunting, look through the table that follows this chapter and plan which objects you want to search for.   After getting some practice with finding and critically looking at galaxies, you'll soon have many favorites that you'll return to time and time again.

The following catalog lists 758 galaxies visible in small telescopes. To best observe them, you'll need to get away from light pollution and avoid the moon to increase the dark sky contrast as much as possible. Use a low power eyepiece to find these objects, then increase the power to the most pleasing view.

Explanation of data: Coordinates are provided for epoch 1950.0. Mag.=visual magnitude; size=apparent diameter in arcminutes. Type=galaxy's classification, according to Hubble, Sandage, de Vaucouleurs, and Corwin.

CATALOG NUMBER	R.A.(1950) Dec. h m ° '	Mag.	Size '	Type
ANDROMEDA				
NGC 205	00 37.6 +41 25	9.4	8.0x3.0	dE6

Satellite galaxy to M31; lies in the same low power field. Low surface brightness elliptical patch showing little central condensation.

NGC 221	00 40.0 +40 36	8.7	3.6x3.1	E2pec

M32 (Arp 168). Small elliptical satellite to M31 in same low power field. Appears as a small round glow with a tiny stellar nucleus and mottled texture.

NGC 224	00 40.0 +41 00	4.8	160.0x35.0	Sb(s)

M31, the Andromeda Galaxy. The finest example of a galaxy in the sky; measures nearly 3° across. Naked eye object--2-inch shows elongated bright patch of nebulosity. 6-inch shows bright oval nucleus and traces of faint spiral arms extending outward--M32 and NGC 205 lie in same low power field. Dust lanes visible in 6-inch as well as star cloud NGC 206--on very dark nights 6-inch shows several globular clusters belonging to our sister spiral in the Local Group.

NGC 404	01 06.6 +35 27	10.7	1.3x1.3	SO

Just 6.4' away is the bright star Beta [β] Andromedae; try moving the star slightly out of the telescope's field of view.

NGC 891	02 19.3 +42 07	12.2	12.0x1.1	Sb(eo)

Faint edge-on galaxy showing a prominent dark lane in 6-inch scopes.

NGC 7640	23 19.7 +40 35	12.5	11.0x1.4	SBb(s)

VV 280; nearly edge-on.

ANTLIA				
NGC 2997	09 43.5 -30 58	11.0	6.0x5.0	Sc(s)
NGC 3095	09 57.9 -31 18	12.7	2.0x1.2	Sc(s)

CATALOG NUMBER	R.A.(1950) Dec. h m ° '		Mag.	Size '	Type

_____AQUARIUS_____

NGC 7184	21 59.9	-21 04	12.0	5.1x0.9	Sb
NGC 7218	22 07.5	-16 54	12.7	1.8x0.7	Sc
NGC 7377	22 45.1	-22 35	12.5	1.1x1.0	S0/Sa
NGC 7392	22 49.2	-20 53	12.6	1.5x0.9	Sb
NGC 7606	23 16.5	-08 46	11.5	6.0x1.6	Sb
NGC 7721	23 36.2	-06 48	12.4	2.6x1.0	Sc
NGC 7723	23 36.4	-13 14	11.1	3.0x2.0	SBb
NGC 7727	23 37.3	-12 34	10.7	2.7x2.7	S0

_____AQUILA_____

| NGC 6814 | 19 39.9 | -10 25 | 12.2 | 2.0x2.0 | Sb |

_____ARIES_____

| NGC 697 | 01 48.6 | +22 06 | 12.5 | 2.0x1.0 | Sbc |
| NGC 772 | 01 56.6 | +18 46 | 10.9 | 5.0x3.0 | Sbpec |

Arp 78. Peculiar galaxy; 6-inch shows a large glow
with stellar nucleus.

NGC 821	02 05.6	+10 46	11.2	1.0x0.9	E6
NGC 877	02 15.3	+14 19	12.4	1.8x1.2	Sc
NGC 972	02 31.3	+29 06	12.7	2.7x1.0	Scpec
NGC 976	02 31.3	+20 44	12.7	0.7x0.7	Sb
NGC 1156	02 56.7	+25 03	12.5	2.0x1.5	I

_____BOOTES_____

| NGC 5248 | 13 35.1 | +09 08 | 11.3 | 6.1x4.8 | Sc(s) |

Low surface brightness spiral; 6-inch shows a
diffuse envelope of gas around a sharp nucleus.

NGC 5533	14 14.1	+35 35	12.6	1.8x0.8	Sb
NGC 5557	14 16.4	+36 43	11.6	0.9x0.8	E2
NGC 5600	14 21.4	+14 52	12.4	1.0x0.9	Sc
NGC 5660	14 28.1	+49 50	12.3	2.2x2.2	Sc
NGC 5665	14 29.9	+08 18	12.7	1.0x0.8	Scpec

Arp 49. Peculiar galaxy; 6-inch shows a tiny nucleus.

NGC 5669	14 30.3	+10 08	12.5	2.5x2.0	Sc
NGC 5676	14 31.0	+49 41	11.2	3.0x1.5	Sc
NGC 5687	14 33.3	+54 42	12.7	0.6x0.4	S0
NGC 5689	14 33.7	+48 57	11.4	2.0x0.6	Sb(s)
NGC 5899	15 13.2	+42 14	12.4	2.3x0.6	Sb

_____CAMELOPARDALIS_____

| IC 342 | 03 41.9 | +67 57 | 12.0 | 15.0x15.0 | Sc(s) |

Nearby large spiral; very faint and of low surface
brightness. 6-inch shows a small nebulous haze.

| NGC 1569 | 04 16.9 | +64 45 | 11.8 | 2.3x0.7 | Ipec. |

Arp 210. Faint peculiar galaxy visible in a 4-inch.

CATALOG NUMBER	R.A.(1950)Dec. h m ° '	Mag.	Size '	Type

CATALOG NUMBER	R.A.(1950)Dec.	Mag.	Size	Type
NGC 1961	05 36.8 +69 24	11.6	3.7x2.5	Sb
NGC 2146	06 10.7 +78 23	11.3	5.0x2.5	Sabpec
NGC 2268	07 01.3 +84 30	12.2	2.2x1.5	Sb
NGC 2347	07 11.6 +64 54	12.7	1.0x0.8	Sb
NGC 2336	07 16.2 +80 20	12.4	5.0x3.0	Sb
NGC 2366	07 23.6 +69 08	12.6	6.0x3.0	I
NGC 2403	07 32.0 +65 43	8.9	16.8x10.0	Sc

One of the finest nearby spirals, appearing as a smaller version of M33. 4-inch shows a large oval patch; 6-inch reveals an elongated structure hinting at spiral shape.

NGC 2441	07 47.1 +73 06	12.7	1.6x1.6	Sc
NGC 2460	07 52.7 +60 31	12.7	1.0x0.7	Sb
NGC 2523	08 09.2 +73 45	12.7	1.8x1.4	SBb(rs)

Arp 9. Shows a tiny core; stellar at low power.

NGC 2633	08 42.7 +74 18	12.6	2.2x1.1	SBbpec
NGC 2655	08 49.4 +78 25	10.7	5.0x3.4	SOpec

Arp 225. Peculiar galaxy showing large diffuse envelope and condensed core.

NGC 2715	09 02.0 +78 16	11.9	4.5x1.2	Sc
NGC 2732	09 07.3 +79 24	11.7	2.0x0.8	SO
NGC 2748	09 08.2 +76 41	11.4	2.1x0.7	Sc

_____CANCER_____

NGC 2672	08 46.6 +19 16	12.2	0.8x0.7	E2pec

Arp 167. Peculiar; shows as a stellar spot.

NGC 2775	09 07.7 +07 15	10.7	2.2x1.4	Sa

_____CANES VENATICI_____

NGC 4111	12 04.5 +43 21	9.7	3.3x0.6	SO(eo)
NGC 4138	12 07.0 +43 58	11.9	1.4x0.8	SO/Sa
NGC 4143	12 07.1 +42 49	11.0	1.3x0.8	SBO
NGC 4145	12 07.5 +40 10	11.9	5.2x3.2	Sc
NGC 4151	12 08.0 +39 41	11.6	2.5x1.6	Sb

Seyfert galaxy. Tiny stellar nucleus visible at high powers in 6-inch; faint halo extends around nucleus.

NGC 4214	12 13.1 +36 36	10.3	7.0x4.5	I

Large irregular glow with mottled texture.

NGC 4217	12 13.3 +47 22	11.9	4.5x0.9	Sb(eo)

Nice faint spiral with a bright center.

NGC 4220	12 13.7 +48 10	11.7	2.5x0.6	SBO/Sa

CATALOG NUMBER	R.A.(1950)Dec. h m ° '	Mag.	Size '	Type

_____CANES VENATICI (Continued)_____

| NGC 4242 | 12 14.9 +45 54 | 11.5 | 4.0x3.0 | S |
| NGC 4244 | 12 15.0 +38 05 | 11.9 | 14.5x1.0 | Sbc(eo) |

Bright edge-on galaxy; 4-inch shows a silvery needle of milky light.

| NGC 4258 | 12 16.5 +47 35 | 8.6 | 19.5x7.0 | Sbpec |

M106. 6-inch shows a mottled irregular core and faint extensions of nebulosity over a large area. Very nice object!

NGC 4346	12 21.0 +47 16	11.6	1.7x0.7	E6
NGC 4369	12 22.1 +39 39	12.6	1.3x1.2	Sa
NGC 4395	12 23.4 +33 49	10.7	10.0x8.0	Sd
NGC 4449	12 25.8 +44 22	9.2	4.2x3.0	I

2-inch shows a hazy patch; 6-inch shows an irregular rectangular appearance with a condensed core.

NGC 4460	12 26.4 +45 08	11.7	2.0x0.5	E7
NGC 4485	12 28.2 +41 58	11.6	1.3x0.7	Ipec
NGC 4490	12 28.3 +41 55	9.7	5.0x2.0	SBdpec

NGC 4485 (VV 30) and NGC 4490 (Arp 269) form an interacting pair; 6-inch shows both--4485 as a small knot of nebulosity, 4490 as a large bright core with faint extended outer envelope of gas.

| NGC 4618 | 12 39.2 +41 25 | 11.7 | 2.0x0.5 | E7 |
| NGC 4631 | 12 39.8 +32 49 | 9.3 | 12.6x1.4 | Sc(eo) |

Arp 281. Peculiar galaxy showing a mottled condensed core in a 6-inch.

| NGC 4656 | 12 41.6 +32 26 | 11.2 | 19.5x2.0 | Sd |

6-inch shows a long irregular bar with bright center.

| NGC 4736 | 12 48.6 +41 23 | 7.9 | 5.0x3.5 | Sb |

M94. 2-inch shows a bright nebulous knot; 6-inch shows a bright circular core with a faint outer envelope.

NGC 4800	12 52.4 +46 48	11.1	1.2x0.9	Sb
NGC 5005	13 08.5 +37 19	9.8	4.7x1.6	Sb
NGC 5033	13 11.2 +36 51	10.3	9.9x4.8	Sb

6-inch shows a circular object with faint nebulosity.

| NGC 5055 | 13 13.5 +42 17 | 9.5 | 9.0x4.0 | Sb |

M63. Just southeast of an 8th mag. star; 6-inch shows a bright oval nucleus with mottled outer nebulosity.

| NGC 5112 | 13 19.6 +39 00 | 12.6 | 3.2x2.3 | Sc |

CATALOG NUMBER	R.A.91950)Dec. h m ° '	Mag.	Size '	Type

NGC 5194	13 27.8 +47 27	8.1	10.0x5.5	Sc(s)pec

M51, the Whirlpool Galaxy (Arp 85, VV 1). One of the finest galaxies in the sky; 2-inch shows a fuzzy elongated patch; 4-inch shows a double patch of bright nebulosity (M51 and connecting NGC 5195). 6-inch scope shows a bright oval face with a faint star projected on it, hints of spiral structure and dark mottling in the galaxy, and the companion, NGC 5195. A fascinating sight in any telescope.

NGC 5195	13 27.9 +47 31	11.0	2.0x1.5	Pec

Connected to M51.

NGC 5273	13 39.9 +35 55	11.5	0.9x0.8	S0
NGC 5297	13 44.3 +44 05	12.0	5.2x0.8	Sb(eo)
NGC 5353	13 51.3 +40 31	12.1	1.1x0.4	E5pec
NGC 5371	13 53.6 +40 43	11.4	3.7x3.3	Sb
NGC 5377	13 54.3 +47 27	11.2	3.0x0.6	Sa(eo)
NGC 5383	13 55.0 +42 05	12.0	2.2x2.0	SBb
NGC 5395	13 56.5 +37 39	12.2	2.1x1.0	SBbpec

_____ CANIS MAJOR

NGC 2207	06 14.3 -21 21	12.3	2.5x1.5	Sc
NGC 2217	06 18.7 -27 14	12.0	4.0x3.0	SB0/SBa
NGC 2223	06 22.5 -22 49	12.7	3.5x2.5	S(B)c(r)

_____ CAPRICORNUS

NGC 6907	20 22.1 -24 58	12.1	2.5x2.0	SBb

_____ CASSIOPEIA

NGC 147	00 30.4 +48 14	12.1	6.5x3.8	dE5

Satellite galaxy to M31. Very low surface brightness; 6-inch shows large diffuse patch of light with star near middle. Difficult object.

NGC 185	00 36.1 +48 04	11.7	3.5x2.8	dE3

Satellite galaxy to M31. Low surface brightness--a bit easier to find than NGC 147. 6-inch shows a large faint patch of nebulosity nestled between three stars arranged in a triangle.

NGC 278	00 49.2 +47 18	11.3	1.2x1.2	Sc

Visible in 6-inch as a small circular nebulosity. A very nice sight!

_____ CENTAURUS

NGC 3557	11 07.5 -37 16	12.1	1.5x1.3	E3
IC 5253	12 21.1 -34 21	12.3	2.5x1.0	SBc(s)

CATALOG NUMBER	R.A.(1950) h m	Dec. ° '	Mag.	Size '	Type

_____CENTAURUS (Continued)_____

CATALOG NUMBER	R.A. h m	Dec. ° '	Mag.	Size	Type
NGC 4373	12 22.7	-39 28	12.2	1.5x1.0	S0
IC 3370	12 25.0	-39 04	12.4	1.4x1.2	E2
NGC 4603	12 38.3	-40 42	12.5	2.5x1.2	Sc(s)
NGC 4696	12 46.1	-41 02	12.5	1.7x1.2	E3
NGC 4835	12 55.3	-45 59	12.5	2.3x0.7	S0
NGC 4936	13 01.5	-30 15	12.6	1.0x1.0	E1
NGC 4945	13 02.4	-49 13	9.2	15.0x2.5	Sc(eo)

Fine edge-on spiral.

NGC 4947	13 02.6	-35 04	12.6	2.0x1.0	S0
NGC 4976	13 05.9	-49 14	11.6	2.8x1.5	S0/Sa
NGC 5102	13 19.1	-36 23	10.8	6.0x2.5	S0
NGC 5121	13 21.9	-37 25	12.5	1.0x0.8	S0
NGC 5128	13 22.4	-42 45	7.2	10.0x8.0	S0pec

Centaurus A (Arp 153). Fine peculiar galaxy showing two distinct halves separated by a broad dust band even in a 2-inch scope. 6-inch shows two large nebulosities with the mottled irregular dust lane; high power shows bright detail in and around dark band. One of the most unusual objects in the sky!

NGC 5161	13 26.3	-32 54	12.5	4.0x1.5	Sc(s)
NGC 5193	13 29.1	-32 58	12.6	1.0x1.0	E1
IC 4296	13 33.8	-33 43	11.9	0.6x0.6	E0
NGC 5253	13 37.1	-31 24	10.8	4.0x1.5	Epec.

Large bright oval nucleus and condensed core.

NGC 5419	14 00.7	-33 44	12.4	1.0x0.7	E3
NGC 5483	14 07.4	-43 05	12.4	2.6x2.4	SBb(s)
NGC 5494	14 09.5	-30 26	12.6	1.5x1.5	Sc(s)

_____CEPHEUS_____

NGC 2276	07 11.0	+85 52	12.4	2.5x2.0	Sc(s)pec

Arp 114. Small round nebular patch in 6-inch.

NGC 2300	07 16.5	+85 50	12.2	1.0x0.7	E3pec
NGC 6946	20 33.9	+59 58	11.1	8.0x8.0	Sc

A fine nearby spiral. 2-inch shows a hazy even patch; 6-inch reveals a ghostly nebulosity with several bright patches. Demands dark sky background.

NGC 6951	20 36.5	+65 56	12.3	3.5x3.5	SBb

_____CETUS_____

NGC 45	00 11.4	-23 27	12.1	8.0x5.5	dSc(s)

Large mottled spiral.

NGC 151	00 31.6	-09 58	12.4	3.1x1.1	SBb(rs)
NGC 157	00 32.3	-08 40	11.2	2.8x2.1	Sc(s)
NGC 210	00 38.0	-14 09	12.0	4.5x2.4	Sb(rs)

CATALOG NUMBER	R.A.(1950) Dec. h m ° '	Mag.	Size '	Type

_____CETUS (Continued)_____

| NGC 247 | 00 44.6 -21 01 | 10.7 | 18.2x5.0 | Sd |

Large bright spiral with a condensed nucleus. Visible as a slim oval core with a faint halo in a 6-inch.

NGC 255	00 45.2 -11 45	12.4	3.3x2.5	Sb
NGC 309	00 54.0 -10 13	12.5	2.4x2.1	Sc(rs)
NGC 337	00 57.3 -07 51	12.2	2.0x1.5	Sc
IC 1613	01 02.5 +01 52	12.0	11.0x9.0	I

Nearby irregular galaxy; difficult to observe, it is visible in a 6-inch at low power on excellent nights.

NGC 428	01 10.4 +00 43	11.7	3.9x3.5	Scpec
NGC 450	01 11.3 -01 07	12.6	2.5x2.0	Sc
NGC 578	01 28.0 -22 56	11.7	4.5x2.5	Sc
NGC 584	01 28.8 -07 07	10.4	1.7x1.0	E3/S0
NGC 596	01 30.3 -07 17	11.5	1.0x0.9	E0
NGC 615	01 32.6 -07 53	11.6	2.7x0.8	Sb(rs)
NGC 636	01 36.6 -07 45	12.6	0.7x0.7	E1
NGC 720	01 50.6 -13 59	10.5	1.3x0.7	E5
NGC 779	01 57.2 -06 12	11.3	3.7x0.9	Sb
NGC 788	01 58.6 -07 03	12.6	1.2x0.9	Sa
NGC 864	02 12.8 +05 45	12.0	2.8x2.8	Sc
NGC 895	02 19.1 -05 45	12.2	2.8x2.2	Sb
NGC 908	02 20.8 -21 27	11.5	4.0x1.3	Sc(s)
NGC 936	02 25.1 -01 22	10.7	3.0x2.0	SB0/SBa
NGC 1022	02 28.1 -06 53	11.2	1.6x0.6	Sb
NGC 1042	02 38.0 -08 40	12.5	4.5x2.6	Sc
NGC 1052	02 38.6 -08 28	11.2	0.7x0.5	E3
NGC 1055	02 39.2 +00 16	12.0	6.7x1.5	Sb

6-inch shows an elongated patch with an 11th mag. star 1' north.

| NGC 1068 | 02 40.1 -00 14 | 8.9 | 2.5x1.7 | Sbpec |

M77 (Arp 37), a Seyfert galaxy. 2-inch shows a nebulous spot of light; 6-inch reveals a bright tiny nucleus and extended outer nebulosity.

NGC 1073	02 41.2 +01 10	12.0	4.5x4.2	SBc
NGC 1087	02 43.9 -00 42	11.9	2.3x1.3	Sc
NGC 1090	02 44.0 -00 27	12.5	4.0x1.5	Sb

_____COLUMBA_____

NGC 1792	05 03.5 -38 04	10.7	3.0x1.0	Sc(s)pec
NGC 1808	05 05.9 -37 34	11.2	4.0x1.0	SB
NGC 2090	05 45.2 -34 15	12.4	2.5x1.0	Sc
NGC 2188	06 08.3 -34 05	12.6	3.0x0.6	Scd

_____COMA BERENICES_____

NGC 4136	12 06.7 +30 12	12.1	3.2x2.9	Sc
NGC 4152	12 08.1 +16 19	12.7	1.3x1.0	Sc
NGC 4162	12 09.4 +24 24	12.6	1.9x1.0	Sc

CATALOG NUMBER	R.A.(1950) Dec., h m ° '	Mag.	Size '	Type

_____COMA BERENICES (Continued)_____

| NGC 4192 | 12 11.3   +15 11 | 10.7 | 8.4x1.4 | Sb |

M98. Elongated edge-on spiral. 6-inch shows a bright streak of nebulosity. Lies 30' west of the 5th mag. star 6 Comae Berenices; M99 lies 1.3° east-southeast.

NGC 4203	12 12.5 +33 29	11.0	2.0x1.8	SB0/S0
NGC 4212	12 13.1 +14 11	11.9	2.4x1.5	Sc
NGC 4245	12 15.2 +29 53	11.1	1.5x0.9	S(B)b
NGC 4251	12 15.7 +28 27	10.2	2.0x0.8	S0
NGC 4254	12 16.3 +14 42	10.1	4.6x3.9	Sc(s)

M99. Large and bright spiral; 2-inch shows a small misty patch. 6-inch shows a bright round nucleus and mottled outer envelope.

| NGC 4274 | 12 17.4   +29 53 | 10.8 | 6.7x1.3 | Sb(r) |

6-inch shows a bright nucleus in an oval nebulosity.

NGC 4278	12 17.7 +29 34	10.3	1.2x1.0	E1
NGC 4293	12 18.7 +18 40	11.7	4.8x1.8	Sapec
NGC 4298	12 19.0 +14 53	11.9	2.7x1.1	Sc
NGC 4302	12 19.2 +14 53	11.6	4.7x0.5	Sc
NGC 4314	12 20.0 +30 10	10.8	3.0x2.7	SBapec

6-inch shows a bright nucleus surounded by faint gas.

| NGC 4321 | 12 20.4   +16 06 | 10.6 | 5.2x5.0 | Sc(s) |

M100. 2-inch shows a bright circular nebula; 6-inch shows a bright condensed core with uneven envelope of faint nebulosity.

| NGC 4350 | 12 21.4   +16 58 | 11.9 | 1.9x0.5 | S0 |
| NGC 4382 | 12 22.8   +18 28 | 9.3 | 3.0x2.0 | S0/E |

M85. Bright but featureless; NGC 4394 lies 7.8' east.

| NGC 4394 | 12 23.4   +18 29 | 11.2 | 2.3x2.3 | SBb |
| NGC 4414 | 12 24.0   +31 30 | 9.7 | 3.1x1.5 | Sc |

Bright nucleus with small grainy halo.

NGC 4419	12 24.4 +15 19	11.4	2.3x0.6	Epec
NGC 4448	12 25.8 +28 54	11.4	2.9x1.0	Sb
NGC 4450	12 25.9 +17 21	10.0	3.8x3.0	Sb

Very bright nucleus with 9th mag. star 4' southwest.

NGC 4459	12 26.5 +14 15	10.9	1.5x1.0	S0
NGC 4477	12 27.6 +13 55	10.7	2.4x2.2	SB0/SBa
NGC 4494	12 28.9 +26 03	9.6	1.3x1.2	E1
NGC 4501	12 29.5 +14 42	10.2	5.7x2.5	Sb

M88. Fine inclined spiral showing a bright condensed nuclear region and large misty envelope.

CATALOG NUMBER	R.A.(1950)Dec. h m ° '	Mag.	Size '	Type
NGC 4548	12 32.9 +14 46	10.8	3.7x3.2	SBb
NGC 4559	12 33.5 +28 14	10.6	11.0x4.5	Sc

Highly inclined spiral appearing in small scopes as a long narrow patch of mottled nebulosity with a bright middle.

NGC 4565	12 33.9 +26 16	10.2	15.0x1.1	Sb

The finest edge-on galaxy in the sky. 2-inch shows a long bright spindle; 4-inch reveals thin dust band running across galaxy's edge. 6-inch easily shows the lane and a tiny stellar nucleus, as well as a bulge of light around the center.

NGC 4571	12 34.3 +14 28	12.2	2.8x2.4	Sc
NGC 4651	12 41.2 +16 40	11.4	3.0x2.5	Scpec

Peculiar galaxy Arp 189 (VV 56).

NGC 4670	12 42.8 +27 23	12.7	0.8x0.6	Epec

Peculiar galaxy Arp 163.

NGC 4689	12 45.2 +14 01	12.0	2.4x1.9	Sb
NGC 4710	12 47.1 +15 26	11.7	3.4x0.5	S0
NGC 4725	12 48.1 +25 46	8.9	7.5x4.8	S(B)b

Large bright spiral; 6-inch shows a bright nucleus encircled by a mottled halo of low surface brightness nebulosity.

NGC 4793	12 52.3 +29 13	11.8	1.9x0.8	Sc
NGC 4826	12 54.3 +21 57	8.8	7.5x3.5	Sb

M64, the Blackeye Galaxy. Visible as large bright oval patch in 2-inch; 6-inch shows a bright elongated nuclear region and a large hazy halo of nebulosity, as well as the conspicuous dark patch which gives the galaxy its name.

NGC 5012	13 09.3 +23 11	11.2	2.2x1.2	Sb

CORVUS

NGC 4027	11 57.0 -18 59	11.6	2.0x1.7	Scpec

Peculiar galaxy Arp 22 (VV 66).

NGC 4038/9	11 59.3 -18 35	11.0	2.5x2.5	Pec

The Ring Tail Galaxy (Arp 244, VV 245). Named for its unusual twisted structure; 6-inch shows evenly illuminated body with a faint tail to the south. 3.7° west-southwest of bright star Gamma [γ] Corvi.

NGC 4050	12 00.4 -16 06	11.6	1.2x0.9	S0

CATALOG NUMBER	R.A.(1950) Dec. h m ° '	Mag.	Size '	Type

CRATER

NGC 3511	11 00.8 -22 50	11.9	4.6x2.0	Sc
NGC 3513	11 01.1 -22 58	12.0	2.0x1.6	SBc
NGC 3672	11 22.5 -09 32	12.4	3.5x1.4	Sb
NGC 3887	11 44.6 -16 35	11.7	2.8x2.0	Sc
NGC 3956	11 51.6 -20 18	12.6	2.8x0.7	Sc
NGC 3962	11 52.2 -13 42	11.3	0.8x0.7	E1
NGC 3981	11 53.7 -19 37	12.7	3.5x1.0	Sb

DRACO

NGC 3147	10 12.8 +73 39	10.9	3.0x2.3	Sb
NGC 4125	12 05.7 +65 27	10.2	2.1x1.1	E6pec
NGC 4236	12 14.3 +69 45	12.4	22.0x5.0	SBd

Large dim loosely structured spiral; visible as a
ghostly patch of milky light in a 4-inch.

NGC 4291	12 18.1 +75 40	11.9	0.7x0.5	E3
NGC 4589	12 35.6 +74 28	10.9	0.9x0.7	E2
NGC 4570	12 48.4 +73 09	11.2	1.7x1.5	Sbpec
NGC 5678	14 30.7 +58 08	11.2	2.4x1.1	Scpec
NGC 5866	15 05.1 +55 57	10.8	2.8x1.0	SO(eo)

M102. Small bright spindle galaxy visible as an
elongated spike in a 4-inch.

| NGC 5879 | 15 08.4 +57 12 | 12.2 | 3.9x1.2 | Sb |
| NGC 5907 | 15 14.6 +56 31 | 11.3 | 11.1x0.7 | Sb(eo) |

Fine edge-on spiral visible as a dim streak of light
in a 2-inch; 6-inch shows bright long nebulosity
with slightly brighter middle and hint of dark lane.

| NGC 5982 | 15 37.6 +59 32 | 10.9 | 1.0x0.8 | E3 |
| NGC 5985 | 15 38.6 +59 30 | 11.4 | 4.9x2.2 | Sb |

Bright inclined spiral; 6-inch shows bright oval
central hub with low surface brightness nebulosity
surrounding it. NGC 5982 in same field.

NGC 6015	15 50.7 +62 28	11.8	5.5x1.9	Sc
NGC 6340	17 11.1 +72 22	12.4	2.0x1.8	Sapec
NGC 6412	17 30.8 +75 45	12.2	1.9x1.5	Sc
NGC 6503	17 49.9 +70 10	9.6	4.5x1.0	Sb

Bright object with diffuse halo.

| NGC 6643 | 18 21.2 +74 33 | 11.3 | 3.0x1.3 | Sc |

ERIDANUS

NGC 1084	02 43.5 -07 47	11.0	2.1x1.0	Sc
NGC 1187	03 00.4 -23 04	11.9	2.2x1.2	Sc
NGC 1209	03 03.8 -15 48	12.6	1.1x0.5	E6
NGC 1232	03 07.5 -20 46	10.7	7.0x5.5	Sc(rs)

Tightly wound face-on spiral; 6-inch shows a bright
core with large grainy halo of gas.

CATALOG NUMBER	R.A.(1950)Dec. h m ° '	Mag.	Size '	Type

ERIDANUS (Continued)

CATALOG NUMBER	R.A.(1950)Dec.	Mag.	Size	Type
NGC 1291	03 15.5 -41 17	10.2	5.0x2.0	S?
NGC 1300	03 17.5 -19 35	11.3	6.0x3.3	SBb(s)

6-inch shows oval nucleus and elongated nebulosity.

CATALOG NUMBER	R.A.(1950)Dec.	Mag.	Size	Type
NGC 1309	03 19.8 -15 35	11.4	1.6x1.5	Sc
NGC 1325	03 22.3 -21 43	12.5	4.2x1.1	Sb
NGC 1332	03 24.1 -21 31	10.4	3.0x0.8	S0
NGC 1337	03 25.6 -08 34	12.4	5.2x0.9	Sc(eo)
NGC 1353	03 29.8 -21 00	12.4	2.5x0.9	Sb
NGC 1357	03 30.9 -13 50	12.5	1.2x1.0	Sa
IC 1953	03 31.4 -21 39	12.5	2.1x1.9	S(B)c
NGC 1359	03 31.5 -19 41	12.5	1.6x1.3	SBpec
NGC 1386	03 35.0 -36 10	12.4	2.5x1.0	S0
NGC 1395	03 36.3 -23 11	11.3	2.1x1.4	E2
NGC 1400	03 37.2 -18 51	10.7	0.8x0.7	E1/S0
NGC 1407	03 37/9 -18 44	10.6	1.1x1.1	E0
NGC 1421	03 40.2 -13 40	12.0	3.0x0.6	Sb(eo)
NGC 1453	03 44.0 -04 08	11.4	0.8x0.6	E2
NGC 1487	03 54.1 -42 31	12.6	1.2x1.0	Spec
NGC 1518	04 04.7 -21 18	12.2	2.6x0.9	SBcpec
NGC 1532	04 10.2 -33 00	11.8	5.0x1.0	Sab(eo)
NGC 1537	04 11.8 -31 41	12.0	1.2x0.6	E6/S0
NGC 1600	04 29.2 -05 10	12.1	0.8x0.6	E4
NGC 1637	04 38.9 -02 56	12.1	2.7x2.0	Scpec
NGC 1640	04 40.1 -20 32	12.5	1.8x0.9	SBb
NGC 1700	04 45.5 -04 56	11.9	0.9x0.8	E3

FORNAX

CATALOG NUMBER	R.A.(1950)Dec.	Mag.	Size	Type
NGC 922	02 22.9 -25 01	12.3	1.2x1.2	SBc
NGC 986	02 31.6 -39 15	11.8	1.5x0.8	SBab(r)
NGC 1079	02 41.6 -29 13	12.6	1.1x0.8	Sa
NGC 1097	02 44.3 -30 29	10.6	9.0x5.5	SBbpec

6-inch shows a bright enlongated nucleus and outer envelope of nebulosity. Fine object.

CATALOG NUMBER	R.A.(1950)Dec.	Mag.	Size	Type
NGC 1201	03 02.0 -26 15	11.8	2.2x1.2	S0
NGC 1255	03 11.4 -25 58	12.1	3.5x2.2	Sc
NGC 1302	03 17.7 -26 14	11.4	2.4x2.1	SBa
NGC 1316	03 20.7 -37 25	10.1	3.5x2.5	E4pec

Brightest member of the Fornax cluster of galaxies. Appears as a roundish high surface brightness patch of hazy light.

CATALOG NUMBER	R.A.(1950)Dec.	Mag.	Size	Type
NGC 1317	03 20.8 -37 17	12.2	0.7x0.6	S0
NGC 1326	03 22.0 -36 39	11.8	3.0x2.5	SB0
NGC 1344	03 26.7 -31 14	11.6	2.0x1.0	E5/S0
NGC 1350	03 29.1 -33 47	11.8	3.0x1.5	SBa(r)
NGC 1365	03 31.8 -36 18	11.2	8.0x3.5	SB

Member of the Fornax galaxy cluster; one of the finest barred spirals in the southern sky. Small scopes show it as a condensed core with low surface brightness extensions on either side.

CATALOG NUMBER	R.A.(1950) h m	Dec. ° '	Mag.	Size '	Type

FORNAX (Continued)

NGC 1371	03 32.8	-25 06	12.2	2.0x1.4	SBa
NGC 1374	03 33.4	-35 24	12.4	0.8x0.8	E0
NGC 1379	03 34.2	-35 37	12.3	0.6x0.6	E0
NGC 1380	03 34.6	-35 09	11.4	3.0x1.0	S0
NGC 1381	03 34.7	-35 28	12.6	2.0x0.5	S0(eo)
NGC 1387	03 35.1	-35 41	12.1	1.0x0.9	SB0
NGC 1385	03 35.2	-24 40	11.8	2.6x1.8	Sc
NGC 1399	03 36.6	-35 37	10.9	1.4x1.4	E1
NGC 1398	03 36.8	-26 30	10.7	4.5x3.8	SBb
NGC 1404	03 37.0	-35 45	11.5	1.0x1.0	E2
NGC 1406	03 37.5	-31 28	12.7	3.0x0.8	Sc
NGC 1425	03 40.1	-30 04	12.1	3.5x1.7	Sb
NGC 1427	03 40.4	-35 34	12.4	1.4x1.0	E5

GEMINI

| NGC 2339 | 07 05.4 | 18 52 | 12.5 | 2.0x1.3 | Sc |

GRUS

NGC 7070	21 27.3	-43 19	12.6	1.9x1.5	S/SBc(s)
NGC 7079	21 29.3	-44 18	12.3	0.5x0.5	E5
NGC 7097	21 37.1	-42 46	12.6	0.6x0.4	E4
NGC 7166	21 57.6	-43 39	12.6	1.5x0.5	S0
IC 5186	22 13.4	-37 05	12.5	2.0x0.8	Sb
NGC 7410	22 52.1	-39 56	11.8	4.0x1.0	SBa(s)
NGC 7412	22 53.0	-42 55	12.2	3.0x2.0	Sc(rs)
NGC 7418	22 53.8	-37 17	11.8	2.5x2.5	S/SBc(rs)
IC 5267	22 54.4	-43 43	11.8	2.0x1.5	S0/Sa
IC 1459	22 54.5	-36 41	11.3	1.0x0.7	E4
NGC 7424	22 54.5	-41 20	12.0	6.0x6.0	Sc(s)

Large but ghostly in a 6-inch scope.

IC 5273	22 56.7	-37 58	12.0	1.8x1.4	SBc(s)
NGC 7456	22 59.3	-39 51	12.5	6.0x1.0	Sc(s)(eo)
NGC 7496	23 07.0	-43 42	12.2	2.0x1.0	SBbc(s)
NGC 7531	23 12.1	-43 53	12.5	1.5x0.5	Sa(r)
NGC 7552	23 13.5	-42 53	11.6	3.0x3.0	SBa
NGC 7582	23 15.8	-42 38	11.8	3.0x0.5	SBb(s)
NGC 7590	23 16.3	-42 31	11.9	2.2x0.8	Sb
NGC 7599	23 16.7	-42 32	12.0	4.0x1.0	SBc(s)

HERCULES

| NGC 6181 | 16 30.1 | +19 56 | 11.9 | 2.0x0.8 | Sc |
| NGC 6207 | 16 41.3 | +36 56 | 11.3 | 2.0x1.0 | Sc |

Small highly inclined spiral just northeast of M13, the Hercules Cluster.

| NGC 6482 | 17 49.8 | +23 05 | 12.2 | 0.7x0.5 | E2 |

HOROLOGIUM

| NGC 1448 | 03 42.9 | -44 48 | 11.8 | 8.0x1.1 | Sc(s)(eo) |
| NGC 1512 | 04 02.3 | -43 29 | 11.8 | 3.0x2.5 | SBa(rs) |

CATALOG NUMBER	R.A.(1950) Dec. h m ° '	Mag.	Size '	Type

_____HYDRA

NGC 2763	09 04.5	-15 17	12.6	1.5x1.5	Sc
NGC 2781	09 09.1	-14 36	11.7	2.0x0.7	SBa
NGC 2784	09 10.1	-23 58	11.8	3.0x1.0	S0
NGC 2811	09 13.9	-16 06	11.7	1.6x0.5	Sa
NGC 2835	09 15.7	-22 08	12.0	5.8x2.8	SBcpec
NGC 2855	09 19.1	-11 41	12.2	1.1x1.0	Sa
NGC 2865	09 21.2	-22 58	12.5	0.8x0.5	E4
NGC 2889	09 24.8	-11 25	12.4	1.3x1.2	Sbc
NGC 2935	09 34.5	-20 54	12.4	3.2x2.4	SBb
NGC 2983	09 41.3	-20 15	12.6	1.4x1.0	SB0/SBa
NGC 2986	09 42.0	-21 03	12.2	1.0x0.9	E2
NGC 3078	09 56.2	-26 41	12.2	0.6x0.4	E3
NGC 3109	10 00.8	-25 55	11.2	12.0x2.0	IB

A low surface brightness mottled bar of gas.

NGC 3145	10 07.7	-12 10	12.5	2.4x1.0	S(B)b(rs)
NGC 3585	11 10.9	-26 29	11.3	1.5x0.8	E7/S0
NGC 3621	11 15.9	-32 32	10.6	5.0x2.0	Scd

Large uneven oval nebulosity.

NGC 3904	11 46.7	-29 02	11.9	1.5x1.0	E2
NGC 3923	11 48.5	-28 33	11.1	1.5x1.2	E4
NGC 4105	12 04.1	-29 30	12.0	1.5x1.5	E3
NGC 4106	12 04.2	-29 31	12.5	1.0x0.8	E2/S0
NGC 4304	12 19.6	-33 12	12.4	1.0x1.0	SBbc(rs)
NGC 5061	13 15.3	-26 36	11.7	1.2x0.9	E2
NGC 5085	13 17.6	-24 09	12.3	2.8x2.0	Sb
NGC 5236	13 34.3	-29 37	10.1	10.0x8.0	S(B)c(s)

M83. A fine face-on spiral; shows mottled patchy arms and a small condensed nucleus with a 6-inch scope. One of the finest face-on galaxies.

_____LACERTA

| BL Lacertae | 22 00.8 | +42 01 | 12.0-15.5 | stellar | BL Lac |

Prototype of a strange class of active violent galaxies called BL Lacertae objects. Visible in 6-inch as a "star" when its variable light is at maximum.

_____LEO

| NGC 2903 | 09 29.3 | +21 44 | 9.1 | 11.0x4.7 | Sb |

4-inch scopes show an elongated nucleus with an extensive oval nebulosity; 6-inch scopes reveal a large nebular glow with a stellar nucleus and some dark patches of dust.

NGC 2964	09 40.0	+32 05	11.0	2.2x1.1	Sc
NGC 2968	09 40.3	+32 10	11.9	1.2x0.7	Pec
NGC 3162	10 10.7	+22 59	12.3	1.9x1.5	Sc
NGC 3190	10 15.4	+22 05	11.3	3.0x1.0	Sb

CATALOG NUMBER	R.A.(1950)Dec. h m ° '	Mag.	Size '	Type

NGC 3193	10 15.7 +22 09	11.5	0.9x0.9	E0
NGC 3226	10 20.7 +20 09	11.4	1.0x0.9	E2pec

Arp 94 (VV 209). 6-inch shows central brightening.

NGC 3227	10 20.7 +20 07	11.4	3.0x1.2	Sbpec

Arp 94 (VV 209). Seyfert galaxy apparently linked to NGC 3226.

NGC 3301	10 34.3 +22 08	11.8	2.5x0.6	SBa(eo)
NGC 3338	10 39.5 +14 00	11.6	4.5x3.0	Sbc
NGC 3346	10 41.0 +15 09	11.7	2.2x2.0	Scd
NGC 3351	10 41.3 +11 58	10.4	4.0x3.0	SBb(r)

M95. 4-inch shows faint nebulosity around slightly brighter core; 6-inch shows a large diffuse ring of gas encircling a stellar nucleus.

NGC 3367	10 44.0 +14 01	12.1	1.9x1.7	Sc
NGC 3368	10 44.2 +12 05	9.1	5.0x4.0	Sb(s)

M96. 6-inch scope shows a slightly elongated envelope brightening to a sharp oval nucleus.

NGC 3370	10 44.5 +17 32	12.4	2.4x1.2	Sc
NGC 3377	10 45.1 +14 15	10.5	1.6x0.9	E6
NGC 3379	10 45.2 +12 51	9.2	2.1x2.0	E0

M105. 6-inch shows a tiny nucleus and wispy outer gas.

NGC 3384	10 45.7 +12 54	10.2	4.0x2.0	SB0
NGC 3389	10 45.8 +12 48	12.5	2.2x1.0	Sc
NGC 3412	10 48.3 +13 41	10.4	2.4x1.1	SB0
NGC 3437	10 49.9 +23 11	11.8	2.1x0.5	Sbc
NGC 3489	10 57.7 +14 10	10.5	2.0x0.9	S0/SB0
NGC 3521	11 03.2 +00 14	9.5	6.0x4.0	Sb

Extensive outer envelope surrounds a very bright core.

NGC 3593	11 11.2 +13 06	11.3	3.0x0.9	Sb
NGC 3607	11 14.3 +18 20	9.6	1.5x1.3	S0

Very bright condensed core of nebulous gas.

NGC 3608	11 14.4 +18 26	11.1	1.0x0.8	E3
NGC 3623	11 16.3 +13 23	9.3	7.8x1.3	Sb(r)(eo)

M65 (Arp 317). 6-inch shows a highly flattened disk with a very bright oval center and a dust lane on one side of the nucleus.

NGC 3626	11 17.5 +18 38	10.5	1.6x1.3	S0
NGC 3627	11 17.6 +13 17	8.4	8.0x2.5	S(B)bpec

M66 (Arp 16). 4-inch scopes show an oval nebulosity while 6-inch scopes show dust patches near the hub.

CATALOG NUMBER	R.A.(1950)Dec. h m ° '	Mag.	Size '	Type

_____LEO (Continued)_____

| NGC 3628 | 11 17.7 +13 53 | 10.9 | 12.0x1.5 | Sb(eo) |

VV 308. Near M65 and M66. Long edge-on galaxy visible in 3-inch scopes as a pale silvery needle of light. 6-inchers show a low surface brightness streak of grey light with a slightly brighter center and a prominent dust band alongside the galaxy.

NGC 3640	11 18.5 +03 31	10.7	1.1x0.9	E2
NGC 3646	11 19.2 +20 27	11.8	3.2x1.9	Sc
NGC 3655	11 20.3 +16 51	11.3	1.2x0.9	Sc
NGC 3666	11 21.9 +11 37	12.2	3.7x0.8	Sbc
NGC 3681	11 23.9 +17 09	12.4	1.0x0.9	Sbc
NGC 3684	11 24.5 +17 18	12.4	1.4x0.9	Sc
NGC 3686	11 25.1 +17 30	11.4	2.2x1.9	Sc
NGC 3705	11 27.6 +09 33	12.2	3.5x1.3	Sb
NGC 3810	11 38.4 +11 45	10.8	3.6x2.5	Sc
NGC 3900	11 46.6 +27 17	11.5	1.7x0.8	Sb
NGC 4008	11 55.7 +28 28	12.2	0.7x0.5	S0

_____LEO MINOR_____

| NGC 2859 | 09 21.3 +34 44 | 10.7 | 4.0x3.5 | SB0 |

6-inch scope shows a small diffuse nebulosity surrounding a bright starlike nucleus.

NGC 3003	09 45.6 +33 39	12.7	5.0x0.9	S(B)c(eo)
NGC 3021	09 48.0 +33 47	11.7	1.1x0.5	Sb
NGC 3245	10 24.5 +28 46	11.2	1.8x0.9	S0
NGC 3254	10 26.5 +29 45	12.2	4.3x1.0	Sb(eo)
NGC 3277	10 30.2 +28 46	12.0	1.0x0.9	Sb
NGC 3294	10 33.4 +37 35	11.4	2.7x1.2	Sc
NGC 3395	10 47.1 +33 15	12.0	1.4x0.8	Sc(s)pec
NGC 3414	10 48.6 +28 15	11.0	1.4x1.0	SB0pec

Arp 162. 4-inch shows an oval nebulosity with a bright center.

| NGC 3430 | 10 49.5 +33 14 | 12.0 | 3.2x1.8 | Sc |

IC 2613. 6-inch shows a low surface brightness smudge near an 8th mag. star.

| NGC 3432 | 10 49.7 +36 54 | 11.4 | 5.9x0.8 | Spec(eo) |

Arp 206 (VV 11). 4-inch shows a bright elliptical nebulosity containing two stars.

NGC 3486	10 57.8 +29 15	11.2	5.5x4.2	Sc
NGC 3504	11 00.5 +28 15	10.9	2.0x1.8	S(B)b(s)
NGC 3512	11 01.3 +28 18	11.7	1.1x1.0	Sc

_____LEPUS_____

| NGC 1744 | 04 57.9 -26 06 | 12.1 | 7.6x3.1 | S(B)c |
| NGC 1832 | 05 10.0 -15 47 | 12.0 | 2.1x1.1 | S(B)b(rs) |

CATALOG NUMBER	R.A.(1950) Dec. h m ° '	Mag.	Size '	Type

_____LEPUS (Continued)

| NGC 1964 | 05 31.2 -21 59 | 11.6 | 5.4x1.1 | Sb(s) |

Astrophysically the largest known spiral galaxy.
6-inch shows an oval bright nucleus encapsulated in
a hazy glow.

| NGC 2139 | 05 59.0 -21 44 | 11.9 | 1.6x1.3 | Scpec |
| NGC 2196 | 06 10.1 -21 47 | 12.6 | 1.7x1.3 | Sb |

_____LIBRA

NGC 5595	14 21.5 -16 30	12.4	1.4x0.8	Sc
NGC 5597	14 21.7 -16 33	12.6	1.3x1.2	Sb
NGC 5728	14 39.6 -17 03	12.4	2.0x0.8	SBb(s)
NGC 5757	14 45.0 -18 53	12.6	1.2x1.0	SBb
NGC 5812	14 58.2 -07 16	11.4	0.7x0.6	E0
NGC 5861	15 06.4 -11 08	12.4	2.3x1.1	Scpec
NGC 5878	15 11.0 -14 05	12.4	2.9x0.9	Sb
NGC 5885	15 12.4 -09 53	12.4	2.2x2.2	Sb
NGC 5898	15 15.2 -23 55	12.6	0.6x0.5	E0
NGC 5915	15 18.8 -12 55	12.5	1.0x0.7	Sb

_____LUPUS

NGC 5530	14 15.4 -43 09	12.3	3.5x2.0	Sbc
IC 4444	14 28.5 -43 12	12.2	1.5x1.3	S(B)bc(s)
NGC 5643	14 29.4 -43 59	11.4	2.5x2.3	S(B)c(s)

_____LYNX

| NGC 2500 | 07 58.2 +50 54 | 12.2 | 2.0x1.6 | SBd |
| NGC 2537 | 08 09.7 +46 09 | 12.3 | 1.0x0.9 | Sdpec |

Arp 6 (VV 138, Mark 86). The Bear's Paw Galaxy. 6-inch
shows a fuzzy looking "star."

NGC 2541	08 11.1 +49 15	12.0	4.5x2.2	Sc
NGC 2549	08 14.9 +57 58	12.1	1.8x0.7	S0
NGC 2552	08 15.4 +50 11	12.5	2.6x2.0	I/Sd
NGC 2683	08 49.6 +33 38	9.6	9.0x1.3	Sb

A bright edge-on spiral; 4-inch shows a thin streak
of light with a condensed nucleus. 6-inch at high
power reveals mottled structure along the galaxy's
disk.

NGC 2712	08 56.2 +45 07	11.7	2.8x2.1	S(B)b
NGC 2776	09 08.9 +45 11	11.7	2.1x2.1	Sc
NGC 2782	09 10.9 +40 19	11.7	1.8x1.6	Sbpec

Arp 215. 6-inch shows a round nebulosity with a 9th
mag. star nearby.

_____OPHIUCHUS

| NGC 6384 | 17 29.9 +07 06 | 12.2 | 4.0x3.0 | Sb |

CATALOG NUMBER	R.A.(1950) Dec. h m ° '	Mag.	Size '	Type

NGC 7814	00 00.7 +15 51	12.0	3.0x0.8	Sa(eo)

Edge-on galaxy visible as a lens-shaped smudge.

NGC 7177	21 58.3 +17 29	12.0	2.1x1.1	Sb
NGC 7217	22 06.6 +31 07	11.0	2.6x2.3	Sb
NGC 7331	22 34.8 +34 10	9.7	10.0x2.3	Sb

Fine highly inclined spiral showing a bright hub and mottled outlying haze to 4-inch scopes on good nights of transparency. 6-inch scopes show the galaxy's dusty structure and small bright nucleus well.

NGC 7332	22 35.0 +23 32	11.8	2.3x0.6	S0(eo)
NGC 7448	22 57.6 +15 43	11.2	2.0x0.9	Scpec

Arp 13. 6-inch shows a small bright round nebulosity.

NGC 7457	22 58.6 +29 53	12.2	1.9x1.0	S0
NGC 7469	23 00.7 +08 36	12.7	1.3x1.0	Spec

Arp 298. Seyfert galaxy which appears as a stellar point surrounded by a faint halo of gas.

NGC 7479	23 02.4 +12 03	11.6	3.2x2.5	SBb(s)

Fine barred spiral showing an elongated nuclear region and tenuous mottled haze.

NGC 7678	23 26.1 +22 09	12.6	1.5x1.1	Sc

Arp 28. Fuzzy but near stellar in a 6-inch. Near a triangle of bright stars.

NGC 7741	23 41.4 +25 48	12.1	3.0x2.0	SBc(s)
NGC 7742	23 41.8 +10 29	12.4	0.8x0.8	E0pec
NGC 7769	23 48.5 +19 52	12.5	1.0x0.8	Sbc

NGC 1023	02 37.2 +38 52	11.0	4.0x1.2	SB0pec

Arp 135. 6-inch shows a bright oval shaped nebulosity with a condensed nucleus.

NGC 1058	02 40.2 +37 08	12.5	2.3x2.1	Sc
NGC 1270	03 15.6 +41 18	12.7	0.6x0.5	E2

NGC 625	01 32.9 -41 41	12.3	2.5x1.0	Sa/Spec
IC 5325	23 26.0 -41 36	12.5	1.6x1.5	Sbc(r)

NGC 470	01 17.1 +03 09	12.5	1.7x1.1	Scpec
NGC 474	01 17.5 +03 10	11.9	0.4x0.4	S0pec

CATALOG NUMBER	R.A.(1950) h m	Dec. ° '	Mag.	Size '	Type

____PISCES (Continued)

| NGC 488 | 01 19.1 | +05 00 | 11.1 | 3.5x3.0 | Sb(rs) |
| NGC 520 | 01 22.0 | +03 32 | 12.4 | 3.0x0.7 | Sbpec |

Arp 157 (VV 231). Distorted galaxy; 6-inch shows an irregular patch of misty light.

| NGC 524 | 01 22.1 | +09 16 | 11.1 | 1.8x1.7 | SO/Sa |
| NGC 628 | 01 34.0 | +15 32 | 10.2 | 10.6x9.0 | Sc(s) |

M74. One of the most difficult Messier objects; 4-inch shows a low surface brightness evenly illuminated nebulosity. 6-inch shows a large faint mass of light around a sharp condensed nucleus.

NGC 718	01 50.7	+03 57	12.6	0.8x0.7	Sb
NGC 7541	23 12.2	+04 15	12.1	2.9x0.9	S(B)c
NGC 7619	23 17.8	+07 55	11.2	0.8x0.6	E3
NGC 7626	23 18.2	+07 56	11.7	0.9x0.7	E2pec

_____PISCIS AUSTRINUS

| NGC 7314 | 22 33.0 | -26 18 | 11.9 | 3.5x1.5 | Sc |
| IC 5271 | 22 55.3 | -34 01 | 12.6 | 2.0x0.8 | SO |

_____PUPPIS

| NGC 2525 | 08 03.3 | -11 17 | 12.3 | 2.2x1.4 | SBc |

_____PYXIS

| NGC 2613 | 08 31.2 | -22 48 | 10.9 | 6.6x1.3 | Sb(s) |

6-inch shows a bright nucleus surrounded by an elongated haze.

_____SAGITTARIUS

| NGC 6822 | 19 42.1 | -14 53 | 11.0 | 20.0x10.0 | I |

Barnard's Galaxy. Nearby irregular system very faint due to absorption from the Milky Way's plane. Visible in a 6-inch with low power as a barely discernable patch of light. Best seen on dark nights with large binoculars.

| NGC 6902 | 20 21.2 | -43 50 | 12.4 | 0.9x0.7 | SBa |

_____SCULPTOR

| NGC 24 | 00 07.4 | -25 15 | 12.2 | 5.0x0.7 | Sb(eo) |
| NGC 55 | 00 12.5 | -39 50 | 9.7 | 25.0x3.0 | SBm(eo) |

Large bright nearly edge-on galaxy showing a mottled nucleus placed slightly off-center.

| NGC 134 | 00 27.9 | -33 32 | 11.4 | 5.0x1.0 | Sbc |

CATALOG NUMBER	R.A.(1950)Dec. h m ° '		Mag.	Size '	Type

SCULPTOR (Continued)

| NGC 150 | 00 31.8 | -28 05 | 12.2 | 2.0x1.0 | SB |
| NGC 253 | 00 45.1 | -25 34 | 8.9 | 24.6x4.5 | S(B)c(s) |

One of the finest galaxies in the sky. 2-inch shows a long thin streak of light; 4-inch reveals a central condensation and extensive outer nebulosity. 6-inch scopes show a huge mottled envelope of nebulosity around a bright condensed nucleus and dark structure in and around the nuclear region.

| NGC 289 | 00 50.4 | -31 29 | 12.1 | 2.0x1.5 | Sbc |
| NGC 300 | 00 52.6 | -37 58 | 11.3 | 21.0x14.0 | Scd(s) |

6-inch shows a sharp stellar nucleus with a large dim halo of low surface brightness nebulosity.

NGC 613	01 32.0	-29 40	10.2	4.0x2.0	SBc
NGC 7507	23 09.5	-28 49	12.0	1.0x1.0	E0
IC 5332	23 31.7	-36 22	11.9	4.0x4.0	Sc(r)
NGC 7713	23 33.8	-38 13	11.8	4.0x1.5	Sc(r)
NGC 7755	23 45.5	-30 48	12.5	4.0x3.0	SBbc(r)
NGC 7793	23 55.3	-32 51	9.7	6.0x4.0	Sd

Large bright oval galaxy showing a faint haze around its nuclear region.

SERPENS

NGC 5921	15 19.5	+05 15	12.2	3.6x3.0	SBb
NGC 5962	15 34.2	+16 46	11.9	2.2x1.8	Sc
NGC 5970	15 36.1	+12 20	12.4	2.3x1.6	Sc
NGC 6070	16 07.4	+00 50	12.3	3.1x1.7	Sc
NGC 6118	16 19.3	-02 11	11.9	4.2x1.2	Sbc

SEXTANS

NGC 2967	09 39.5	+00 34	12.4	2.0x1.8	Sc
NGC 2974	09 40.0	-03 29	11.0	1.0x0.6	E4
NGC 3044	09 51.0	+01 49	12.6	4.9x0.5	Sc(eo)
NGC 3055	09 52.7	+04 31	12.5	1.4x0.8	Sc
NGC 3115	10 02.8	-07 27	9.3	4.0x1.0	Sa

Bright spindle shaped galaxy showing a sharp nucleus and faint halo of gas.

NGC 3166	10 11.2	+03 40	11.4	4.0x1.5	Sa
NGC 3169	10 11.7	+03 43	11.7	3.9x1.7	Sb
NGC 3423	10 48.7	+06 07	11.5	3.5x2.8	Sc

TELESCOPIUM

NGC 6861	20 03.7	-48 31	12.3	1.3x0.7	E6
NGC 6868	20 06.3	-48 31	12.1	1.4x1.0	E3
NGC 6875	20 09.6	-46 19	12.6	1.0x0.5	S0
NGC 6893	20 17.2	-48 25	12.5	1.5x1.0	E3/S0

CATALOG NUMBER	R.A.(1950) Dec. h m ° '	Mag.	Size '	Type

TRIANGULUM

| NGC 598 | 01 31.1   +30 24 | 6.5 | 65.0x35.0 | Sc(s) |

M33. Huge relatively low surface brightness galaxy showing a bright central area and faint nebulosity in large binoculars. 4-inch scopes show a hazy oval central region surrounded by an enormous faint halo. 6-inch scopes on dark nights show bright condensations in the faint gas -- including at least one HII region -- and delicate spiral structure in the arms, as well as a sharp stellar nucleus and mottled central hub.

| IC 1727 | 01 44.6   +27 05 | 12.0 | 1.0x0.5 | I |
| NGC 672 | 01 45.0   +27 11 | 12.2 | 5.5x1.5 | SBc |

VV 338. Large ghostly patch of grey light.

| NGC 925 | 02 24.3   +33 22 | 12.0 | 9.4x4.0 | SBc(s) |

Large irregular low surface brightness patch; only slightly condensed in the central region.

| NGC 949 | 02 27.6   +36 56 | 12.7 | 1.1x0.4 | Sb |

URSA MAJOR

NGC 2639	08 40.1 +50 24	11.6	1.2x0.6	S0/Sa
NGC 2681	08 50.0 +51 31	10.4	2.8x2.5	S0/Sa
NGC 2685	08 52.2 +58 59	12.2	3.0x1.6	S0pec

Arp 336. Distorted "gyroscope galaxy" showing as a faint mottled patch of uneven light.

NGC 2693	08 53.5 +51 33	11.7	0.7x0.5	E2
NGC 2742	09 03.7 +60 41	11.2	2.5x1.0	Sc
NGC 2768	09 07.8 +60 16	10.5	1.6x0.8	E6
NGC 2787	09 14.9 +69 25	10.9	2.0x1.3	SB0
NGC 2841	09 18.6 +51 12	9.3	6.4x2.4	Sb

Large inclined spiral showing a bright stellar nucleus within an extensive halo of mottled nebulosity. 6-inch shows dark structure on one side of the galaxy's hub.

NGC 2880	09 25.7 +62 44	11.4	1.2x0.7	E3/S0
NGC 2950	09 39.1 +59 05	10.9	1.3x0.9	SB0
NGC 2976	09 43.2 +68 08	11.4	3.4x1.3	Sc
NGC 2985	09 46.0 +72 31	10.6	4.0x3.0	Sab
NGC 3031	09 51.5 +69 18	7.9	21.0x9.8	Sb(rs)

M81. One of the best spiral galaxies in the sky. Visible as an oval smudge in 2-inch scopes; 4-inch scopes at high power show a sharp nucleus embedded in a large outer halo of nebulous gas. 6-inch scopes show a bright oval hub centered on a stellar nucleus with mottled spiral arms arcing about; on good nights they reveal a prominent dust lane running alongside the galaxy's core.

CATALOG NUMBER	R.A.(1950) Dec. h m ° '	Mag.	Size '	Type

| NGC 3034 | 09 51.9   +69 56 | 8.8 | 9.0x4.0 | Ipec |

M82 (Arp 337). Bright spindle shaped distorted galaxy
in same low power field as M81. 2-inch shows a high
surface brightness edge-on streak of grey-green gas.
4-inch shows a bright long sliver of nebulosity with
faint mottling across parts of the edge. 6-inch on
good nights shows a bright spindle crosscut by large
dark patches centered on a sharp nucleus.

| NGC 3079 | 09 58.6   +55 57 | 11.2 | 8.0x1.0 | Sc(eo) |

6-inch shows a large mottled nebulosity with a bright
star on the galaxy's northern end.

| NGC 3077 | 09 59.4   +68 58 | 10.9 | 2.3x1.9 | E2/Ipec |
| NGC 3184 | 10 15.2   +41 40 | 9.6 | 5.5x5.5 | Sc |

Large round nebulosity with a bright nucleus; a star
appears near the galaxy's center.

| NGC 3310 | 10 35.7   +53 46 | 10.1 | 3.0x2.0 | Ipec |

Arp 217. Round nebulosity with a bright sharp core.

NGC 3319	10 36.4 +41 56	11.8	6.0x3.2	S(B)c
NGC 3359	10 43.4 +63 30	11.0	7.0x3.5	S(B)c
NGC 3348	10 43.5 +73 07	11.2	0.9x0.8	E1
NGC 3445	10 51.6 +57 15	12.5	1.1x1.1	Scpec

Arp 24 (VV 14). Peculiar galaxy visible as an even
patch of light.

NGC 3448	10 51.7 +54 34	11.7	1.8x0.3	Spec(eo)
NGC 3458	10 53.0 +57 22	12.2	0.8x0.6	S0
NGC 3516	11 03.4 +72 50	11.6	1.0x0.8	SB0
NGC 3556	11 08.7 +55 57	10.7	7.7x1.3	Sc(eo)

M108. Long thin streak of light; 6-inch at high power
shows dark patches and bright knots across the
galaxy's face, and a stellar nucleus.

NGC 3583	11 11.4 +48 39	12.2	2.2x1.4	Sbc
NGC 3610	11 15.6 +59 04	11.2	1.3x1.0	E5pec
NGC 3613	11 15.7 +58 17	11.2	1.6x0.8	E6
NGC 3619	11 16.5 +58 02	11.7	1.0x1.0	S0
NGC 3631	11 18.3 +53 28	11.2	4.3x3.2	Scpec

Arp 27. 6-inch shows a stellar nucleus surrounded by
a faint round halo.

NGC 3642	11 19.6 +59 21	11.4	5.5x4.2	Sc
NGC 3665	11 22.1 +39 02	11.4	1.3x1.0	S0
NGC 3675	11 23.5 +43 52	10.6	3.5x1.7	Sb

Bright elliptical nebulosity just 40' east of the 5th
mag. star 56 Ursae Majoris.

CATALOG NUMBER	R.A.(1950) Dec. h m ° '	Mag.	Size '	Type
NGC 3690	11 26.0 +58 49	12.0	1.4x0.4	Sbcpec

IC 694 (Arp 296, VV 118, Markarian 171). Faint small galaxy appearing as a nebulous patch at low power.

NGC 3718	11 29.9 +53 21	11.2	3.0x3.0	SOpec

Arp 214. 6-inch shows a round nebulosity with no central condensation. NGC 3729 in same field.

NGC 3726	11 30.7 +47 19	11.3	5.0x3.3	Sc
NGC 3729	11 31.0 +53 24	11.7	1.8x1.3	SBpec
NGC 3738	11 33.1 +54 48	11.8	1.2x0.9	Pec

Arp 234. 6-inch shows a fuzzy "star."

NGC 3756	11 34.1 +48 11	12.5	3.3x1.6	Sc
NGC 3780	11 36.7 +56 33	12.4	2.4x1.9	Sc
NGC 3813	11 38.7 +36 49	11.7	1.9x0.8	Sb
NGC 3877	11 43.5 +47 46	10.9	4.4x0.8	Sb(eo)
NGC 3893	11 46.1 +49 00	11.3	3.7x1.9	Sc
NGC 3898	11 46.7 +56 22	11.4	2.6x0.9	Sb
NGC 3917	11 48.3 +52 06	12.8	4.4x0.7	Scd(eo)
NGC 3938	11 50.2 +44 24	11.5	4.5x3.8	Sc
NGC 3941	11 50.3 +37 16	9.8	1.8x1.2	SB0
NGC 3945	11 50.6 +60 57	10.8	5.0x2.0	SB0
NGC 3949	11 51.1 +48 08	11.0	2.2x1.1	Sbc
NGC 3953	11 51.2 +52 37	10.7	5.6x2.3	S(B)b

Large bright galaxy; 6-inch shows a condensed center with mottled envelope. A faint star lies on the eastern edge of the galaxy.

NGC 3982	11 53.9 +55 24	11.3	1.7x1.3	Sb
NGC 3992	11 55.0 +53 39	10.8	6.2x3.5	SBb

M109. 4-inch shows an oval nebulosity with a slightly brighter nuclear region; 6-inch reveals a condensed center and faint extensions leading to a faint star on one edge of the galaxy.

NGC 3998	11 55.3 +55 44	11.3	1.6x1.2	SO
NGC 4036	11 58.9 +62 10	10.7	2.4x0.9	SO
NGC 4041	11 59.7 +62 25	11.0	2.2x1.9	Sc
NGC 4047	12 00.2 +48 55	12.0	1.1x1.0	Sb
NGC 4051	12 00.6 +44 48	11.0	4.2x3.0	Scpec

Markarian 79. A Seyfert galaxy, it shows as a bright elliptical nebulosity surrounding a bright nucleus.

NGC 4062	12 01.5 +32 10	12.0	3.2x1.1	Sbc
NGC 4085	12 02.8 +50 38	11.8	2.2x0.5	Sbc
NGC 4088	12 03.0 +50 49	10.9	4.5x1.5	Scpec

Arp 18. An irregular low surface brightness object.

NGC 4096	12 03.5 +47 45	11.9	5.8x1.0	Sc

CATALOG NUMBER	R.A.(1950) h m	Dec. ° '	Mag.	Size '	Type

_____ URSA MAJOR (Continued)_____

NGC 4100	12 03.6	+49 51	11.9	5.0x1.2	Sbc(eo)
NGC 4102	12 03.8	+52 59	11.8	2.2x1.2	Sbc
NGC 4111	12 04.5	+43 21	9.7	3.3x0.6	S0(eo)
NGC 4144	12 07.5	+46 44	12.4	5.2x0.7	Scd
NGC 4157	12 08.6	+50 46	11.9	6.5x0.8	Sb(eo)
NGC 4290	12 18.5	+58 22	12.7	1.5x0.9	SBab
NGC 4605	12 37.8	+61 53	9.6	5.0x1.2	Scpec

Bright galaxy showing a mottled core and extensive halo of nebulosity.

NGC 4814	12 53.3	+58 37	12.1	2.2x2.1	Sbpec
NGC 5204	13 28.3	+58 40	12.2	3.9x2.2	I/Sd
NGC 5308	13 45.4	+61 14	11.7	2.1x0.5	Sa
NGC 5322	13 47.6	+60 26	10.0	1.4x1.0	E4
NGC 5376	13 53.6	+59 45	12.2	1.2x0.8	Sab
NGC 5422	13 59.0	+55 24	11.5	2.9x0.4	S0
NGC 5448	14 00.9	+49 25	12.3	4.0x1.2	Sb
NGC 5457	14 01.4	+54 35	9.6	22.0x20.0	Scpec

M101. One of the largest galaxies in the sky, it is face-on and has a low surface brightness. 2-inch on dark nights show it as a circular dim patch of grey light; 4-inch at high power shows a small nucleus and extensive faint outer nebulosity. 6-inch scopes on good nights show a small bright nucleus, enormous nebulous condensations and a hint of spiral structure.

| NGC 5473 | 14 03.0 | +55 08 | 11.4 | 0.9x0.7 | SB0 |
| NGC 5474 | 14 03.2 | +53 54 | 11.4 | 4.0x2.9 | Scpec |

VV 344. A faint more-or-less circular smudge.

NGC 5480	14 04.6	+50 57	12.6	1.1x0.9	S(B)c
NGC 5485	14 05.5	+55 14	11.7	0.8x0.7	S0
NGC 5585	14 18.0	+56 57	11.7	4.5x2.3	S(B)d
NGC 5631	14 25.1	+56 48	11.4	0.7x0.7	S0

_____ URSA MINOR_____

| NGC 6217 | 16 34.8 | +78 18 | 11.5 | 1.8x1.2 | Sc |

_____ VELA_____

| NGC 3256 | 10 25.7 | -43 38 | 12.1 | 2.0x1.5 | Sb(s)pec |
| NGC 3318 | 10 35.1 | -41 22 | 12.6 | 2.0x1.2 | SBb(rs) |

_____ VIRGO_____

NGC 3976	11 53.4	+07 02	12.4	3.6x0.8	Sb(eo)
NGC 4030	11 57.8	-00 49	11.0	3.1x2.2	Sc
NGC 4116	12 05.1	+02 58	12.3	3.1x1.2	SBc
NGC 4123	12 05.6	+03 09	12.0	3.2x2.0	SBb
NGC 4168	12 09.8	+13 29	12.3	1.0x1.0	E0
NGC 4178	12 10.2	+11 09	11.8	4.4x1.1	SBa
NGC 4179	12 10.3	+01 35	11.6	2.7x0.6	S0(eo)
NGC 4189	12 11.2	+13 42	12.5	1.7x1.5	Sc

CATALOG NUMBER	R.A.(1950) h m	Dec. ° '	Mag.	Size '	Type

| NGC 4216 | 12 13.4 | +13 25 | 10.4 | 7.4x0.9 | Sb(eo) |

Large bright nearly edge-on spiral with a stellar
nucleus somewhat offcenter.

NGC 4235	12 14.6	+07 28	12.6	2.6x0.5	Sa
NGC 4260	12 16.8	+06 23	12.7	2.0x0.9	SBbc
NGC 4261	12 16.8	+06 06	10.3	0.9x0.7	E3
NGC 4267	12 17.2	+13 03	12.0	2.2x2.2	SB0
NGC 4270	12 17.3	+05 44	11.9	1.2x0.4	S0
NGC 4273	12 17.4	+05 37	12.6	2.4x0.9	Sc
NGC 4281	12 17.8	+05 40	11.3	1.1x0.6	S0
NGC 4294	12 18.7	+11 47	12.6	2.4x0.9	S(B)c
NGC 4303	12 19.4	+04 45	10.1	5.6x5.3	Sc(s)

M61. Bright face-on spiral with a high surface
brightness; 4-inch scopes show a hazy circular patch
with a condensed nucleus. 6-inch scopes show a
stellar nucleus and mottled haze surrounding it. The
double star 17 Virginis lies 50' north, next to faint
galaxy NGC 4324.

NGC 4324	12 20.6	+05 31	12.5	1.3x0.6	Sa(r)
NGC 4339	12 21.0	+06 22	12.6	0.7x0.7	S0/E0
NGC 4365	12 22.0	+07 36	11.1	1.3x1.0	E3
NGC 4371	12 22.4	+11 59	11.6	2.0x1.2	SB0
NGC 4374	12 22.6	+13 10	9.3	1.6x1.4	E1

M84. Small bright elliptical near the heart of the
Virgo cluster; 6-inch shows a round high surface
brightness ball of nebulosity. M86 lies 17' east
which, along with galaxies NGC 4388 (16' south) and
NGC 4402 (10' north), form the western end of the
Virgo cluster's center.

NGC 4378	12 22.8	+05 12	11.7	3.0x2.7	Sa
NGC 4388	12 23.3	+12 56	11.7	5.0x0.9	Sb(eo)
NGC 4406	12 23.7	+13 13	9.7	2.1x1.4	E2

M86. Small bright elliptical almost identical to M84
but slightly larger. A high surface brightness object,
it shows well as a round condensed patch in a 4- or
6-inch scope. In same field as M84, NGC 4388 and NGC
4402.

NGC 4417	12 24.3	+09 52	12.2	1.8x0.5	E7/S0
NGC 4420	12 24.4	+02 46	12.5	1.9x0.7	Sc
NGC 4424	12 24.6	+09 42	12.5	2.0x1.0	Sb
NGC 4429	12 24.9	+11 23	11.2	3.0x1.0	S0/Sa
NGC 4435	12 25.2	+13 21	11.9	1.3x1.0	SB0pec
NGC 4438	12 25.3	+13 17	10.8	4.0x1.5	Sapec

Large distorted galaxy showing an elongated nucleus.
NGC 4435 in same field.

NGC 4442	12 25.6	+10 05	10.8	1.8x0.9	SB0
NGC 4457	12 26.4	+03 51	11.7	2.0x1.6	S(B)a
NGC 4461	12 26.6	+13 28	12.2	1.6x0.7	S0/Sa

CATALOG NUMBER	R.A.(1950) Dec. h m ° '	Mag.	Size '	Type

_____VIRGO (Continued)_____

| NGC 4472 | 12 27.3 +08 16 | 8.6 | 2.8x1.8 | E4 |

M49. Bright round elliptical bracketed between two 6th magnitude stars.

NGC 4473	12 27.3 +13 43	10.1	1.6x0.9	E5
NGC 4478	12 27.8 +12 36	10.9	0.8x0.7	E2
NGC 4486	12 28.3 +12 40	9.2	3.0x3.0	E0pec

M87. Physically the center of the Virgo cluster, this is one of the most massive and luminous galaxies known. 6-inch scopes show a bright condensed core and faint outer halo of nebulosity. South of an 8th mag. star.

NGC 4487	12 28.3 -07 48	12.0	3.3x2.5	Sc
NGC 4496	12 29.1 +04 12	12.0	3.0x2.0	S(B)cpec
NGC 4504	12 29.7 -07 17	11.7	4.0x2.0	Sc
NGC 4517	12 30.2 +00 23	12.0	8.9x0.9	Sc(eo)

Large dim edge-on galaxy with low surface brightness.

NGC 4519	12 31.0 +08 56	12.2	2.2x1.7	S(B)c
NGC 4526	12 31.6 +07 58	10.9	3.3x1.0	S0/Sa
NGC 4527	12 31.6 +02 56	11.3	5.3x1.0	Sb(eo)

Edge-on galaxy appearing as a dim sliver of light.

| NGC 4532 | 12 31.8 +06 44 | 12.1 | 2.2x0.5 | I |
| NGC 4535 | 12 31.8 +08 28 | 10.7 | 6.0x4.0 | S(B)c |

Large bright galaxy; 6-inch shows stellar nucleus and faint outer halo of misty gas.

NGC 4536	12 31.9 +02 28	11.9	6.9x2.6	Sc
NGC 4546	12 32.9 -03 31	10.0	1.8x0.8	E6/S0
NGC 4550	12 32.9 +12 30	11.7	1.4x0.4	E7/S0pec
NGC 4552	12 33.1 +12 50	9.5	1.3x1.3	E0

M89. Elliptical galaxy resembling a fainter version of M87.

| NGC 4564 | 12 34.0 +11 43 | 12.2 | 1.6x0.6 | E6/S0 |
| NGC 4567 | 12 34.0 +11 32 | 12.0 | 2.4x1.6 | Scpec |

Forms an interacting pair -- the "Siamese Twins" -- along with NGC 4568. 6-inch shows two dim patches apparently in contact.

| NGC 4568 | 12 34.1 +11 31 | 11.9 | 3.6x1.8 | Scpec |
| NGC 4569 | 12 34.3 +13 26 | 10.0 | 7.0x2.5 | Sb |

M90. Large bright highly-inclined spiral showing a condensed core and diffuse outer envelope of gas.

| NGC 4570 | 12 34.4 +07 31 | 10.9 | 2.4x0.5 | S0/E7 |
| NGC 4578 | 12 35.0 +09 50 | 12.5 | 1.9x1.3 | E3 |

CATALOG NUMBER	R.A.(1950)Dec. h m ° '	Mag.	Size '	Type
NGC 4579	12 35.1 +12 05	9.2	4.0x3.5	Sb

M58. A fine spiral, it shows as a bright elongated nucleus wrapped by faint tenuous haze. The faint interacting pair NGC 4567/8 lies about 30' southwest.

NGC 4580	12 35.3 +05 38	11.7	1.3x1.0	Sa/Sb
NGC 4586	12 35.9 +04 35	12.5	2.6x0.7	Sab
NGC 4592	12 36.7 -00 16	12.4	3.0x0.7	Sbc
NGC 4593	12 37.0 -05 04	12.0	3.2x2.5	SBb
NGC 4594	12 37.3 -11 21	8.7	7.0x1.5	Sab(eo)

M104, the Sombrero Galaxy. Beautiful edge-on system showing a lens-shaped structure bisected by a broad dust lane visible even in a 2-inch telescope.

NGC 4596	12 37.4 +10 27	11.4	2.4x0.9	SB0/a
NGC 4602	12 38.0 -04 52	12.4	3.0x1.5	Sc
NGC 4608	12 38.7 +10 26	12.1	1.4x1.4	SBa
NGC 4612	12 39.0 +07 35	12.6	0.9x0.8	S0/Epec
NGC 4621	12 39.5 +11 55	9.6	2.0x1.5	E5

M59. Small bright elliptical galaxy visible as a fainter version of M87.

NGC 4632	12 40.0 +00 11	12.5	2.6x0.8	Sc
NGC 4636	12 40.3 +02 57	10.4	1.3x1.2	E0
NGC 4639	12 40.3 +13 31	12.2	2.0x1.3	SBb
NGC 4643	12 40.8 +02 15	10.6	1.5x0.9	SBa
NGC 4647	12 41.0 +11 51	12.0	2.0x1.5	Scpec
NGC 4649	12 41.1 +11 49	8.9	2.0x1.8	E2/S0pec

M60. Small bright elliptical galaxy showing as a smooth round ball of gas in small scopes. NGC 4647 lies just 2.5' northwest.

NGC 4654	12 41.4 +13 23	11.2	4.2x2.2	Sc
NGC 4658	12 42.0 -09 49	12.4	1.3x0.5	S(B)c
NGC 4660	12 42.0 +11 26	10.9	1.3x0.6	E6
NGC 4665	12 42.6 +03 19	11.1	3.0x2.0	S0/SBa
NGC 4666	12 42.6 -00 12	11.4	3.9x0.7	Sc(eo)
NGC 4684	12 44.7 -02 28	11.6	1.8x0.5	S0
NGC 4691	12 45.6 -03 04	11.8	2.0x1.5	SBa
NGC 4694	12 45.7 +11 15	12.6	1.8x0.7	E5/S0
NGC 4697	12 46.0 -05 32	9.6	2.2x1.4	E6
NGC 4698	12 45.8 +08 45	11.3	2.8x1.0	Sb
NGC 4699	12 46.5 -08 24	9.3	3.0x2.0	Sab(rs)

Bright spiral with a condensed core.

NGC 4700	12 46.5 -11 08	12.5	2.2x0.3	S(eo)
NGC 4713	12 47.5 +05 35	11.7	2.2x1.3	Sc
NGC 4731	12 48.4 -06 08	10.8	5.5x2.5	SBcpec
NGC 4742	12 49.2 -10 12	11.7	0.9x0.6	E4
NGC 4753	12 49.7 -00 55	10.8	3.3x1.1	S0pec
NGC 4754	12 49.8 +11 35	10.5	2.0x1.2	SB0

CATALOG NUMBER	R.A.(1950) Dec. h m ° '	Mag.	Size '	Type
NGC 4760	12 50.5 -10 13	12.5	0.6x0.5	E1
NGC 4762	12 50.5 +11 31	11.0	3.7x0.4	S0(eo)
NGC 4772	12 51.0 +02 27	12.6	2.3x1.0	Sa
NGC 4775	12 51.1 -06 21	11.6	1.7x1.6	Sc
NGC 4781	12 51.8 -10 16	11.2	2.3x1.1	Sc
NGC 4786	12 52.0 -06 35	12.7	0.6x0.5	E3pec
NGC 4790	12 52.2 -09 58	12.5	1.2x0.9	S(B)c
NGC 4808	12 53.3 +04 35	12.0	2.2x0.8	Sc
NGC 4818	12 54.3 -08 15	12.1	3.4x1.0	S(B)a
NGC 4845	12 55.5 +01 51	12.6	4.2x0.7	Sb(eo)
NGC 4856	12 56.7 -14 46	11.4	2.0x0.7	SBa
NGC 4866	12 57.0 +14 27	11.4	6.8x0.8	Sa(eo)
NGC 4899	12 58.3 -13 41	12.7	1.8x1.0	Scpec
NGC 4900	12 58.2 +02 46	11.3	1.7x1.5	Sc
NGC 4902	12 58.3 -14 15	11.6	2.0x2.0	SBb
NGC 4939	13 01.7 -10 05	12.2	5.0x1.9	Sbc
NGC 4941	13 01.6 -05 17	12.2	3.0x1.0	S(B)a
NGC 4951	13 02.5 -06 14	12.7	4.0x1.0	Sc
NGC 4958	13 03.1 -07 45	10.9	1.7x0.7	S0
NGC 4981	13 06.1 -06 31	12.2	2.0x1.5	Sbc
NGC 4984	13 06.4 -15 15	11.9	1.1x0.9	Sa
NGC 4995	13 07.0 -07 34	11.2	2.0x1.1	Sb
NGC 5018	13 10.3 -19 15	12.2	1.5x0.8	E4
NGC 5044	13 12.8 -16 08	11.2	0.9x0.9	E0
NGC 5054	13 14.3 -16 23	11.9	3.8x2.2	Sb
NGC 5068	13 16.2 -20 47	11.6	5.6x5.6	SBc
NGC 5077	13 16.9 -12 24	12.4	0.9x0.6	E3
NGC 5084	13 17.5· -21 34	12.4	6.6x1.0	S0
NGC 5087	13 17.7 -20 21	12.4	0.8x0.5	S0
NGC 5134	13 22.6 -20 51	12.4	1.8x0.8	Sb
NGC 5147	13 23.7 +02 22	12.1	1.3x1.0	Sc
NGC 5170	13 27.1 -17 42	12.6	7.6x0.7	Sc(eo)
NGC 5247	13 35.3 -17 38	12.7	4.4x3.7	Sbc
NGC 5300	13 45.7 +04 11	12.3	3.1x2.1	Sc
NGC 5324	13 49.4 -05 48	12.6	1.6x1.5	Sc
NGC 5334	13 50.4 -00 53	12.5	3.3x2.2	SBc
NGC 5363	13 53.6 +05 29	10.7	1.7x1.5	S0/Epec
NGC 5364	13 53.7 +05 15	11.5	5.0x4.0	S(B)bpec

Fine inclined system visible in a 6-inch as a tight oval core with loose faint haze suggested spiral arms.

| NGC 5426 | 14 00.8   -05 49 | 12.7 | 1.5x1.1 | Sc |
| NGC 5427 | 14 00.8   -05 47 | 12.0 | 2.0x1.6 | Sc |

NGC 5426 lies in same field.

NGC 5468	14 04.0 -05 14	12.4	2.0x1.9	Sc
NGC 5493	14 08.9 -04 49	12.5	0.8x0.5	E7/S0
NGC 5566	14 17.8 +04 11	10.4	5.6x1.1	SBabpec

Visible in 6-inch as a compact nucleus surrounded by faint outer haze.

NGC 5576	14 18.5 +03 30	11.7	0.8x0.6	E4
NGC 5584	14 19.8 -00 10	12.2	2.6x1.0	Sc
NGC 5638	14 27.1 +03 27	12.5	0.9x0.8	E1
NGC 5668	14 30.9 +04 40	12.3	2.0x1.6	Sc

VIRGO (Continued)

CATALOG NUMBER	R.A.(1950) Dec. h m ° '	Mag.	Size '	Type

CATALOG NUMBER	R.A.(1950) Dec. h m ° '	Mag.	Size	Type
NGC 5701	14 36.7 +05 34	11.8	3.0x2.0	S(B)b
NGC 5713	14 37.6 -00 05	11.7	2.0x1.8	Scpec
NGC 5740	14 41.9 +01 54	11.7	2.2x1.0	Sb
NGC 5746	14 42.3 +02 10	10.1	6.5x0.8	Sb(eo)

Fine large edge-on galaxy.

CATALOG NUMBER	R.A.(1950) Dec.	Mag.	Size	Type
NGC 5750	14 43.6 -00 01	12.2	1.5x0.9	SBc
NGC 5775	14 51.5 +03 45	12.3	4.0x0.7	Sb(eo)
NGC 5806	14 57.5 +02 05	11.7	1.8x0.8	Sb
NGC 5813	14 58.7 +01 54	12.0	0.9x0.8	E1
NGC 5831	15 01.6 +01 24	12.7	0.6x0.5	E4pec
NGC 5838	15 02.9 +02 18	12.0	3.2x0.7	S0
NGC 5846	15 04.0 +01 48	10.5	0.9x0.9	E1
NGC 5850	15 04.6 +01 44	12.0	2.6x2.1	SBb
NGC 5854	15 05.3 +02 45	12.6	2.0x0.4	SBa

The Eagle Nebula

Appendix 1:
Reflections on
Amateur Astronomy

Amateur astronomy is undergoing a revolutionary change. New technologies, ideas, and easily available high-quality information are changing the hobby of observing the sky just as they are changing everything else. Eleven years ago, when I first became obsessed with observing deep-sky objects at age 15, things were relatively simple. Many people who became interested in star gazing purchased simple reflecting or refracting telescopes, observed the planets and bright deep-sky objects, and perhaps dabbled in astrophotography. Telescopes with large mirrors, permitting observers to see thousands of faint galaxies and nebulae, were difficult to obtain and extremely expensive, limiting their availability largely to institutions.

However, things began to change in the late 1970s. Telescope manufacturers started offering large reflecting telescopes mounted on simple altazimuth mountings called Dobsonians. (They were named for John Dobson, a California telescope maker who popularized the design.) This meant that for the price of a good 8-inch telescope, observers could suddenly buy a 17.5-inch scope that would collect 5.5 times more light and show much fainter objects. Because many deep-sky objects are quite faint, this enabled those with large telescopes to see a multitude of objects they had never been able to see before. Thus began a revolution in deep-sky observing.

This development shed light on the problem of information on deep-sky objects. For many years observing guides for backyard observers have relied on and perpetuated the use of ancient data, and most amateur star atlases showed only the brightest few hundred objects. In 1981 the excellent Sky Atlas 2000.0 was published, a folio-size group of foldout charts of the sky showing stars down to magnitude 7.5 and thousands of deep-sky objects. The companion book of data, Sky Catalogue 2000.0, volume 2, contains a valuable listing of recent astronomical data for deep-sky objects; positions, magnitudes, sizes, types, and other important basic information. This atlas and accompanying book form a valuable addition to the literature for backyard astronomers. In 1987 an even more thorough atlas was published called Uranometria 2000.0. In two volumes, it promises to become the standard atlas for deep-sky observers. Up until now, there hasn't been a modern one-volume reference for deep-sky observers with small telescopes. This book is aimed at filling that gap. And deep-sky observers have their own magazine containing large amounts of valuable information, photographs, and sketches in Deep Sky Monthly (1977-1982) and its successor, the quarterly Deep Sky (1982-). Between these sources and others to come, the problem of outdated information for deep-sky observers is slowly becoming vastly improved.

As I write this during the mid-1980s another development has occurred. Two companies are now offering computer-control mechanisms for telescopes that contain databases of several thousand deep-sky objects. These devices couple to telescopes and, once aligned and calibrated, automatically aim or assist the observer in aiming a telescope at any of the objects in their databases. While they take the thrill of finding objects out of observing, computer-control for telescopes may revolutionize the hobby again. Imagine seeing 100 or 200 galaxies per night as a computer finds them for you!

Where will all of this technology and information take you as you pursue the gentle hobby of backyard astronomy? Certainly better and more thorough information will help you see more objects and understand and enjoy those you view more. However, no matter how much technology is available to help you observe deep-sky objects, the ultimate thrill of the hobby is simply setting up your telescope and viewing the wonders of the universe.

David J. Eicher

Lagoon and Trifid Nebulae

Appendix 2:
A Deep-Sky
Bibliography

The following books and periodicals contain useful observing information, catalogues of objects, maps, and photographs and sketches of interest to deep-sky observers.

Astronomical Objects for Southern Telescopes. E.J. Hartung. 238 pp., Cambridge University Press, Cambridge, 1968. A compendium of high-quality observing notes on objects in the southern hemisphere; many are visible from the northern hemisphere as well.

The Astronomical Scrapbook. Joseph Ashbrook. 468 pp., Cambridge University Press and Sky Publishing Corp., Cambridge, 1984. A fascinating collection of historical tales in astronomy, many of which relate to deep-sky pioneers or early deep-sky observing.

Astronomy. Richard Berry, ed. Kalmbach Publishing Co., 1027 North 7th St., Milwaukee, Wisconsin 53233. The largest English-language astronomy periodical, Astronomy often features departmental articles relating to deep-sky observing. Monthly.

Atlas of Deep-Sky Splendors. Third ed. Hans Vehrenberg. 246 pp., Treugesell-Verlag and Sky Publishing Corp., Dusseldorf, 1978. A marvelous photographic album of hundreds of deep-sky objects all recorded at the same scale for easy comparison.

Burnham's Celestial Handbook. Robert Burnham, Jr. Three vols., 2138 pp., Dover Publications, New York, 1978. An enormous constellation-by-constellation listing of stars and deep-sky objects containing great amounts of information and many photographs and charts.

The Cambridge Deep-Sky Album. Jack Newton and Philip Teece. 126 pp., Cambridge University Press and AstroMedia Corp., Cambridge, 1984. A colorful photo album of Messier and bright NGC objects produced by two Canadian amateur astronomers.

Deep Sky. David J. Eicher, ed. Kalmbach Publishing Co., 1027 North 7th St., Milwaukee, Wisconsin 53233. Founded in 1977 as Deep Sky Monthly, this publication is the only magazine in existence centered on deep-sky observing and astrophotography. Begun as a quarterly in 1982 and called simply Deep Sky, the magazine's 192 annual pages feature articles, maps, charts, photographs, eyepiece drawings, and observing hints for clusters, nebulae, and galaxies. Departments cover double stars, variable stars, small telescope observing, and astronomical research news.

Deep Sky Objects: A guide for the Amateur Astronomer. Jack Newton. 160 pp., Gall Publications, Toronto, 1977. This reference book contains a photograph and map for each Messier object and a handful of bright NGC objects.

Discover the Stars. Richard Berry. 120 pp., paper, Harmony Books, New York, 1987. This book is an introductory guide to observing the sky and contains 12 monthly star maps, 23 close up star maps, and information on 300 deep-sky objects. The maps show stars to magnitude 5.5.

Galaxies. Paul Hodge. 174 pp., Harvard University Press, Cambridge, Massachusetts, 1986. An excellent introduction to the field of galaxy research and the properties of galaxies, this is a revision of a classic work originally written by Harlow Shapley.

Galaxies. Timothy Ferris. 191 pp., Stewart, Tabori & Chang, New

York, 1980. This is a folio-sized colorful picture book of galaxies that includes an unusually lucid and informative text on the astrophysical nature of these objects.

Leslie Peltier's Guide to the Stars. Leslie Peltier. 185 pp., AstroMedia Corp. and Cambridge University Pres, Milwaukee, 1986. A fine introduction to observing the sky with binoculars.

Man Discovers the Galaxies. Richard Berendzen, Richard Hart, and Daniel Seeley. 228 pp., Columbia University Press, New York, 1984. An historical detective story of how astronomers unraveled the basic structure of the Milky Way Galaxy, including biographical information on Shapley, Hubble, Einstein, Jeans, Barnard, and many others.

The Messier Album. John H. Mallas and Evered Kreimer. 216 pp., Sky Publishing Corp., Cambridge, Massachusetts, 1978. This book provides a short description, photograph, and sketch for each Messier object.

The Milky Way. Bart J. Bok and Priscilla F. Bok. Fifth ed., 356 pp., Harvard University Press, Cambridge, Massachusetts, 1981. Generally regarded as the standard semi-technical introduction to our Galaxy, This is an extremely valuable sourcebook of information for those interested in the nature of galaxies.

The Revised New General Catalogue of Nonstellar Astronomical Objects. Jack W. Sulentic and William G. Tifft. 383 pp., the University of Arizona Press, Tuscon, 1973. A listing of the Revised New General Catalogue, the standard list of bright deep-sky objects originated by William and John Herschel, with positional, magnitude, and type descriptions.

Sky and Telescope. Leif Robinson, ed. Sky Publishing Corp., 49 Bay State Road, Cambridge, Massachusetts 02138. The nation's oldest astronomy periodical contains the much-respected department "Deep Sky Wonders." written by Walter Scott Houston. Monthly.

Sky Atlas 2000.0. Wil Tirion. Twenty-six fold-out folio charts, Cambridge University Press and Sky Publishing Corp., Cambridge, 1981. An excellent large-scale atlas showing 43,000 stars down to magnitude 8 and 2,500 deep-sky objects.

Sky Catalogue 2000.0. Alan Hirshfeld and Roger W. Sinnot, eds. Two vols. Cambridge University Press and Sky Publishing Corp., Cambridge, 1982-1985. Volume two (385 pp.) lists fundamental data on thousands of double and variable stars, 750 open clusters, 150 globular clusters, 283 bright nebulae, 150 dark nebulae, 564 planetary nebulae, 3116 galaxies, and 297 quasars.

A Starhopper's Guide to Messier Objects. Lenore Freeman. 23 pp., Everything in the Universe, Oakland, California, 1983. Simple star-hopping charts for constellations containing Messier objects showing how to find them easily.

Starlight Nights. Leslie Peltier. 236 pp., Sky Publishing Corp., Cambridge, Massachusetts, 1965. This is the story of Leslie C. Peltier, one of the greatest amateur astronomers of all time. It contains no "how-to" observing information, but is an interesting read.

Uranometria 2000.0, Vol. 1. Wil Tirion, Barry Rappaport, and George Lovi. 259 pp., Willmann-Bell, Inc., Richmond, 1987. This first volume of a two-volume set is a sky atlas covering the northern hemisphere down to -6° declination. The work is more thorough than Tirion's Sky Atlas 2000.0, showing stars down to magnitude 9.5 and many more deep-sky objects.

The Visibility of Deep Sky Objects. Fred Klein. Five vols., 283 pp., Klein Publications, Los Altos, California, 1984. A series of booklets offering a "visibility index" for 2400 deep-sky objects.

The Webb Society Deep Sky Observer's Handbook. Seven vols., 1334 pp., Enslow Publishers, Hillside, New Jersey, 1979-1987. A compilation of observing notes and sketches on double stars (vol. 1), planetary and gaseous nebulae (vol. 2), open and globular clusters (vol. 3), galaxies (vol. 4), clusters of galaxies (vol. 5), anonymous galaxies (vol. 6), and southern hemisphere objects (vol. 7).

The Crab Nebula

Appendix 3:
The Messier
Catalogue

The most famous catalogue of deep-sky objects, the Messier Catalogue, was compiled in the 18th century by French comet hunter Charles Messier and contains 107 of the sky's best deep-sky objects. As such, the objects it contains are among the most observed deep-sky objects in the sky. The list below gives M numbers and their identities, as well as their NGC numbers. Information on each object can be found in the appropriate section of the book (i.e.,open clusters, planetary nebulae, etc.).

Messier	NGC	Description
1	1952	Crab Nebula, bright neb. in Taurus
2	7089	globular in Aquarius
3	5272	globular in Canes Venatici
4	6121	globular in Scorpius
5	5904	globular in Serpens
6	6405	open cluster in Scorpius
7	6475	open cluster in Scorpius
8	6523	Lagoon Nebula, br. neb. in Sgr.
9	6333	globular in Ophiuchus
10	6254	globular in Ophiuchus
11	6705	Wild Duck Cl., open cl. in Sct.
12	6218	globular in Ophiuchus
13	6205	Hercules Cl., globular in Her.
14	6402	globular in Ophiuchus
15	7078	globular in Pegasus
16	6611	Eagle Neb., br. neb. in Serpens
17	6618	Omega Neb., br. neb. in Sagittarius
18	6613	open cluster in Sagittarius
19	6273	globular in Ophiuchus
20	6514	Trifid Neb., br. neb. in Sagittarius
21	6531	open cluster in Sagittarius
22	6656	globular in Sagittarius
23	6494	open cluster in Sagittarius
24	----	star cloud in Sagittarius
25	----	open cluster in Sagittarius
26	6694	open cluster in Scutum
27	6853	Dumbbell Neb., planetary in Vulpecula
28	6626	globular in Sagittarius
29	6913	open cluster in Cygnus
30	7099	globular in Capricornus
31	224	Andromeda Galaxy, gal. in Andromeda
32	221	galaxy in Andromeda
33	598	galaxy in Triangulum
34	1039	open cluster in Perseus
35	2168	open cluster in Gemini
36	1960	open cluster in Auriga
37	2099	open cluster in Auriga
38	1912	open cluster in Auriga
39	7092	open cluster in Cygnus
40	----	mistaken object
41	2287	open cluster in Canis Major
42	1976	Orion Neb., br. neb. in Orion
43	1982	bright nebula in Orion
44	2632	Beehive Cl., open cluster in Cancer
45	----	Pleiades, open cluster in Taurus
46	2437	open cluster in Puppis
47	2422	open cluster in Puppis
48	2548	open cluster in Hydra
49	4472	galaxy in Virgo
50	2323	open cluster in Monoceros
51	5194	Whirlpool Gal., galaxy in CVn.
52	7654	open cluster in Cassiopeia

53	5024	globular in Coma Berenices
54	6715	globular in Sagittarius
55	6809	globular in Sagittarius
56	6779	globular in Lyra
57	6720	Ring Neb., planetary in Lyra
58	4579	galaxy in Virgo
59	4621	galaxy in Virgo
60	4649	galaxy in Virgo
61	4303	galaxy in Virgo
62	6266	globular in Ophiuchus
63	5055	galaxy in Canes Venatici
64	4826	Blackeye Gal., galaxy in Com.
65	3623	galaxy in Leo
66	3627	galaxy in Leo
67	2682	open cluster in Cancer
68	4590	globular in Hydra
69	6637	globular in Sagittarius
70	6681	globular in Sagittarius
71	6838	globular in Sagittarius
72	6981	globular in Aquarius
73	6994	asterism of 4 stars in Aquarius
74	628	galaxy in Pisces
75	6864	globular in Sagittarius
76	650-1	Little Dumbbell Neb., plan. in Per.
77	1068	galaxy in Cetus
78	2068	bright nebula in Orion
79	1904	globular in Lepus
80	6093	globular in Scorpius
81	3031	galaxy in Ursa Major
82	3034	galaxy in Ursa Major
83	5236	galaxy in Hydra
84	4374	galaxy in Virgo
85	4382	galaxy in Coma Berenices
86	4406	galaxy in Virgo
87	4486	galaxy in Virgo
88	4501	galaxy in Coma Berenices
89	4552	galaxy in Virgo
90	4569	galaxy in Virgo
91	----	mistaken object
92	6341	globular in Hercules
93	2447	open cluster in Puppis
94	4736	galaxy in Canes Venatici
95	3351	galaxy in Leo
96	3368	galaxy in Leo
97	3587	Owl Nebula, plan. in Ursa Major
98	4192	galaxy in Coma Berenices
99	4254	galaxy in Coma Berenices
100	4321	galaxy in Coma Berenices
101	5457	galaxy in Ursa Major
102	5866	galaxy in Draco
103	581	open cluster in Cassiopeia
104	4594	galaxy in Virgo
105	3379	galaxy in Leo
106	4258	galaxy in Canes Venatici
107	6171	globular in Ophiuchus
108	3556	galaxy in Ursa Major
109	3992	galaxy in Ursa Major

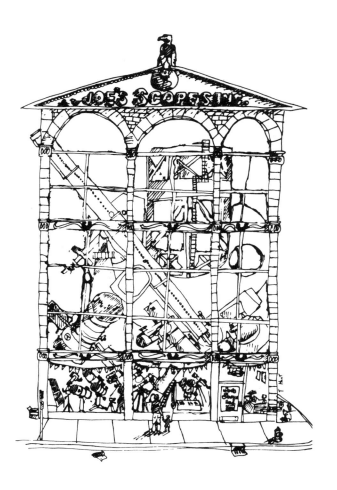

Appendix 4:
Telescope
Manufacturers

The following lists telescope manufacturers who can provide you with information on their telescopes and accessories for deep-sky observing.

Astro-Physics
7470 Forest Hills Road
Loves Park, Illinois 61111
(815) 282-1513

Manufactures refracting telescopes.

Bausch & Lomb
Criterion Division
135 Prestige Park Circle
East Hartford, Connecticut 06108
(203) 282-0768

Manufactures Schmidt-Cassegrain telescopes.

Celestron International
2835 Columbia Street
Torrance, California 90503
1-800-421-1526

Manufactures Schmidt-Cassegrain, Maksutov-Cassegrain,
Schmidt-Newtonian, and refracting telescopes.

Coulter Optical, Inc.
P.O. Box K
Idyllwild, California 92349
(714) 659-4621

Manufactures Dobsonian reflector telescopes.

Edmund Scientific Co.
Edscorp Building
Barrington, New Jersey 08007
(609) 573-6250

Manufactures reflecting and refracting telescopes.

Meade Instruments Corporation
1675 Toronto Way
Costa Mesa, California 92626
(714) 556-2291

Manufactures Schmidt-Cassegrain, Maksutov-Cassegrain,
Schmidt-Newtonian, reflecting and refracting telescopes.

Questar Corporation
P.O. Box 59
New Hope, Pennsylvania 18938
(215) 862-5277

Manufactures Maksutov-Cassegrain telescopes.

Unitron, Inc.
175 Express Street
Plainview, New York 118-3
(516) 822-4601

Manufactures refracting telescopes.

Index

Curtis, Heber D., 266

D

dark-adaption, 22, 38
dark nebulae, *See* bright and dark nebulae
Darquier, Antoine, 197
Dawes Limit, 40
Dawes, William Rutter, 33, 40
de Cheseaux, Philippe Loys, 131
declination, 25
Deep Sky, 11, 31, 103, 125, 195, 263, 315, 317
Deep Sky Monthly, 125, 315
Deep Sky Objects: A Guide for the Amateur Astronomer, 317
deep-sky observing, introduction to, 10
Deslile, J.N., 131
Delta Cancri, 129, 141
Delta Cassiopeiae, 142
Delta Cephei, 104, 106, 109, 119, 165
Delta Ceti, 279
Delta Cygni, 207
Delta Herculis, 215
Dembowski, Baron Ercole, 33
Deneb, 108, 144, 205, 246
Dickenson, Terence, 24, 31
Discover the Stars, 317
Dobson, John, 17, 315
Dobsonian telescopes, 19, 315
Dorpat Observatory, 33
Double Cluster, *See* NGC 869 and NGC 884
double stars, 13, 30 *See also* binary stars
Drake, Frank, 168
Draper, Henry, 230
Dreyer, John L.E., 132
Dumbbell Nebula, *See* M27
Dunlop, J., 181

E

Eagle Nebula, *See* M16
eclipsing binary stars, 36, 106
Edmund Mag. 6 Star Atlas, 31, 38

Eicher, David J., 21, 31, 103, 125, 315, 318
Eight-Burst Nebula, *See* NGC 3132
Einstein Observatory, 105
Electra, 148
elliptical galaxies, 270
emission nebulae, *See* bright and dark nebulae
Ephemerides, 129
Epsilon Bootis, 40
Epsilon Cephei, 109
Epsilon Corvi, 285
Epsilon Lyrae, *42*
Epsilon Pegasi, 181
Erfle eyepiece, 28
Eskimo Nebula, *See* NGC 2392
Espin, T.E.H., 34, 144
Eta Cancri, 141
Eta Carinae Nebula, *See* NGC 3372
Eta Herculis, 165
Eta Piscium, 277
Eta Ursae Majoris, 281
eyepieces, 26

F

Fabricius, David, 104
Ferris, Timothy, 317
Field Book of the Skies, 35
filar micrometer, 41
filters, 28
Finsen, W.S., 34
5 Serpentis, 178
Flaming Star Nebula, *See* IC 405
Flamsteed, John, 131
Fornax Dwarf Galaxy, 183, 275
41 Capricorni, 182
47 Tucanae, 171, 177, 178, 180, 181
Freeman, Lenore, 318

G

GK Persei, 106
galaxies, 14, 262
Galaxies, 317
Galileo, 128, 129
Gamma Andromedae, 283

331